Solving People Problems

For

The Creation and Preservation

Of

Family Wealth

Peter G. Sandwell MD

Salt Pond Press / North Haven, CT

FIRST EDITION

Published by Salt Pond Press
P.O. Box 2010, North Haven, CT 06473

Printed in the United States of America

LCCN: 2008925551
ISBN-13: 978-0-9793186-0-3
ISBN-10: 0-9793186-0-2

Dedication

To

Thomas William Brown

My Grandfather

*Whose Love Made
This Journey Possible*

Contents

Part Two - Practical Applications

Part Three - Neuroscience

Warning - Disclaimer

Note to the Reader

Acknowledgments

I would first like to thank my parents, who worked tirelessly to prepare me for life. It was their extensive preparation that enabled me to tackle this project. I would next like to thank a whole host of very generous teachers who encouraged me and challenged me at every step of my educational process. I would particularly like to thank Daniel Hoyt, my high school physics teacher, who first opened my eyes to the possibility that I could contribute something unique if I set my mind to it. I would like to thank David Morgenstern, from whom I received indispensible training that was full of both generosity and genius. I want to thank Jay Haley, who initially got me interested in a career in child psychiatry; when he very generously gave a talk to a small group of medical students which I was lucky enough to attend. I would like to thank Salvador Minuchin, who worked generously, brilliantly, and tirelessly, to build the field of family therapy and the Philadelphia Child Guidance Clinic, where I was lucky enough to get much of my training. I would like to thank all of the staff of the Philadelphia Child Guidance Clinc, from whom I learned so much about working with families. I would particularly like to thank Lydia Linan, who took the time to show me the importance and the method of making a developmental diagnosis. Her efforts forever set an entire direction to my professional thinking. I would like to thank all of my peers and colleagues at the Philadephia Child Guidance Clinic, from whom I received so much support and peer learning. I would particularly like to thank Ann Itzkowitz, Olga Falcetto, Edwin Castillo, and Jose Nogueira, who provided me with so much support and friendship. I would like to thank Carl Whitaker, who worked a lifetime to open up to others the field of family therapy. His personal and professional efforts introduced me to an entire professional landscape. And it was the exploration of this new landscape that made the work that this book is based on possible. I would like to thank Sandy Whipple, who gave me great support, both professionally and personally, during a most difficult time of the early discovery of this new knowledge.

I would like to thank all of the individuals and families I have worked with during my professional career. They taught me so much; through their generous sharing of their struggles and through their courageous efforts to tackle their people problems. I would especially like to thank all of the extended families who have honored me by working with me. It was they who showed me the power of the extended family to heal its members.

I would like to thank countless professionals and researchers whose life works has made this work possible. My work is a grain of sand on a mountain of other individual's lifetimes of effort and genius. I would to thank Martin Gilbert for his brilliant work documenting the life of Winston Churchill. Without his work, I would never have been able to examine and delineate the patterns in Winston Churchill's life. I would also like to thank Michael Kaufman for his exquisite biography of George Soros. And I would like especially to thank George Soros for his generosity in sharing information about his life and the life of his extended family with Michael Kaufman, which made his biography possible.

I would like to thank Kenneth Rocklin and Jessica Assard- Wu, who have been expertly assisting me and supporting me in my current work with extended families. And I would like to especially thank Jessica Assard-Wu for her generous and skillful reading and commenting on this manuscript.

Finally, I would like to thank my wife Lanna, for her constant support and patience with this project, and my daughter Sarina, for her patience and for the constant pleasure she brings to our family.

Solving People Problems

For

The Creation and Preservation

OF

Family Wealth

Chapter 1

If you want to be rich for one year, grow rice
If you want to be rich for ten years, grow trees
If you want to be rich for one hundred years, grow people
Chinese Proverb

All families want to be rich. They want to have enough money and more. They want to be rich in intellectual capital, so that their members can be competent at what they do and can deal with the world effectively. But most of all, they want to be rich in human capital[1]. They want their members to be emotionally happy and effective at each stage of life and they want the relationship between family members to be harmonious and supportive. Money as a form of wealth is really a tool that helps to achieve the other kinds of wealth. Intellectual capital is easy to build if family members are provided with the right example from elders and the right educational experiences. It is human capital that is hard to come by. And in building family wealth and preserving it from one generation to the next, it is the people problems that are the most vexing. They are the problems that interefere the most with the family's growing prosperity.

Family members have all sorts of emotional problems that are patched up these days with a variety of medicines, leaving the members and their families to hobble along as best they can. Divorces, running at about 50%, cut deeply into family assets, both financial and human, and they leave a long trail of suffering children. A large number of people never reach even half of their possible career fulfillment or potential. Stress, much of it emotional in origin, undermines people's health more than any other single factor[2]. According to Williams and Preisser in their book, <u>Preparing Heirs</u>, 70% of wealth transitions from one generation to the next fail. They defined failure as the "involuntary loss of control of the assets" by the inheritors[3]. They go on to say that the cause of these failed estate transitions lies "within the family itself"[4]. For families that own family businesses, less that two-thirds of these businesses survive to the second generation and less than 30% make it to the third generation[5]. At the heart of this frequent loss of the valuable family business are the people problems involved in keeping the business in the family.

This book will introduce you to a new methodology for solving a wide array of these people problems. Like the introduction of the laser, which had a wide variety of successful applications, this new people technology has a wide variety of very fruitful uses. At its center, it involves harnessing the power of the extended family as an organizational unit. Families who make use of this inherent extended family power end up being able to create large amounts of value for themselves in a relatively short period of time. How would you and your family like to create $5 million dollars worth of long term value in a period of 12 to 16 months? For some families, depending on their situation, the possible value creation could easily top $30 million dollars.

This book is intended as a kind of "show and tell" for families who are interested. It is not intended as an attempt to reform our present culture's approach to these people problems. Like Harvard University in 1760, it is intended to educate the few rather than to uplift the many. New knowledge takes a long time to work its way into the infrastructure of society. Reading and writing were a powerful skill in ancient Greece and Rome. Yet it has taken society about 2000 years to put educational structures in place so that the *Many* can reliably benefit from these skills. Much discussion and effort within the society had to take place to accomplish this goal of near universal literacy. Big cultural changes that require a large group investment always take a long time to achieve. My goal is merely to introduce the notion of this technology and its power to the few who are interested now. I leave it to God and mankind to slowly bring these fruits to the *Many*.

In Part 1 of this book, I will introduce you to this new way of thinking, this new people technology. In Part 2, I will show you how it can be applied successfully to a number of different types of people problems. So you will understand the scope of this way of thinking, I will now list the kinds of people problems that I will cover in Part 2. In my experience, all of these types of problems can be solved with the application of this new knowledge. They include:

- Emotional problems and problems of immaturity
    Examples: an emotional disorder in a family
    member; anorexia, bipolar disorder,
    bulimia, obsessive-compulsive
    disorder, severe anxiety disorder,
    depression, early psychosis

-Problems of intergenerational preservation of family
    capital
    Examples: heirs who are immature and unlikely
    to be able to make good use of, or
    even hold on to an inheritance

- Relationship problems between spouses or career
    partners
    Examples: impending divorce, or
    a vital partnership under severe
    interpersonal strain, ready to
    rupture

- Relationship problems within an extended family
    Example: family strife that threatens the
    existence of a family business

- Personality flaws or derailers in the character of a
    leader or CEO
    Examples: blocks to career fulfillment or
    to attaining one's true potential

-Problems of high stress levels in family members that
    leave them vulnerable to the onset of serious
    illness

-Disaster prevention

In Part 3, I will present a brief overview of the neurobiology behind this new people technology. In Appendix 1, I will provide a summary of the 12 developmental stages.

How can one new technology be successfully applied to such a wide range of people problems? The answer is that all of these problems have certain fundamentals in common. They involve the ongoing interaction between the ever developing individual and the extended family context in which he or she is imbedded. The success of this new technology lies in making needed changes to the extended family context. It turns out that if you change the extended family culture sufficiently, you can greatly increase the functioning of both the individual family members and the group as a whole.

But before I explain why and how this is possible, let me digress to give you some examples that I hope you will find both interesting and intriguing.

Chapter 2

The power of changing the context

Take a situation that had a very happy and initially unexpected ending. John, a six year old boy, was brought to me by his parents, Mr. and Mr. B. He had been fine until a month before our meeting when he started to be totally preoccupied with something bad happening to the family. He began asking the parents twenty times an hour if the house was going to burn down or if a robber was going to break in and kill them. His behavior was driving the family crazy. After examining him, it was clear that he had all of the symptoms needed to make a diagnosis of Obsessive-Compulsive Disorder (OCD). Nowadays, the common approach to such a problem would be to explain to the parents that the child has a chemical imbalance and that he would have it for life. The parents would then be reassured that there are medicines to treat OCD. The child would then be tried on a series of medicines in search of some symptomatic relief.

Because I was trained in the old school, which included a lot of child development, I took things a step further. I proceeded to make what is called a developmental diagnosis. That is, I looked at the child's problem from the point of view of what developmental stages he was having trouble with (See Appendix 1 for a Summary of the Developmental Stages). He was clearly having trouble with six year old issues, because his affliction had started at age six. He was also having trouble with Basic Trust issues, which are the focus of the first year of life. The Basic Trust phase (See Appendix 1) involves learning to feel safe in the world and he was clearly not feeling safe.

Because I was also trained as an expert family therapist, I was curious to see if John's parents had problems with either six year old issues or Basic Trust issues. Family therapists think that the apple usually doesn't fall far from the tree. So I was expecting that his parents may have such problems. What are six year old issues? At six, John should be just finishing up the Initiative Phase (See Appendix 1) and moving into the Industry Phase (See Appendix 1). In the Initiative Phase, he was working on learning that he had the capacity to charm the parent and relatives of the opposite sex, the way a four year old boy can charm a group of his female relatives. By six however, John should be moving toward the Industry Phase. He should be learning that charm has its limits and he should be starting to become very interested in being good at things.

The natural person to learn from is his father. So he should be starting to identify with his father more and more. He also should be starting to join with dad to work intently on being good at things. This phase is called the Industry phase because the child learns to enjoy being a young worker, whether he is working at baseball, schoolwork, piano lessons or Cub Scouts. If a child has trouble with this phase, they may have trouble immersing themselves in the working world as adults, even though they may have all the aptitude and education needed.

Sure enough, John's father had trouble with Industry phase too. Mr. B, a very bright professional in his late thirties, had always had trouble immersing himself in his career. While he had achieved a reasonable level of success, he said that he had never functioned at more than half of his potential.

The second phase John was having trouble with was the Basic Trust phase. This is the phase where an infant learns to trust their family and their world. If all goes well, the infant leaves this phase with a fairly solid sense that the world is basically a safe place. This phase forms the foundation for every future relationship that follows. If this phase is damaged, the child may later manifest depression or great anxiety. And they often attempt to cope with such depression or anxiety by using alcohol or drugs as an adult. Sure enough, Mr. B had trouble with this phase too. He had a history of anxiety and depression. He also had a history of a drinking problem which he had finally conquered by going to Alcoholics Anonymous.

About the same time I saw John, I had been working with Dr. Carl Whitaker in a professional coaching relationship. As Warren Buffett said "It is hard to teach a young dog old tricks", so I had been learning from Dr. Whitaker slowly. He was 76 at the time. He had been urging me during our coaching sessions to invite grandparents and other extended family members into my therapy sessions. This was something new. Traditional training in family therapy involved focusing on the nuclear family (mom, dad and the kids), not the extended family.

Since OCD was considered a very difficult problem to treat when I was trained, I decided to follow my coach's advice. I would try something new and invite the grandparents to the sessions. I scheduled the first meeting with the paternal grandparents, the parents, John, and his two sisters. During the first meeting I wanted to focus on the paternal grandfather. I found out that he had been an alcoholic all of his life (Severe Basic Trust problems). In addition, though he was considered bright, he had only been able to hold menial jobs (Severe Industry Phase problems). Then I found out that his parents had both died within the same week during a flu epidemic when he was six years old. As a result, he was sent to an orphanage. I got the chills as I listened to this part of the story.

Now, paternal grandfather's lifelong symptoms made sense to me. Any six year old child who lost both parents so suddenly would lose most of their trust in the world (Severe Basic Trust problems). And it made sense that he was forever attempting to cope with his unresolved losses by drinking. It also made sense that he was never able to settle into the working world (Severe Industry phase problems). As a six year old child, he had no father to join with, identify with, or learn from.

I scheduled the second meeting with this same group a few weeks later. This time, I wanted to get to know paternal grandmother's story. She told me that she had suffered greatly being married to such an impaired husband. But she had stayed with him for 50 years. She then related that when she was six, her mother had died of pneumonia and she was sent to live with relatives. These relatives had made it plain to her as she was growing up that they didn't want her. Do birds of a feather flock together? In this marriage, when it came to developmental wounds, they did.

Both paternal grandfather and grandmother had experienced severe wounds to their Industry phase of development. They were both six when they lost one or both parents. And both had suffered severe damage to their Basic Trust phase, because of the severe nature of their losses.

For the third session, I turned my attention to Mrs. B's side of the family. It was less obvious how Mrs. B was injured in her Basic Trust phase and Industry phase. She did, however, suffer from chronic anxiety related to Mr. B's work difficulties and past drinking problems. With regard to the Industry phase, Mrs. B seemed to be chronically over-functioning to make up for Mr. B's inadequacies. Again following my coach's advice, I wanted to invite Mrs. B's parents in for some extended family sessions. Unfortunately, both her parents were deceased. But she did have an aunt who she was very close to, her father's older sister. At Dr. Whitaker's urging, we scheduled an extended session a few weeks later where we invited this aunt to join Mr. and Mrs. B and their children. I wanted to get the aunt's help to hear the story of she and her younger brother's childhood. I asked her to talk about their growing up together. Very soon, the aunt revealed that her mother had died when she was ten and Mrs. B's father was six. Mrs. B was very surprised. She had never heard this part of her father's story. The aunt then went on to remember what Mrs. B's father had been like as an adult. She described him as having been reclusive. She said that he was always afraid to leave the house (Severe Basic Trust problems) and that he was not much of a worker or provider (Severe Industry phase problems). She said he had worked as an adult as a clerk in the family store but that he wasn't very effective. His wife, Mrs. B's mother, had to carry the main burden of running the store to provide for the family. Mrs. B's father was thus much like Mr. B's father. Both were very impaired.

Two weeks after the meeting with Mrs. B's aunt, a strange thing happened! Mrs. B called me to report, much to their delight, that all of John's symptoms had disappeared. I saw the parents and the children for a regular family therapy session the next week and indeed, John was symptom free. His problem had resolved after one evaluation session and three extended family sessions. Subsequent follow-up showed that John's symptoms were gone for good. He reported that he didn't worry about his previous fears any longer. The two extended families, working in tandem, had created tremendous value in a very short period of time. By current standards, John should have remained chronically emotionally disabled for the rest of his life. Instead, he had become completely free of his affliction. This outcome was entirely unexpected when I began learning this prototype methodology from Dr. Whitaker. But the extended families that I have worked with in the last 18 years have showed me that I should expect this kind of success.

In this kind of work, my client is no longer the impaired individual. It is the extended family as a whole. It is the extended family's power that creates such valuable changes in their impaired members. While I play the role of symphony conductor, providing the needed leadership, the extended family members play the instruments, create the results. They use their collective power to make needed changes in their extended family culture. These changes free up their members who were previously trapped in emotionally wounded and immature familial developmental patterns.

Chapter 3

Great wealth can be created by working with the family manure.

The Author

There is tremendous value to be reaped by being able to rapidly change the course of a family member's life. This is now possible using the extended family consulting approach. Alan, a man I had known for many years died recently[1]. He was in his seventies when he died. Alan was an Ivy League trained professional, but he had been plagued by severe emotional problems since early adolescence. He received all of the standard treatment approaches to his difficulties, including multiple hospitalizations and more than thirty years of individual therapy and psychotropic medications. Yet he suffered a high degree of personal and professional dysfunction all his life. Alan was never able to marry successfully. He never achieved even a fraction of his professional potential. He never made more than $35,000 per year in his field, even though an average practitioner earned well over $100,000 per year. He lived in a rooming house for most of his adult life and suffered a high degree of social isolation. Few people wanted to spend time with such a "loser".

What was the loss to his family to have such an emotionally disabled member? And what was the loss to Alan to lead such a burdened life? Your first reaction may be to say that it can't be measured. But it is important to try and assign some value to such a loss. Families need a way to begin to measure the cost vs. benefits to be derived since they now have a way to work together to avoid such a tragedy. Trial lawyers and juries come to our aid here as it is their job to try to assign value to large, long-term quality of life losses.

If we take their lead, we would first look at loss of earnings over Alan's working life. He had established his ability by being an Ivy League graduate in his field. If he had done even reasonable well, he would have earned more than $150,000 per year. So if we take the more conservative figure of $100,000 per year as his projected earnings had he been emotionally well, we have a loss of about $70,000 per year. Assuming that his earning power had been established by the time he was 30, he would have had a working life of 35 years if he retired at age 65. With a loss of $70,000 per year due to his emotional disability, his total professional loss of earnings over his lifetime would have been $2,450,000.

Emotionally, he suffered greatly from early adolescence on. Assuming that his emotional suffering started at age 13 and that he lived to 73, Alan experienced 60 years of suffering. His emotional suffering was extensive and continual throughout this period. Nobody with any sense would have walked in his shoes for $30,000 per year. Those with a wide variety of choice and comforts in life wouldn't walk in his shoes for even $100,000 per year. But to be conservative, we can take the lower figure of $30,000 per year for emotional pain and suffering. That gives us a lifetime pain and suffering figure of $1.8 million. Taken together, his loss of earnings and pain and suffering come out to $4.25 million. If his problems could have been resolved soon after their onset, he and his family could have created at least $4.25 million dollars of lifetime value, figured conservatively.

But how is it possible for an extended family working together to create changes of such high value? In the next chapter, I will tell you how I have come to understand this power inherent in the extended family.

[1] All case histories presented are based on truth. But to preserve confidentiality, names and details have been changed and composites have been used, so as to protect the individual or family's identity, from whose case materials the cases in this book have been derived. Any resemblance to an actual individual or family is purely coincidental.

Chapter 4

If I can see further, it is because I am standing on the shoulders of giants.

Sir Isaac Newton

After applying this extended family consulting methodology to one family after another, I found that the results have astounded me each time. This methodology was solving problems for families that I could never help before, whether I used individual therapy, regular family therapy, medication, or any combination of these. What is more, the results were very rapid! After having worked with about 35 extended families, my best estimate was that 1 hour of the extended family work got about the same amount accomplished as 25 hours of working with the nuclear family. That means that one 3 hour extended family retreat gets the same results as 1 ½ years of regular family therapy.

I was now faced with an interesting problem. How were these results possible? Dr. Whitaker provided no guidance for me in this area. In fact, he presented this methodology as just a more powerful version of regular family therapy. He said nothing about what it could accomplish in terms of speed or power. I was on my own here to answer my questions. But the results I was seeing were shocking.

As a child, I was always fascinated with the evolution of aviation. From the start, the developments in aviation advanced year by year. The field moved from the Wright brother's biplane in 1903 to the supersonic jet in less than 60 years. Progress in aviation provides a good yardstick to use as a comparison when viewing this new advance of working with extended families. The leap from family therapy to extended family work is huge. It was as if I had been at the Paris Air Show in 1920. First, I saw a biplane traveling at 100 miles per hour and then I witnessed a new plane traveling at 2500 miles per hour. It was a 50 year leap. To me, the new results with extended families were such a leap.

It seemed to me that there must be new fundamental principles operating in extended family work. I did not understand these new principles; they needed explaining. This was a scientific breakthrough staring me in the face. I decided that I would never be able to make efficient use of this breakthrough unless I understood it. What is more, I would never be able to properly introduce this new method into the marketplace unless I could explain why it worked. So I decided to review the facts I was observing, and at the same time, to search out knowledge in other fields that might help me to understand this phenomenon.

It took me about eight years to fully understand what was happening and why. To do so, I needed to make use of knowledge from a wide range of fields. I benefited from a vast array of scientific work. What I will present to you now is what I came up with as a workable theory. This theory satisfies me because it explains all the observable facts of this process. Also, it is grounded in knowledge from a whole host of other fields. What is more, this theory has enabled me to predict accurately how this knowledge can be applied in other new areas. I will leave it up to you, the reader, to see if what I have come up with makes sense to you.

Chapter 5

If we don't all hang together, surely we will all hang separately.

Benjamin Franklin

The defining characteristic that made this way of working unique was the focus on the extended family as the working unit. They were like a powerful orchestra whereas the nuclear family was like a string quartet. By working together, it seemed that the extended family members were tapping into some sort of built in capacity to effect rapid change or healing. I started with the premise that what I was witnessing was an innate but as yet unrecognized capability of the extended family. Since the power of this capacity was so extensive, I assumed that it was part of a long evolutionary heritage, like the ability of the body to heal a broken bone if it is set properly.

Dr. Whitaker used to say that he didn't believe in individuals, he saw them as merely family fragments. In the same way, I started to see the extended family unit as the whole chess board. And I now saw the nuclear family as merely four or five pieces in one corner of the board. Everyone who is familiar with chess knows that if you want to win, you need to work with the overall patterns of pieces on the entire board. That creates great power in your game. If you work only with one piece at a time and its neighboring pieces, you will lose badly to an experienced player.

I decided to go to the primate scientific literature for guidance. I found that we humans are part of a long line of primate ancestors going back over 53 million years. Throughout this history, primates have been living together in moderate sized family groups of about 25 to 50 related individuals. Chimpanzees, our closest primate relatives, shed further light. Jane Goodall's research found that chimpanzees live in family units of about 30 members and that their behavior is very group-coordinated in order to foster survival.

I then went to the anthropology scientific literature to

find out the historical size of the human family. What I found was that in all societies in the world, except for the Eskimos and industrialized man, the basic family unit has always been the extended family. The typical size of this extended family had been from 30 to 150 members. It is not much different from the size of the average chimpanzee group. The exceptions to this rule, the Eskimos and industrialized man, have used the nuclear family, mom, dad, and the kids, as the basic unit. But the Eskimos used the nuclear family as the basic unit only during the winter months. During the summer thaw, they typically brought the extended family together for a large two month reunion, thus renewing extended family ties.

One can view the Eskimos as extended family teams that break up into smaller groups during the winter season. It appears that the Eskimos divided into smaller nuclear family units in winter because it was too hard to find enough food in one location to keep a larger group together. The extended family could be more successful if it temporarily split up. But their two month reunion each summer suggests that they saw the extended family as very important.

It is only in the industrialized world that the nuclear family, or the even smaller single parent family, has come to be seen as complete and self-sufficient. It seems that industrialized man has gradually moved away from the extended family model for the same kinds of economic reasons that motivate the Eskimo's winter separations. Economic opportunities in industrialized society lure individuals away from their extended families. Alone, the individuals marry, set up nuclear families, and try to make it in this way. A large part of the immigration history of the United States is made up of individuals or nuclear families setting out for greener pastures on their own.

There are currently a lot of questions about how well the nuclear family is making out as a survival unit. And the single parent family is obviously under great strain. The extended family has been the basic evolutionary unit for a long time. Nuclear families and smaller units are very recent experiments. If we count our early primate history, we could say that the extended family has been the basic unit for about 53 million years. That is certainly long enough for some special group related capacities to have evolved.

We tend to think of evolutionary advances as characteristics that belong to individuals, such as good eyesight or large size. Is there such a thing as a group related evolutionary advance? Yes there is. The modern Homo sapiens' language is an example of such a group evolutionary capability. An updated larynx arose about 100,000 years ago and made human language as we know it possible. A human type voice box and the language that it can produce is not, however, at heart, an individual characteristic. Complex human language is a shared attribute, a group capability. Language advances tremendously the groups ability to coordinate its efforts. It promotes team related behavior.

So group related evolutionary advances do occur and human language is a quintessential example. And since the extended family has been the basic evolutionary unit for millions of years, there has certainly been enough time for special group-related capacities to evolve. But why did this innate capacity for emotional healing evolve primarily as a group capacity? Why didn't the main capacity for emotional healing evolve as an individual capacity? Certainly, individuals are capable of slow emotional healing such as is seen in individual therapy. But why is the healing power greatly augmented when the extended family is working together?

It seems that the capacity to heal, as a group function, must somehow be related to the group's main role of functioning as a team in the environment. It also must somehow be advantageous for the group to be able to trigger healing in each other. Otherwise, it would not have conferred survival value and it would not have been selected for in the evolutionary process. From an evolutionary point of view, there must have been some strong advantage for this capacity to be in the repertoire of the team rather that in the repertoire of the individual.

This realization led me to look at sociobiology, the study of the biology of social organization, with particular focus on their genetic and evolutionary roots. Within sociobiology, I was drawn especially to the work of Edward O. Wilson and the biology of ants. They are a quintessential team organism. Ants' whole team behavior has evolved as an innate group capacity. There are no ants that can make it alone. Workers are sterile and so they can't reproduce. Queens and drones are helpless without the workers. The survival unit is the whole hive, not individual ants. What is more, one of their main survival tools is their capacity to have a coordinated team approach to dealing with the environment. We could call their team approach to the environment their organizational culture. This is very similar to the organizational culture of a modern corporation, its collective approach to dealing with the environment. Ants as team players are extraordinarily successful. It is said that all ant species, taken together, make up 10% of the earth's animal biomass. That is quite an accomplishment. It attests to the great merit of a coordinated teamwork approach. So it makes some sense in the biological world that teams may have special capacities that are specific group capacities. What is more, these capacities can confer great survival advantage.

But ants have their teamwork scripts written into their brains in a hard-wired, species-specific way. Carpenter ants are stuck being carpenter ants no matter what is happening in the environment. They cannot switch over to being soldier ants if that approach becomes more advantageous. Their team brain circuits are hard-wired or fixed. They are stuck with them the way they are. Only exceedingly slow genetic change can modify their team brain circuits.

In contrast, an extended family's approach to the environment can change if they have enough impetuous and drive to accomplish the change. An extended family that has always been farmers can move to another country, settle in a city, and become urban workers. Granted, the change can be very stressful but it can be done. So the basic organizational culture of the extended family, while quite stable, is nevertheless able to be changed. This is much superior to the fixed organizational culture of an ant species which cannot be readily modified in response to a change in the environment.

So it appeared to me that this capacity for the extended family to make great and efficient healing changes was somehow related to its evolutionary heritage as the fundamental unit of human survival. And it also appeared that this extended family group healing capability was somehow related to its capacity to change its organizational culture, under the right set of circumstances. I was toying with the idea that emotional healing may somehow be related to group organizational change. But at this point, I could not take my ideas any further.

Sociobiology offered me one more theory to support the idea that group-related characteristics could be selected for on an evolutionary basis. The theory is called Kin selection. It says that human genetic traits may be selected for because they promote group survival of related individuals. This is true even if these traits are not favorable to the survival of the individual family member. An example is a U.S. Marine's willingness to fight on the beaches of Iwo Jima during WWII. The casualty rate for that amphibious landing was over 50%. It doesn't appear that the Marine's biological capacity for bravery would do him any good personally. If anything, this capacity appears to work very much against his chances for individual survival. Yet his willingness to risk dying to defend his family group protects the collective genes of his family group, even as it risks his individual genes. Over evolutionary time, the capacity for such selfless bravery has favored the chances for genes to be passed down, even if some individuals get sacrificed along the way.

It is hard to trace how some ideas finally come together. Our minds often work along parallel paths of inquiry until we are finally able to put together a solution. Such parallel thought processes were occurring to me as I groped toward a solution to this puzzle.

Chapter 6

The apple doesn't fall far from the tree.

Anonymous

From the very beginning of my work with extended families, I had always been working with a parallel set of thoughts and observations. This parallel way of thinking was child development. As a child psychiatrist, I had been trained to take a close look at the developmental status of any child or adolescent that I evaluated. Our training included how to make a diagnosis of a child with emotional difficulties based on the DSM IV symptom-based diagnostic system. But we were also trained to pay particular attention to which developmental phases the child or adolescent was having trouble with. In the case of the six year old boy in chapter two, his symptom based DSM IV diagnosis would be Obsessive-Compulsive Disorder, because he had the right number of required symptoms from the list in the diagnostic manual. DSM IV is the diagnosis system that most people are familiar with and that is constantly referred to in the media. It is especially useful as a way for clinicians to communicate accurately with each other. A developmental diagnosis is more useful in zeroing in on the themes that are problematic.

A developmental diagnosis of John in chapter 2 would note that he was having trouble with the Basic Trust phase, because he was constantly distrustful about the safety of his environment. He would also be diagnosed as having trouble with the transition between the late Initiative phase and early Industry phase. During this transition, he would be working on identifying and joining with his father and moving toward focusing on being competent at a variety of tasks and skills. He would be diagnosed developmentally as having trouble with this transition because this was the point at which he became symptomatic. The transition he was now in at age six was being interfered with by his symptoms.

While I was being trained in developmentally-based child psychiatry, I was simultaneously receiving training in family therapy. We were trained as family therapists to look at whether the parents had difficulties with any of the same developmental phases that their symptomatic child was struggling with. We found during our training that parents usually had such difficulties. When we found such a correlation, we would take it into account in our therapeutic approach. We would work with the family to help both the child and the parents to get unstuck with regard to the problematic developmental phases.

Once I started working with the three-generational extended family, a whole new vista opened up. I began to discover that in many families, one or more of the grandparents were having trouble with the same developmental phases that were giving the parents and symptomatic child difficulty. In addition, I observed that frequently, one or more grandparents had sustained a specific traumatic life event during the same developmental phase that the parents and symptomatic grandchild were having difficulty with. In the case of the six year old boy, John, his paternal grandparents had each been six when they lost one or more parents to a sudden death, ending their familiar home life. What is more, John's maternal grandfather had had the exact same experience with the death of his mother when he was six. As I saw more three-generational extended families, I began to notice this pattern or a variation of it over and over again.

Once I had observed this connection between a grandchild's emotional distress related to a particular developmental phase and the childhood trauma of one or more grandparents at the same developmental age, I started to search further. I began to seek histories not only of the grandparents' lives but also of the lives of their parents and grandparents. I was now reaching back 5 generations. What I found was that if the grandparent themselves had not been the victim of a specific, matching, traumatic event, then invariably either their parents or their grandparents were. In other words, a child in emotional distress always had ancestors, usually 3-5 generations back, who had experienced a severe trauma at the same developmental stage at which the child was having their problems.

As I gathered data from more and more families, I also found that the emotional wounds were always both bilateral and matching. That is, the wounds were present on both mother's and father's side. And, the emotional wounds on mother's side matched those on father's side; that is, they occurred to the same developmental themes. Usually however, I found the wounds to be generationally staggered. By this, I mean that a traumatic event to the grandparent generation on one side was matched by an equally traumatic event one generation or two earlier on the other side. I was explaining this once to a psychiatric colleague. He had told me that his wife's father had died when she was four. But he protested that nothing like that had happened to him when he was four. I then asked, "What about your parents?" I could feel a chill flash between us as he realized that his father was four when one of his parents died.

Chapter 7

The Past is never dead, it isn't even past.

William Faulkner

Eventually, a coherent picture came together for me. The child or adolescent's problem with a developmental phase was really just a continuation of longstanding difficulty with the same phase in their mother's and father's extended families. What is more, the trouble usually started 3-5 generations back in each ancestral line. The problem invariably had it's origins in a severe trauma to individual ancestors when they were at the same developmental stage as the current symptomatic child. The child's present developmental difficulty was the result of this continuous chain of trouble with that phase. This chain always stretched back to ancestors on both sides who had been the original recipients of the developmentally specific wounds.

The results of the original trauma were being carried forward to each successive generation. Eventually, a child 3-5 generations downstream from the original trauma on each side was the one appearing as the current index patient. In fact, both extended families were still wounded with regard to the problematic developmental phase.

Why would it be advantageous to an extended family group to carrying a wound forward generation after generation? Why wouldn't it be better for the extended family to have evolved some mechanism to get the wound healed, so that the group could move on with things?

About the time I was pondering these questions, I came across a book by Kevin Kelly called <u>Out of Control, the Rise of Neo-biological Civilization</u>. It is a book about complex adaptive systems. The author presents the thesis that the technological systems and components that man is producing now do not resemble the top-down control-oriented systems characteristic of the past several centuries of industrialization. Rather, they resemble much more closely the complex interactive systems seen in nature.

The title of the second chapter is his book is the <u>Hive Mind</u>, where he looks at the wisdom of teams, starting with a look at beehives. He talks about the idea of a bee colony as a single organism. As he was making comparisons in the book between man-made systems and biological systems, he stated at one point that the essence of a living organism is its ability to remember and its ability to adapt. And in order to adapt, a living system has to be able to remember.

This got me to thinking. What about a team's ability to adapt? What would a wounding event have to do with team adaptation? A traumatic event is exactly the kind of event a human team would want to adapt to. If an extended family team did not adapt to a serious trauma, the next occurrence might wipe the extended family out. So if extended family teams need to adapt to injurious events, then how does the <u>team</u> remember the event until it has time to adapt? And how does the team system change once it has adapted.

I had been studying for a certificate in Small Business Management at the same time that I was working on these problems. One of the concepts that I was exposed to in my business courses was the idea of the "culture" of a business. A business' culture comprises all the ways in which business and its personnel go about doing things in order to prosper. In business theory, it is understood that the "culture" of a business needs to learn and adapt in order to survive and excel.

If you think about IBM when it was growing rapidly under its founder, Tom Watson Sr.'s, leadership, what made it different from other competitors? If you took all of the buildings, physical resources, and a group of equally talented personnel and just put them together, they would not equal IBM as a company. What would be missing would be all of the behavior patterns between the people and things in the organization that were practiced in an ongoing manner, its business or corporate culture. Once you take away all the particular ongoing patterns of transactions between people and things at the company, all you have left is an array of uncoordinated assets. The functioning, vibrant company is worth much more than the sum of its component parts. That something extra, the precise reoccurring ways in which the components of the system interact, its "corporate culture", is often a company's most valuable asset. It is the corporate culture that gives a company its great competitive advantage.

It is the same with extended families. It is the ways in which family members interact with each other and with the outside environment, both human and non-human, that give each extended family its competitive advantage. To give a very simple example: take two extended families 10,000 years ago, with the same number of members of the same ages, abilities and health statuses. Assume that you could find two such extended families that matched in every way. But assume that one extended family had a style of working together and the other had a style of "everyone for themselves". In a very short time, the extended family that worked together would run circles around its' non-cooperating competitor. If you are still not so sure, imagine two ice hockey teams that are playing each other. One has the ingrained habit of working together for the good of the team and one has the credo, "everyone is out for themselves". If they were evenly matched player for player in terms of size and ability, then the team that could work successfully together would have a great competitive advantage, because of their cooperative "team culture". So the nature of a team's internal culture or the nature of an extended family's culture has a great bearing on its long-term success.

For ants of a particular species, their hive culture is very fixed, hard-wired into their brains. What is more, each ant's hard-wired brain circuits correspond to the patterns that it needs to play in the overall choreography of the group's coordinated behaviors. Thus, all of the ants of a particular hive have brains that are hard-wired in a corresponding and coordinated way. With human groups, the map of the culture also resides in the brains of the members of the group. But, it is written into each member's brain in a modifiable way.

If a particular species of ant needs to change its hard-wired approach to the environment because of changing conditions, it needs to wait for a genetic change. A genetic change of the right kind would be needed to create a corresponding change in the hard-wiring of the brains of some or all of its members. If the genetic change was just right, then the hard-wired change would be just right, and the group would now have an improved approach to the environment. The genetic change would have resulted in the group modification of its hard-wired culture. Change to its hard-wired culture depends on random genetic changes that either make things better or worse for the group, governed by the laws of natural selection. Other things being equal, the groups with the best hard-wired behavior patterns will triumph over the groups with less advantageous behavior patterns. If at any time all groups have equally advantageous hardwired behavior patterns, then one group can only gain advantage over another group by being lucky enough to experience the right genetic change. The occurrence of a genetic change that could produce a behavioral advantage depends on genetic variability being introduced by sexual reproduction or by a genetic mutation. Ant groups just have to wait until they get lucky.

With humans, cultural change in an extended family group is much more malleable. The group can have an important collective experience and as a result, modify its group cultural approach to the environment in a coordinated way. The group does not have to depend on a genetic change to achieve a group cultural change. An educated extended family that leaves Russia to immigrate to New York can learn as a group to speak English. Switching to English would be a change to their extended family culture.

But learning which changes the extended family's culture could benefit from needs to be a group-wide affair. The whole group needs to adjust to the new extended family cultural patterns.

Chapter 8

That which wounds instructs.

Benjamin Franklin

It is now time to revisit one of our previous questions. What is the advantage to an extended family group of having their emotional wounds move forward from one generation to the next? The advantage is predicated on the emotional wound being the consequence of an important group experience. The wound results from an important experience with the environment that the group needs to learn from. It is very advantageous for the group not to forget this kind of experience. What the group needs to do is to remember the experience long enough to have a chance to <u>integrate</u> the experience into a modification of the extended family's culture. This leaves the extended family better prepared to deal with the same kind of injurious experience next time. What is more, the integrative process needs to be group-wide. A cultural change that would result in the extended family being better prepared next time involves changes to the coordinated behavior of the group as a whole.

At about the time I was working on these ideas, I came across an interesting article in the National Geographic Magazine. The issue was devoted to the Americas before the arrival of Christopher Columbus and the influx of the Europeans[1]. One of the articles was by a Native American man who told of the role his forefathers played as shamans in their tribe. He told of how his ancestors believed that if a tragedy such as the death of a tribal hunter occurred, his shaman forefathers were required to lead a ceremony to respond to the death. The author told how his shaman ancestor would gather the whole group together for three days in a ceremony devoted to placating the spirit of the tragically deceased hunter. The tribe believed that this gathering satisfied the spirit of the deceased member. They also believed that if this three day meeting did not take place, then the spirit of the deceased member would attach itself to one of the young children of the group and burden that child's life forever.

I saw this prediction, should the meeting not take place, as essentially a Native American description of how a child member of the group could end up becoming the carrier of a severe emotional wound to the group, in this case, the death of a member. I believe holding the meetings is a description of what this Native American group saw as necessary to avoid burdening this child's fate. The three day process reminded me of Dr. Whitaker's three day retreats with his extended families. It occurred to me that this three day process was an integrative process. It was meant to take the information inherent in the loss/death of the hunter member and integrate it into the group's culture, resulting in a slight extended family cultural change. As I saw it, the goal was to have the group end up changing their culture in such a way as to try to prevent this tragedy from reoccurring.

This article referred to two possible responses to a trauma to the group. The first was to schedule an integrative tribal meeting to work the experience into a resulting modification of the group's culture; a modification that would render the group better prepared to avoid such a tragedy in the future. The alternative outcome would occur if the integrative meeting was not held. In this second possible outcome, the impact of the tragedy would be passed on to the next generation as a kind of internal enactment or play. In this enactment or play, the group would unconsciously direct the emotional impact of the loss at one group member, usually a young child. The child would thus take on the role of the lost member in the group's enactment process. By this mechanism, the emotional impact of the loss would remain remembered by the group.

In other words, if the group couldn't integrate the experience, then the group would remember the experience through an ongoing internal play, waiting for a chance to integrate it later. The experience was too valuable to forget. It inherently contained information that was essential to the group's future welfare. It was better to integrate it eventually, rather than forget it. And it was better for a child's life to get saddled with representing this tragic loss than for the group to forget. For, if the group forgets the trauma, it may happen to them again. If they are blindsided a few times, the entire group might perish. It seems that it was better for the group for a child's life be sacrificed to become a living memory vehicle, a living bookmark, if that is what it takes to greatly enhance the group's chances for survival.

Now it was beginning to make sense. A child's emotional difficulties might actually be a part of a very valuable extended family memory process. This would begin to explain why getting the extended family together in some sort of integrative process might rapidly free the child from their affliction. But what if the individual child carrying the emotional problems grows up, goes into individual therapy, and slowly gets better? How do we explain this third possible outcome? We are all familiar with such scenarios. After all, individual therapy is the mainstay of all the psychotherapies. In comparison, family therapy represents a very small effort nationwide, maybe less than 20% of all psychotherapy.

An understanding of how the individual could resolve their emotional difficulties on their own came to me as I read one of the works of Joseph Campbell. In his book, Hero With a Thousand Faces, he introduces the idea of the hero's journey. Joseph Campbell was a world renowned professor of mythology. In part of his work, he analyzed the structure of myths throughout the world and concluded that all myths from all cultures have the same basic structure. In all myths, a group has arrived at a point where there is a basic deficit in their living. A hero is somehow mobilized from within their ranks and forced in some way to leave the group and seek a solution to the deficit. In the first phase of the hero's journey, the excluded member ventures out into the world or recedes deep into themselves, like Buddha, to seek a solution. In the second phase of the hero's journey, the hero somehow succeeds where others have failed and attains the powers or knowledge that their group needs. In the final phase, the hero returns with the life-enhancing knowledge and bestows it on the group or infuses it into the group in some way.

So we actually have three possible outcomes. In the first scenario, after a group sustains a life-instructing traumatic event, the shaman leads the group in a more or less immediate integration and all is well. During the integration process, the group extracts the essential lessons from the tragedy and encodes them into its culture so that it is better prepared for such an occurrence in the future. In the second possible scenario, the group is unable to stage an integrative retreat. Maybe the shaman who knows how to lead the retreat is among those who have died. Or maybe the group has been dispersed or has no time or safety to hold the retreat. In the absence of a retreat, the group preserves the crucial experience by setting up an internal enactment. The group will repeat this enactment from generation to generation until it finally has a chance to stage an integrative retreat. This allows the group to preserve the valuable knowledge inherent in the traumatic experience. But it isn't so healthy for the singled out individual in each generation who must constantly bear the stress imposed by the group, as he or she acts as the focal point of the enactment. If the trauma to the group is severe, then this individual will be at the focal point of heavy group-directed stress, and his or her life will be forever burdened unless they are released from their Herculean task by the group's eventual staging of the needed integration.

For this burdened individual, life is bleak indeed. They can never hope to have a normal life until their group stages an integration. But in most cases in modern society, their extended family doesn't even know that such an integration is needed. Thus the stage is set for the burdened individual to try to free themselves from their predicament. They are thus set up to try to embark on the hero's journey. Their attempt to free themselves using the hero's journey is the third scenario.

The quest to free themselves has all the elements of the hero's journey as Campbell describes it. Their extended family is experiencing a serious deficit. They need to stage an integration in order to incorporate into their extended family culture the information inherent in a recent traumatic experience that their group has suffered. The individual at the focal point of the internal group enactment has become a symptom bearer or scapegoat under his or her burden of chronic stress. As a result of the enactment, this individual has been singled out by the group in a non-verbal group process to be excluded from the normal life and developmental support of the group. This burdened individual either has to accept his or her doomed fate and remain emotionally crippled for life, or rise to the challenge and go on a quest to succeed at the hero's journey. This burdened individual will only have a normal life to the extent that they succeed on their hero's journey.

If the trauma to the group was mild to moderate, and the burdened individual enters effective individual therapy and stays with it long enough, they may end up completing enough of their hero's journey to regain a more normal life. But if the trauma to the group was severe, even with prolonged individual therapy, the individual's quest to complete their major league hero's journey usually fails.

Chapter 9

The Major League Hero's Journey; Success and Failure

"The myths agree that an extraordinary capacity is required to face and survive such experience."

Joseph Campbell

I want to highlight the rarely completed major league hero's journey and also the ruined life of the perpetually burdened individual because these are the two scenarios out of the three that we are most familiar with. The most useful scenario is the one that we have become unfamiliar with in industrialized society, the extended family integrative process. While I will spend some time delineating the hero's journey, my purpose is to show how this scenario, familiar in myths, legends, and in historical heroes, fits into this overall puzzle. A good theory accounts for all of the facts, and the hero's journey is an important part of the fact picture.

The nature of the hero's journey for the individual who is at the focal point of the extended family's unintegrated trauma is like all hero's journey's, extremely difficult. What is more, the individual is without any formal instructions on how to go about it. While the burdened individual sets about to try to extricate themselves from their predicament, they try many things. The problem is to find the path from tragedy to comedy, to a happy personal ending. If they arrive at a happy ending themselves, then they will de facto impose a shift on the extended family's culture by holding their new healthier position. The role of the burdened individual, if they succeed, is to ultimately force a change, an integration of the previous trauma, on the extended family system. The burdened individual has to generate enough power within themselves to impose that change on the rest of the extended family. The more severe the previous trauma, the more force they will need to generate, because a more severe trauma will require a larger change to the extended family culture.

As the burdened individual tries things in the outer world,

including perhaps individual therapy, they are actually trying to achieve an inner change. Remember that the developmental reality of the burdened individual's inner world is linked to the developmental reality of the extended family as a whole. They are part of one system, like all the chess pieces are part of one game. Thus, any change that the burdened individual makes which brings him back toward developmental normality will force the extended family system to change. Such a change on the part of the burdened individual will shift the emotional stress of the unintegrated trauma back on the extended family, were it will be slowly integrated.

This is tortuously difficult work. It is also an agonizingly slow and inefficient process. For the integration is occurring through being imposed by the force exerted slowly from the burdened individual. It is not occurring by a consensual mutual effort on the part of the extended family as a whole. Campbell refers to this hero's process leading to group change. He says, "The passage of the mythological hero may be over-ground incidentally; fundamentally it is inward- into depths where obscure resistances are overcome, and long lost forgotten powers are revivified, to be made available for the transfiguration of the world"[1].When Campbell refers to "long lost forgotten powers being revivified", he is referring in our case to the individual making internal changes. These internal changes lead to the burdened individual's wounded developmental stages being revised to a healthy configuration. When Campbell refers to the powers thus reclaimed as being "made available for the transfiguration of the world", he is referring in our case to the transformation of the extended family.

Basically, the burdened individual has to slowly discover the elements of the needed integration and impose them on their group. Campbell says that when the hero's journey starts in childhood, then, "The myths agree that an extraordinary capacity is required to face and survive such experience"[2]. In other words, if the burdened individual is a child and the wounds they carry are severe, the vast majority of such children don't make it. They might complete a small part of the journey in their lifetime, but most don't complete enough to regain their developmental health. Thus, while most struggle endlessly, few succeed. This is what is happening with children and adolescents who become emotionally crippled for life. Those that become chronically emotionally crippled do so because they remain the carriers of the unintegrated information of their extended families. Their lives are thus severely burdened by the resulting distortions to their development stages that result from being in the focal point role. For those very few children who do complete the hero's journey, it takes them a lifetime. Their reward of a normal life that others take for granted may come after 50 to 60 years of struggle.

The problem with the hero's journey as a path to extended family integration is that it also has grave pitfalls for the group as a whole. Forced integration may lead to a change that is undesirable for the group as a whole. In addition, it is very costly for the burdened individual attempting it. In fact, the extended family is tremendously resistant to integration being forced upon it by this mechanism. So success for the extended family as well as freedom for the burdened individual is very difficult to achieve this way.

This makes good sense from an evolutionary point of view because this method of imposed integration has a serious inherent danger. The danger involves the risk that an individual might impose a change that is very advantageous for themselves but very unfavorable for the group. Individuals are naturally at the center of their own world. If the extended family group had no mechanism to resist change imposed by the individual, then eventually, an individual might impose a very self-centered cultural change. And this selfish change, since it doesn't take into account the welfare of the group, might happen to be very detrimental to the group, seriously compromising the extended family's survival.

The extended family's survival depends greatly on its overall approach to the environment. And its overall approach to the environment is its group culture. Thus the extended family might end up having its environmental game plan altered in a fatal way because of the short-sighted self-interest of a single member. As an analogy, consider a football team in a huddle. What if an individual player could call a play whenever he felt like it, a play that would make his abilities stand out? What if he could call such a play even if it was absolutely the wrong thing to do at that time, and would risk the team losing the game. If a particular team allowed such behavior on the part of individual members, the team would eventually lose many games. A football team needs a mechanism to prevent such self-centered direction of the group's efforts by individuals behaving selfishly.

For the extended family team, permitting the individual easy access to imposing change would also eventually lead to game losses. In the case of the extended family, however, the "game loss" might mean being wiped out of existence. So, evolution, favoring extended family teams according to the principles of natural selection, selected for teams that had barriers to such unilateral influence exerted by individuals.

In fact, this is exactly what I have observed. It is very difficult indeed for a single member to impose a change on the extended family. That is why individual therapy is so slow. Any change that an individual member makes in individual therapy simultaneously forces a corresponding change to the entire extended family's culture. As a therapist working with an individual, you actually have to make changes to the entire extended family, while only having access to the individual. The extended family is not participating in the change process by offering its power. It is like trying to change the position of the U.S. Congress but only having access to one member of the House of Representatives. You can do it, but it is very slow indeed. Compared to the change process I see when the extended family is working together, individual therapy is not only slow but very painful for the individual. From my observations, I have concluded that individual therapy requires the patient to feel fully each increment of emotion that stands in the way of change, that is, each increment of emotion that anchors the individual to past maladaptive patterns.

This mechanism of individually imposed change, while greatly inhibited by the nature of the human brain, is not entirely forbidden. I believe that we humans have a team brain. But I believe that the brain is set up to allow the individual to initiate change. But to do so, the individual needs to feel each uncomfortable feeling fully, in terms of both intensity and quantity, before the individual can institute a change. By restricting the process of individual change such that it is both slow and extremely painful, our team brain insures that an individual does not make a decision to impose change lightly. Only when the individual is in dire straits and cannot have a satisfying life does unilateral change make sense. And indeed, this is what you see. Individuals don't venture into individual therapy unless they are in a lot of emotional pain. This mechanism built into our team brains to greatly inhibit individual change acts like an insurance policy. Only an individual pushed by being at the focal point of their extended family's enactment process will attempt a hero's journey. An individual who is just out for personal gain will never attempt such a painful journey to force the group to change. Their selfish potential gain would never be worth the extended sacrifice the journey would require. Thus, this brain mechanism guards the extended family against exploitation by a selfish group member.

In contrast to the hero's journey, when the three-generational group is working together to accomplish an integration, they trigger in each other a kind of anesthesia that allows for a great deal of change at a very low emotional price. They trigger in each other a significant uncoupling of the link between the amount and intensity of emotion that needs to be felt and the amount of change achieved. It is like having all change be on sale at 96% off the regular individual price. Imagine going into a jewelry store and finding out that you only need to pay 4 cents on the dollar. Suddenly, you can afford a lot more.

When an extended family changes together in the same room, the change is simultaneously coordinated in real time. This is possible because of all the parallel non-verbal communication that is occurring between members. And, because the group changes together, there is no risk that the change will be anything but beneficial to the group as a whole. Everyone's interests are taken into account because everyone is present. The changes that occur when the extended family is working together are also very rapid, because all the communication between members is happening at the same time. Even though only one member may be speaking at a time, all members are signaling each other non-verbally in every moment. This greatly speeds up the process. It would be of great survival advantage for a group to be able to accomplish coordinated group change quickly. Such rapid group change would allow an extended family to revise its group culture quickly. Being able to adapt to changing conditions is one of the hallmarks of a successful living organism or team. To be able to accomplish such a change rapidly would be of great competitive advantage.

I believe that evolutionary pressures favored the development of such a rapid coordinated group change capacity, just as it favored the development of modern language, another adaptive group mechanism that allows for rapid coordination of group behavior. Language is definitely a group attribute. It is of little use to the individual alone. True, he could talk to himself out loud and thus occasionally it might help to clarify his thinking. But the real payoff from language comes from its <u>utility in coordinating group behavior</u>. It is an evolutionary achievement for the group as a whole. Because the extended family group has been the unit of survival for millions of years, going back to our primate ancestors, evolution has been acting for all of that time on the group as a whole. Characteristics that have favored group survival have been selected for by the process of natural selection working on the success or failure of the extended family as a whole. Just as with the ants and bees, the mechanisms of evolution have slowly been favoring changes to the capabilities of the human "team" brain that have made possible highly adaptive and <u>coordinated group activity</u>. The principle: "If we don't all hang together, surely we will all hang separately"[3] has been shaping the capacities of the human team brain. The ability of the extended family to come together in a group meeting and communicate in a deep way so as to revise their "team" brain circuits in order to optimize their collective approach to the environment is a mechanism that was developed through the evolutionary natural selection process.

The capacity for an individual to impose change on the set of "team brains" that make up their extended family was also selected for but with accompanying built-in inhibitions and limitations. Each individuals feelings, behaviors and thought patterns are anchored by the emotions resulting from deep experiences. If an individual is bitten by a dog as a child, fear of dogs will persist, even if the person encounters a friendly, harmless dog. Their fear persists as long as the emotions that accompanied their experience of being bitten remain in storage. I call the original emotions related to the experience of being bitten the "anchoring emotions". These emotions anchor the person's thoughts, feeling and behaviors toward dogs as being dangerous forever, unless they are cleared out by being vented or re-experienced in a safe setting. All deeply engrained thought patterns, feelings, and behavior patterns toward any situation are held securely in place by "anchoring emotions". This is what keeps a person's reactions to situations stable over time.

In order to change a person's basic responses to any given situation, the anchoring emotions that keep their thought patterns, feelings, and behavior patterns stable need to be processed or re-felt and thus moved out of the way. This is accomplished by feeling all of the anchoring feelings, one feeling at a time, until they are all cleared out. Two regions of the limbic system, the emotional brain, are responsible for storing the anchoring emotions, the hippocampus and amygdala. Just as they are the site of the anchoring emotions for the individual, they are also the site of the anchoring emotions related to coordinated extended family behavior. These two brain structures provide stability to group related thoughts, feelings, and behavior patterns by containing within their vast circuitry mechanisms to prevent or limit change. The feelings that need to be felt by the individual in order to impose group change require great effort because they are so uncomfortable. These include anxiety, fear, anger and pain etc., and are the currency of the amygdala. Because these feelings are so uncomfortable, the internal feeling work the individual has to do to impose group change proceeds extremely slowly and requires great and sustained effort. Any individual looking for a quick way to change the group's culture in a selfish direction will be quickly discouraged by the necessary emotional work required. Consequently, only changes that are extremely important to the individual will be worth such effort. These changes are limited to the ones that a burdened individual finds necessary to make in order to have a satisfying life. No other types of changes are worth trying to impose. These changes that would free the burdened individual are the very ones that she intuitively finds must be made to escape her untenable life position if she happens to be the current emotional wound carrier of her extended family. As a result, only changes related to undertaking the hero's journey are worth such effort.

Thus, the brain evolved to allow for the hero's journey as a mechanism to force integration of the old upstream wounds on the extended family. But our human team brain only allows for slow, painful, costly progress using this mechanism. Compared to change accomplished by extended family group effort, the hero's journey is a much less favored substitute. It is the utter agony and hopelessness of the hero-scapegoat's wound carrying position that drives them to even consider undertaking such a slow painful journey.

The myths provide us with metaphorical accounts of the dynamics of the very human hero's journey. One such story from the <u>Arabian Nights</u> provides us with a good example. The story is about the parallel journeys of Prince Kamar al-Zaman and Princess Budur. Prince Kamar was the handsome only son of the King of Persia. At this time, it was expected that a young prince would take a wife when he came of age. This was the time of marriage for the sake of practicality, not love. When it was Prince Kamar's time to marry, he showed no interest. When his father the King began to press him, he continually refused. At first, the King was patient with his only son, but after several years passed, he grew angry with his son's refusal to wed. Eventually, enraged, he had his son imprisoned in a tower. The King would not release his son until he agreed to wed. The deficit in this extended family has to do with a pattern whereby love is not considered as the grounds for marriage. The Prince's intuitive refusal to settle for a practical marriage led to his internal exile in the tower. He has been singled out and forced to consider the hero's journey.

At the same time, in distant China, the same sort of problem was occurring with a King and his daughter, Princess Budur. This Princess was exceedingly beautiful and all the Kings of neighboring kingdoms had contacted her father, asking for her hand in marriage for their sons. But again, the subject of marriage was being presented to her as a practical matter. There was no consideration of her finding a mate based on love. Princess Budur, like Prince Kamar, refused all of her father's requests to consider marrying. Eventually, her father lost all patience and had her chained to the walls of a prison room in the castle. He refused to release her until she agreed to marry one of the suitors, even though she had not even so much as met any of them.

What happens next in the story is characteristic of myths. The weaver of the story now begins to include magical elements. All weavers of myths from all over the world have repeatedly resorted to this device as a shorthand way to explain the next part of the hero's journey, the inward exploration. In this case, the storyteller introduced two spirits to keep the story moving forward.

It so happened that while this recalcitrant Prince and Princess, separated by thousands of miles, were suffering in their internal exile, a female spirit happened on the scene. She beheld the sleeping Prince Kamar and marveled at his beauty. She immediately became concerned that other spirit relatives of hers in the neighborhood might do him harm. So she flew up into the sky to have a look around. Presently, she came across a male spirit and challenged him. She wanted to know what he was doing in the area. He said he had just returned from a kingdom in China thousands of miles away. He said that while he was there, he had seen a Princess Budur, who he declared was the most beautiful young woman of her time. He then went on and on about her loveliness. The female spirit, smitten with Prince Kamar, was offended that the male spirit would exalt Princess Budur to such a degree. So she suggested that they both go look at the Prince, so the male spirit could see for himself how handsome he was. They both flew down to the prison room where the Prince was sleeping. The male spirit agreed he was handsome but said that his Princess Budur was even more appealing. This incensed the female spirit. She decided that they should bring Princess Budur to the Prince's prison room. Then they could look at them side by side and decide which was more beautiful.

So the two spirits proceeded to magically transport the Princess from China. They placed her next to the sleeping Prince. As they looked at them, they both marveled that the Prince and Princess were like twins, they were both so beautiful. Nevertheless, the male spirit insisted that the Princess was more superb. The female spirit disagreed and they argued back and forth. Finally, they decided they needed an impartial judge to settle the matter. The female spirit summoned an old, monstrous-looking, inferior spirit. He asked how he could serve them. They asked him which one of the two sleeping humans was more beautiful. He said that they were equal, but he proposed a test to establish which one was superior. He suggested that they awaken the Prince and Princess in turn while the other lay asleep. Then they could judge which one was more enamored of their sleeping counterpart. Whichever was more enamored would be judged to be the inferior one. The female and male spirit agreed to use this way to settle the matter.

They first woke the Prince. Upon awakening, he found Princess Budur sleeping beside him. He was struck with her beauty. He tried to wake her but the spirits had put her into a deep sleep. He was full of eagerness, for he thought that this was a woman that his father had put beside him to entice him finally to marry. Unable to wake her, he restrained himself and settled for removing the seal ring from her finger and putting it on his finger. Then the spirits put him back to sleep and woke up the Princess.

When Princess Budur was awoken by the spirits, she saw that the Prince sleeping beside her was in every way her counterpart. She was completely taken with him. She tried to wake him but it was impossible. She saw that he had removed her ring and she did not know what other liberties he had taken with her. She became consumed with love. She took his seal ring from his finger and put it on her own hand to replace the ring he had removed. Then she set about kissing him on the lips and hands. From there she proceeded to kiss him all over. Finally, she hugged him and with her arms around him, she fell asleep. It was clear that the male spirit had lost the argument, for the Princess showed the least restraint. With the argument settled, the spirits returned the Princess to China. When the Prince and Princess woke up the next morning, each found that they were now alone. Their new respective beloveds were nowhere to be found. They each called to their households, seeking the whereabouts of the one they had fallen in love with. Finding that no one knew where the beautiful woman had gone, Prince Kamar sank into a depression. His father the King became so concerned with him that he sat at his son's beside day and night. Princess Budur was in even worse distress. She went completely mad and had to be shackled to the iron grate of one of the windows of her room.

Neither the Prince nor the Princess could forget their encounter with their new beloved. And what is more, each had a ring to attest to the reality of the meeting with the other. At this point in the story, each of the young people had achieved a breakthrough and had been able to fall in love. They had each achieved a breakthrough with respect to the Intimacy Phase. They could now see that a marital union based on love was possible, because they had now experienced such a connection. Now the suffering phase of their journey had begun. They had each made the breakthrough to experience love, and now they had to make this possibility a reality. Campbell notes at this point: "The encounter and separation, for all its wildness, is typical of the sufferings of love. For when a heart insists on its destiny, resisting the general blandishment, then the agony is great, so too the danger." Campbell goes on to say that myths from all over the world inform us that if the hero persists in seeking to bring their newfound realization into reality, forces within their unconscious and within the world, responding to the power of their quest, will slowly bring the inevitable to pass. That is, if they persist through their suffering, they will eventually meet with success. The myths inform us that our nature (our brain) is so composed that if a hero seeks out what is missing for them and their group, and if they seek it out skillfully and with courage and determination, they will eventually unearth the missing elements of the developmental theme in question. And once empowered with the needed information, found in the night sea of their unconscious, they will be able, through great persistence, to bring these missing elements back into their group. For although the group greatly resists the transformation that the hero will impose by bringing back the discovery, the group will not resist it all together. In fact, the extended family is set up to embrace the change that the hero will force upon it. It just won't yield to the change easily. Like iron, it will resist attempts to change its form, but like iron, it will eventually yield to the unrelenting force of the hero blacksmith.

The rest of the story of Prince Kamar and Princess Budur chronicles their long journey, whereby they found each other, and then eventually found their way back to Prince Kamar's kingdom. Along the way of this long journey, little by little they acquired the power they would eventually need to assume their place as the new rulers. They also acquired the power they would need to set a new standard for their groups, in this case the standard of love as an essential ingredient in the marriage arrangement. So the myths from all over the world attest to the validity of the hero's journey and of its inevitable success if the hero is up to the incredibly difficult task of completing such a journey. But as an everyday way to resolve upstream extended family wounds, it leaves a great deal to be desired.

Chapter 10

Understanding the Extended Family Adaptation Mechanism, the
Key to Solving People Problems

So now, finally we have a picture of what is going on.
The extended family gets injured.

The Extended Family Integrative Process

In order to change its culture (its collective soft-wired
approach to the environment written into the group's team brains)
to better adapt to the environment, the family can come together
for an extended family integrative session. This leads to the
updating of the extended family culture through a process of group
coordinated transformation. Some of the circuitry in each member's
brains gets revised to support the needed changes. The group
leaves the integration session with each member now carrying
revised circuitry that determines revised group coordination
patterns. These collective revised circuits allow the group to
handle the kind of environmental injury they just sustained much
more successfully next time. This is the mechanism that we do
not use in modern industrialized society. This is the mechanism
that would spare us the creation of emotionally crippled family
members. It is the mechanism that does not require the wasteful
hero's journey process with its thousands of attempts for each rare
success.

The Enactment Process with Burdened Individuals in Each Generation

If the extended family member with the capacity to lead
such an integration is not available, or if enough of the group
cannot assemble to mutually trigger the integrative process, then

the extended family reverts to relying on enactment mode. This is a primitive but very effective way to preserve the emotional impact and learning content of the injury, until such time as an integration session is possible. Such an internal "play" or enactment requires the singling out of a younger group member to be the focal point of the stress of the unintegrated trauma. In the unconscious process of the group, it goes something like this. We, the group, need to remember this trauma until we have a chance to learn from it. In the meantime, lets have little Johnny represent the traumatic injury, for example, the death of the three uncles on a hunting expedition that we have not yet come to terms with. Little Johnny then becomes the focal point of the group's internal memory "play", the point were all of the emotional pressure is applied.

Thus, little Johnny's normal developmental process is set aside and he is commandeered for the group benefit, at great pain and detriment to him. Because each child's emotional development is absolutely dependant on the group communicative process, Johnny cannot get out from under the burden. There is no other family that he is bonded to that can trigger his development, and his family is busy focusing stress on him to preserve its memory of the trauma. Also, the child's brain contains the tendency to acquiesce to being the extended family's burden carrier, even if the price is extremely high personally. This is because the role of the extended family burden carrier is a vital one for group survival. By being the extended family's burden carrier, the young member plays a key role in helping the group preserve vital group experiences. Over time, evolution favored brain circuits that allowed for members to sacrifice themselves for group welfare.

Thus every member of the extended family is a potential burden carrier. If they are selected for the role, we can call them a hero, one who sacrifices their own well-being for the benefit of the extended family's survival. Remember the previous example of the Marines who landed on the beaches of Iwo Jima during WWII. They acted for the benefit of their families back home. It certainly wasn't in their individual best interest to charge a hale of bullets, with casualties running to 50% per landing. The difference between the Marine hero and the extended family burden carrier is that the burden carrier is currently an unsung and unrecognized hero.

Because the burdened member's developmental process is co-opted, they are deprived of a developmentally dependent, satisfying life, as long the needed group trauma integration remains undone.   So the burdened member becomes the proverbial worm on the hook, struggling to get free in order to have his quality of life restored. All his life force gets put into the struggle to try to get free. That pain of being deprived of any semblance of a satisfying life drives the burdened individual toward attempting a hero's journey.   The odds are not good that he will succeed, and the journey, if attempted will be very long. If he fails, which happens most of the time, we get the chronic emotional cripple.

The Rarely Successful Hero's Journey

For the rare burdened individual who might succeed at the hero's journey, Campbell says that the answer to their dilemma always ends up residing with the hero herself. For she is the one who is in agony now.   Her brain circuits are constantly being flooded with the emotional and informational content of the group's unintegrated traumatic stress. She becomes in essence the hub of the group's dilemma. Whenever another extended family member relates to her, the non-verbal communication directed toward her is infused in every moment with the traumatic themes that the group has not yet settled. That constant emotionally laden communication directed at her ends up continually coursing through her brain circuits, just like constant loud background music. As the burdened individual, her brain cannot help but be unconsciously aware of the themes the group is struggling with. She is constantly having the circuits connected to those themes continually activated in an emotionally distressing way. This leads directly to her emotional dysfunction, behavioral dysfunction and distortions of judgment and thinking.

How is it possible that non-verbal communication directed at the burdened individual can be so precise? Is there any scientific evidence that non-verbal communication has such precision? Here, Dr. Paul Ekman[1] comes to our rescue.   He has spent an entire career researching facial expressions and non-verbal communication. His research has found that humans display thousands of finely graded facial expressions that convey precise emotional meaning. He has also found that a majority of these facial expressions are universal for all mankind. Because facial expressions are the product of all sorts of combinations and degrees of facial muscle contractions, they come in as wide a variety of forms as the distinct colors of an artist's palette or the distinct hues of a color TV. When one adds in gestures, tone of voice, posture, and sequential behavioral signals, you have a very full non-verbal language to convey accurate emotional meaning. What is more, a huge number of these non-verbal communications are automatic. That is, we use them all the time unconsciously. We convey them to each other whether we want to or not. Compared to Swahili, a widely used language with less that 1000 words; non-verbal communication is much more complex.

Human communication is always multi-layered. Many meanings are being communicated simultaneously. We might say certain words, but our tone of voice alters the meaning because our tone of voice is sending additional information. That is why watching a Shakespeare play is so much richer than just reading the script. All of the non-verbal communication that is absent in the script comes through in the play.

When members of an extended family in enactment mode are relating to the burdened individual, they are always sending two sorts of communications. On the one hand, they may be telling him something like "Tie your shoes" or "It's time for dinner". At the same time, they are relating to him emotionally and non-verbally as the focus in their trauma enactment to keep these unintegrated themes remembered. So they are sending him information about the trauma theme and the accompanying unintegrated emotions, every time they interact with him. The burdened individual always receives both types of messages. He responds to the invitation to come to dinner and at the same time, he responds internally to the second covert layer of non-verbal trauma messages.

One can perhaps get a feel for this by imagining a black student in a mostly white southern college in the late 1960's. The black student is at the focal point of major unresolved issues of racial prejudice. Likewise, a majority of the white students are bound up in the racial prejudicial ignorance. The communications between the black student and the prejudiced white students are constantly infused with prejudicial themes, each time they interact. What is more, most of their communications relating to the unresolved racial issues are being conveyed non-verbally through facial expression, tone of voice, and other non-verbal behavioral patterns. The black student cannot escape her role as the focal point of such massive unresolved racial issues, even if she forgets about it consciously for a time. This is because her receptive communication systems, both visual and auditory, are constantly being bombarded with signals whose emotional content is full of the unresolved racial issues. This is true, no matter what she is doing, whether she is participating in class, walking across campus, or engaged in any other activity.

The black student thus has inside herself, by virtue of the constant stream of non-verbal communication to which she is exposed, implicit knowledge of what the problematic prejudicial themes are. The communication she is receiving is activating the relevant brain circuits related to these problematic racial themes all the time.

All of us seem to carry normative maps about how extended family issues can be resolved, if only the group could implement them. The black student knows what it feels like to be related to, without the burden of prejudice as a constant undercurrent. She has had this kind of positive experience at home. She has also experienced this kind of unburdened group-regard in other relationships she has experienced in the black community. The themes related to racial prejudice are inside her, because they are being constantly etched into her brain circuits. Like a fish that is constantly assaulted by the water of its dirty aquarium, she is constantly exposed to the prejudice communication matrix in which she is imbedded at the white college. And some answers about how things should be, rather than how they are at present, are also inside her. She has a large experience with prejudice-free relationships to draw on. The problem is how to go inside to retrieve the relevant information and bring it forth to be used for group transformation.

Similarly, the extended family's burdened individual, Campbell's hero, has the answers within. But bringing them forth and using them to forge group transformation is Herculean work. If the burdened individual accepts the status quo of his position and avoids ruffling any feathers in other extended family members, then no one else but he will feel any disturbing emotions. The individual at the focal point of the group's enactment will remain burdened and in emotional agony. The rest of his group will remain stuck.

If however, he goes inside and brings forth some small increment of the needed change and tries to implement that change in relating to the rest of the group, this act of courage will trigger disturbing feelings within him. For, he will first confront very uncomfortable feelings as he tries to access this small inner change. Accessing this small change will trigger him to feel the emotional difference between this new small change and the previous status quo. In other words, his act of inner courage to bring a small piece of what is needed to the fore will immediately put him in touch, within himself, with the difference emotionally between these two positions. If he tolerates his uncomfortable feelings related to this shift and holds on to his new way of relating to the group, then the group will start to become uncomfortable with the change he has induced. For then, they will start to feel the feelings associated with the change.

Sidney Poitier comes to mind. In some of his movies, he acts toward whites as if he is just as good as they are, and that puts them in touch instantaneously, whether they realize it or not, with their prejudicial stuckness. If instead he related to everyone just as they had come to expect based on the ways of prejudice; if he was an "Uncle Tom", then the themes of prejudice would remain asleep in both the black man and the white men he is relating to. Then no change would be triggered.

To repeat what Joseph Campbell said, the answer to the dilemma of the hero lies within. Once an enactment gets going, there is no other place from within the group to get much help. And to repeat what he said of the passage or journey of the hero: "fundamentally it is inward - into depths where obscure resistances are overcome and long lost, forgotten powers are revivified, to be made available for the transfiguration of the world". As the reader reads this sentence, she should understand "where obscure resistances are overcome" to mean: internal inhibiting feelings are felt and thus processed by the hero and corresponding brain circuits are rerouted. As the reader reads the phrase "long lost, forgotten powers are revivified", she should understand it to mean: brain circuits are activated that are needed to bring an adaptive approach to the problematic themes. It is as if the needed circuits are dusted off and finally put into use. Finally, as the reader reads the phrase "to be made available of the transfiguration of the world", she should understand it to mean: to be made available to be used, so that the changed hero can act as a wedge or lever required to impose the needed shift on the group.

The problem for the potential hero is thus two-fold. First, what is the answer to how the group should change, in order to relate more successfully to the recent traumatic experience? Second, how does the hero get the group to make the transition from its current approach to the new needed approach? The answers to both are already in the vast library of the human brain. The library has been built based on 53 million years of primates relating to each other, to the environment and to other competing primate groups[2]. The problem for the hero then becomes; to find within himself, what are the internal brain "patterns that connect" with the dilemma?[3] Like it is said of great literature, all the important themes are enduring. They come up over and over again in their myriad variations. The reason this is so is because we as primates have encountered them millions of times and thus our brains have co-evolved with these dilemmas. Also, a whole host of possible solutions to these dilemmas have been part of our evolution. Thus, the possible solutions have been etched into the human brain library. The problem is, how can the group activate and put into place the new needed approach from the vast array of possible approaches in their brain libraries? We should note that the solution that is finally put into place is always a human solution. We never solve the dilemma the way a group of horses would, because we don't have horse brains and we don't have the horse brain library of possible replacement scenarios. The themes and the possible solutions are both part of our evolutionary heritage.

Extended Family Adaptation Mechanism

One might ask; why isn't it easy for the extended family to change its approach to important themes? Why is it adaptive to have this change mechanism so difficult to deploy? The answer is that the extended family's culture needs to be resistant to change so that its approach to the environment can remain steadfast in the face of adversity. If the group culture was easily modifiable, then it would have all the collective determination of a jellyfish. Instead, the culture of the successful extended family consistently exhibits determination, like the determination of a seedling to force its way up through a crack in the sidewalk to reach the sun. The extended family culture needs to be like steel. It needs to hold its shape most of the time to embody the determination of a steel chisel to break rock if it has to. On the other hand, it also needs to be malleable like steel. Under special conditions, for brief periods of time, it needs to be able to be reshaped to a more useful form when necessary. For steel, it is the heating to a great temperature that allows for the needed malleability. Sudden cooling allows for the re-emergence of the required toughness.

If you heat steel hot enough it will become liquid and you can reshape it easily and instantaneously. This is akin to utilizing the coordinated extended family change process. If you have to reshape steel cold by striking it with a hammer over and over again, you can succeed but it takes a very long time and a great effort. This is akin to the hero's journey. In this case, the extended family uses the burdened individual as the hammer. If the burdened individual persists in pressuring the group with the needed changes, then the extended family will slowly change. The problems with the hero's journey method are that it is very slow, and it is very hard on the burdened individual, who has to give up being a normal person to the extent that he or she is deployed as a hammer.

In summary, if the burdened individual can somehow go against the continuous crippling stress exerted by the extended family and if he can slowly regain his developmental norms from his "brain library" within, then he will at the same time force a slow integration of the old traumatic event onto the extended family system. The problem is that these are two big "ifs". Most of the burdened individuals don't make much progress. Instead, they languish, paralyzed by their position at the focal point of the group stress. So the group makes no progress at integrating the old wound, and a member's life gets wasted. This continues from one generation to the next. Collaborative integration is in every way superior to the imposed integration that is the product of the completed hero's journey. Imposed integration is only superior, from a group survival point of view, to the group's forgetting the trauma and its lessons completely. The human team brain has learned through eons of natural selection that forgetting is a short trip to extinction. So it is better to waste the lives of burdened individual members in 10 generations and get things integrated in the 11th generation, rather than forget the traumatic lesson. The human team brain has learned that survival knowledge is extremely valuable and must be preserved at all cost. It is better to have dysfunctional, wasted members in each generation rather than have the whole group get wiped out.

So the three possible extended family mechanisms that we find as a response to a severe trauma to the group are:

1. Extended Family Integration - The extended family uses a collaborative integration approach to dealing with traumatic experiences - This is by far the most desirable method, but we have not been using this method in modern industrialized society. Using this process is the key to the creation and preservation of tremendous family wealth. In the second part of this book, I will be discussing specific ways that this mechanism can be used for wealth creation.

2. Enactment Mode and a Completed Hero's Journey - The extended family moves into enactment mode with the hope that one of the burdened individuals in a subsequent generation will be successful in the hero's journey. If the upstream wounds have been mild, this method can often work if the burdened individual seeks the help of skillful psychotherapy. For upstream wounds of moderate severity, this method takes an enormous effort and most such burdened individuals accomplish only partial success. For upstream wounds that were severe, this almost never works. There

are thousands of burdened individuals who struggle hopelessly for each individual who completes enough of their hero's journey to enjoy some success. And if the hero does complete this kind of enormous journey to a significant degree, it will take him a lifetime.

3. <u>Enactment Mode, Waiting for a Chance to Integrate - Using Burdened Individuals as Bookmarks in the Meantime</u> The extended family makes use of a burdened individual as the focal point of an enactment process to remember the upstream traumatic event, until the group has an opportunity to complete an integrative process. This may take 5 to 10 generations. In the meantime, burdened individuals are sacrificed in each generation as their lives are consumed by acting as the group's bookmark. This is a very poor approach, but it is better than forgetting. It creates psychiatric patients and dysfunctional members as burdened individuals, but at least the essence of the traumatic event is preserved.

This is the process that is primarily being used in modern society by extended families with severe upstream wounds. The American Psychiatric Association (APA) estimates that 10% of all children and adolescents have serious emotional disorders and that half of those, or 5%, have profound emotional disorders from which they will most likely be crippled for life. Medications are widely used in modern society to alleviate some of the emotional pain and other disturbing symptoms of the burdened individuals, but medications do not fix the underlying problem, the extended family's need for an integrative process. Not only do the burdened individuals become lifetime emotional cripples under this approach, but the extended families remain crippled themselves. For their developmental phases remain wounded, affecting all of their members to varying degrees. These developmental wounds cause great marital distress, health problems, and career dysfunction in many other extended family members.

What we don't see is the fourth logically possible mechanism, forgetting the traumatic experience. All the groups who have relied extensively on this method over the millennia have become extinct. Remember, in all of biology, adaptation is necessary for continued survival, and to adapt, the organism or group must remember. So forgetting is not an option if the group wants to survive. The failure to remember leads to a failure to adapt, which leads to extinction.

We have now looked at the extended family adaptation process as an evolutionarily derived learning response to group trauma. We have looked at its three parts in depth; the extended family integration processes, the enactment process that produces a burdened and symptomatic individual, and the hero's journey. I now want to examine some of the characteristics of the extended family wound patterns in more detail. In particular, I want to look at issues of symmetry and timing.

Chapter 11

Birds of a feather flock together
Anonymous

As I continued to do more retreats with three-generational families, I made some additional observations which I mentioned briefly in chapter 6. One observation was that the developmental phases that were wounded in father's extended family were always the same as the ones that were wounded in mother's extended family. The second observation was that the severity of the emotional wounds on mother's and father's sides was always about the same. Each member of the couple had selected a mate that matched them. If father's side had trouble with Autonomy and Control issues because of upstream wounds, then mother's side also had trouble with these issues. While they matched in terms of which developmental phases their families had trouble with, the spouses often showed complementary behavioral styles. For example, the over-controlling wife was often matched with the overly compliant husband. In this case, they both had trouble with the Autonomy and Control themes in their relationships, but the way they were misconfigured was in opposite directions behaviorally.

So empirically, I determined that spouses will have trouble with the same themes and to the same degree of severity. But behaviorally, they will often express their difficulty with these themes in opposite ways. These two observations make sense. If a man who is over controlling goes out on a date with a woman who is configured normally for this theme, she will not be able to tolerate his over-controlling behavior toward her and she will most likely not agree to go out with him again. If the man has problems with the Autonomy and Control phase but manifests these in an under-controlling way, a woman with a normal configuration in this phase will also be highly unlikely to go out with this man. She won't be able to stand his constant deferring to her. She won't like it if he continually asks her to make all the decisions, from which movie they should see to where they should sit, to what drinks and snacks they should get.

The man with control issues will only be able to get repeat dates with a woman with the same kind of wound. For rather than being exasperated, she will implicitly appreciate how hard it is for him to go through life with this wound to the Autonomy and Control theme, because she has been suffering with the same affliction. In addition, if he is over-controlling and she is under-controlling, they will get along better because their behavioral style will be complementary. The same will be true if he happens to be under-controlling and she is over-controlling.

Another observation I made over and over was that the occurrence of the specific wounding event in each family line usually occurred 3 – 5 generations back from the family member who was now symptomatic. This was not always the case, but I observed it very frequently. In addition, when a spouse had been the direct recipient of a wounding event as a child, they usually married someone whose parent had been the direct recipient of a wounding event to the same developmental phase and of the same magnitude. They rarely married someone who had been the direct wound recipient, as they had been.

As I mentioned previously, I was once describing these observations to a physician. He shared that his wife's father had died when she was four but that he had not experienced the death of a parent. I then asked about his parents. We both shared a chill as he recalled that his father had lost a parent when he was four. This kind of staggered matching became very familiar to me. I saw it over and over again.

When one reflects on it, it makes perfect sense. A wife who lost her father when she was four had suffered a severe disruption to the developmental stages occurring at the 4 year age level. A husband who grew up with a father with the same kind of injury would know very well how much suffering that kind of injury inflicts, because he saw it in his own father. And because all children love their parents, he would have great empathy for his father's wounds. Therefore, he would already have the capacity to deeply understand and empathize with his wife's childhood suffering. And she would instantly recognize that he understood her in a way that other dating partners could never understand her, even if she didn't know why. He would have a compassion for her childhood suffering that he had developed from loving a father who had suffered similarly. And this compassion would be an important element in their love. In addition, because his father had specific developmental wounds related to age 4, he as the son would also suffer from misconfiguration of the same developmental themes. As we have seen previously, his father's impairment with particular developmental themes would be carried over to him as his father raised him.

Since potential spouses match each other with regard to which developmental themes are wounded and to what degree, their children will be born into two extended family systems, both mother's and father's, that are a match for unintegrated, upstream developmental wounds. Most families in modern society are in enactment mode with respect to upstream wounds, having no access to an integrative process. And for many of these extended families, the upstream wounds are severe. It is therefore no surprise that the occurrence of dysfunctional children and adolescents, where at least one child in each generation becomes a burden carrier for their two wounded extended families, will be widespread.

Chapter 12

Three sex markers and a death marker.
The Author

Having seen the symmetry of wound patterns in extended families, the next thing that puzzled me was the question of timing. When will the burdened child in the next generation have her difficulties and become symptomatic? Since all children go through the same developmental phases at predictable times, the burdened child will have trouble when she reaches the stage of the theme where her mother's and father's extended families are wounded. After all, how can the two extended families to which she belongs give her a good interactive experience with regards to a developmental phase, that they themselves still have so much trouble with? What is more, as we have seen, the two extended families need a burdened child as part of the enactment memory mechanism.

Children go through the first 9 developmental stages before the age of twelve. From age 12 to about age 24, they go through the 10th developmental stage called the Identity phase. But the Identity phase is very special. During the Identity phase, starting at age 12, the child revisits the previous 9 stages in the same order, and for the same duration each, as they did in the first 12 years of childhood. In childhood, they visited these 9 stages, with an emphasis on these themes, as they relate to relationships in the family. In adolescence, they revisit these 9 stages but this time, the emphasis is on their relationships to the community.

If a child has trouble with a particular developmental stage in childhood, then they will have trouble when they revisit the same theme during adolescence. So a child who has trouble with the Autonomy and Control phase from age 1 to 3 will have trouble with Autonomy and Control issues again in adolescences. Since the Autonomy and Control theme shows up with the same chronology during adolescence as it did in childhood, the child will have trouble with this theme beginning 1 year into adolescence and continuing until 3 years into adolescence (12 + 1 to 12 + 3 or from ages 13 to 15). What is also very clear is that when the child or adolescent is having trouble with a developmental theme, her parents are also having trouble with the same theme at the same time. If you missed most of geometry in 9th grade, because you were frequently sick, then you will have trouble with geometry again as a parent, when you try to help your child with his 9th grade geometry homework.

So, all children will deal with the same developmental themes twice; once in childhood and once in adolescence. And the parents will revisit these same themes at the same time that their children do. Is this what we find when we observe families? The answer is yes. I have had the opportunity to do more than 600 family interviews in the last five years, where a child or adolescent was symptomatic and having trouble with particular developmental phases. What I found was that the parents revisit the same themes two more times for each of their children. And they revisit the same themes precisely when their children do and again when their adolescents do.

To help visualize this childhood developmental chronology and the revisitation chronology during adolescence, I came up with the idea of a <u>developmental clock</u>. Look at the picture of the clock on the next page.

The Developmental Clock

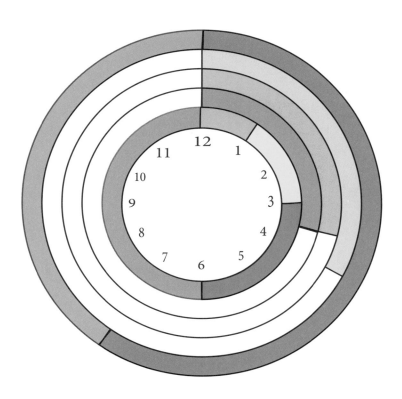

Basic Trust - Birth to 1 Year

Autonomy - 1 Year to 3 Years

Initiative - 3 1/2 to 6 1/2 Years

Industry - 6 1/2 to 12 Years

Separation-Individuation - Birth to 3 Years

Affect Regulation - 6 Months to 3 1/2 Years

Gender Identity - Birth to 4 Years

Sense of Self Established - Birth to 7 Years

Sense of Self Solidified - 7 to 12 Years

Imagine that each numeral on the clock represents one year. The small hand will go around year by year, visiting the developmental stages as they are arranged chronologically around the clock dial. Once the small hand has completed one revolution, the passage of time will be 12 years. At this point, the small hand will start around again. The first complete revolution of the small hand is called childhood. As the small hand starts to go around again for the second time, it will revisit all the same developmental themes as it did the first time around, and in the same chronological order. The second complete revolution of the small hand is called adolescence.

After doing this work with families for a number of years, I began to notice that married adults had trouble with their marriages at characteristic times. What is more, these times correlated with the developmental timing of themes that their extended families had trouble with. What do I mean by this? If a husband and wife came from extended families that had wounds to the Autonomy and Control stage, then I found that the couple, sooner of later, had trouble with Autonomy and Control issues with each other. The problems usually came about 2 years into the marriage and almost always occurred between 1 and 3 years into the marriage. I noticed that for couples with Basic trust problems in their relationship, the problems surfaced during the first year of the marriage. This is just what we see in children, where Basic Trust issues are central during the first year of life. What I finally realized, after seeing many, many families, was that the same developmental themes of childhood were being revisited by the couple during their marriage, with the date of their marriage as the starting point.

This makes sense. The deepest relationship we will ever have is with our parents. We work on the developmental themes in relationship to our parents in a regular predictable sequence. First we learn to trust them. Then we work on how to share power and control with them, the Autonomy and Control phase. We are also, from the beginning, working on our self-esteem, vis à vis our parents. Marriage is the second deepest relationship we have with another person. It makes sense that we need to work on all the developmental themes in our relationship to our marital partner. For the developmental themes are the foundation of any relationship.   And as with any relationship, but especially in a marriage, these themes form the deeper vital infrastructure of the marital relationship.   First we work on trust with our marriage partner.   Then we work on how to share power.   And from the beginning, we are working on mutual self-esteem.   In fact, all the same themes of childhood get revisited as we build our marital relationship.   And they get revisited in the same chronology as we visited them in childhood. If we go back to our developmental clock, we see that the clock not only starts at birth and begins again at 12, the beginning of adolescence; but also a second developmental clock for the marital relationship begins on the day the marriage starts.

Once I recognized these patterns, it became possible to predict when a particular marital couple would have relationship difficulties.   A man from an extended family with wounds to a particular developmental phase "A" ("A" being any particular developmental phase) will have trouble when it is time for the couple to work on the same "A" themes in their relationship.   He will have married a woman from an extended family that also has trouble with the same developmental phase "A".   When they get to the timing point in their marital relationship for their developmental phase "A" issues to be worked on, they will both struggle, because they are both misconfigured for that phase. When their first child gets to the same phase, they will have trouble again, but this time it will usually be more severe.   This is because their connection to their child is more intense than the marital bond.   Dr. Whitaker used to say that the parent – child bond was 220 volts and that the marital bond was 110 volts.

If a couple has such severe problems that a separation and divorce ensues, the marital breakup invariable occurs at one of three points.   First, it may occur in conjunction with the <u>couple's arrival</u> at the particular developmental phase where they are wounded.   If the couple and their extended families have trouble with issues corresponding to age 4, then the marital breakup could occur 4 years into the marriage.   The small hand on the couple's marital developmental clock will have gotten to the 4th year and the couple will be revisiting these wounded themes together.

The second and more frequent possibility is that the marital relationship will break up when their child arrives at the corresponding wounded developmental phase point. In the above example where the couple and their extended families have trouble with issues of the 4th year, the marriage more often will break up when their child turn 4 and begins working on the 4th year wounded developmental issues.

Frequently, I have seen a third marital pattern, where the couple and their extended family with wounded 4th year issues will have significant marital difficulties 4 years into their marriage. Then, when their child turns 4, they will have a more severe marital crisis, but it still won't lead to divorce. Finally, when their adolescent is 16 and her developmental clock revisits the 4th year in adolescence, the couple's marriage will finally break up. I have observed that the more severe the developmental wound for a particular couple and their extended families, the more likely the marriage will break up when their child gets to the age where they are working on the wounded developmental theme for the first time. In other words, the more severe the developmental wounds, the less likely that the marriage will survive until their offspring gets to adolescence.

In addition to being able to predict the timing of marital discord, I was now able to predict the nature of the marital discord. If a couple and their extended families had trouble with wounds to the Basic Trust phase, then the couple will have difficulty with issues of trust in their relationship. If the couple and their extended families had trouble with wounds to the Autonomy and Control phase, then the couple will struggle with power issues is their relationship. So it now became possible to predict when a couple would have marital difficulties and what the nature of these marital difficulties would be.

A good theory allows one to explain all the observations in the simplest way. It also allows one to make predictions that turn out to be accurate. This developmentally-based way of looking at the lifecycle of individuals and families has allowed me to predict when severe marital dysfunction will occur. It has also allowed me to predict when a child will become emotionally or behaviorally symptomatic. With this theory, the key is to know which developmental stages in mother's and father's extended families have unintegrated wounds.

With this theory, one can also predict the nature of the

trouble in the marriage or the nature of the child's emotional or behavioral trouble by knowing which developmental phases are wounded. It also works in reverse. If you know which developmental themes the child or the marital relationship is having trouble with, then you know that there will invariably be corresponding upstream wounds. When you look, you will invariably find that the mother's and father's extended families both suffered specific trauma to these very same developmental themes, usually 3-5 generations upstream.

I began this chapter with the phrase: Three sex markers and a death marker. If you will notice, the three points at which the developmental clock begins are: the start of the marriage, the birth of the child, and the beginning of adolescence at age 12. These also happen to be the most basic anthropologic time markers in all societies throughout the world. And these time markers all have to do with sex and the possibility of new life. The onset of marriage is marked by all human societies, for it is the beginning of the union of the couple, which makes new life possible. The birth of the child is the beginning of new life. And the onset of puberty is the beginning of the maturing child's capacity as a new adolescent to be capable of reproduction. When it became clear to me that my new theory dovetailed with these three most basic anthropologic time markers, I became convinced that the theory was grounded on the bedrock of human nature and its biology.

The last marker I mentioned in the introductory phrase at the beginning of this chapter is the "death marker". Death plays a central role in all human extended families, for it marks the subtraction of critical members from the extended family team, by the inevitable ending of the individual life cycle. As I will illustrate in chapter 17, the death of a parent in old age restarts the developmental clock for the now parentless adult child. When a parent dies, their adult child starts a new parentless life. This results in the adult child revisiting their developmental themes anew. The death of the parent requires a readjustment of all of the adult child's developmental themes, because the adult child will now be moving forward in life under the new parentless circumstances.

I have also found that death plays a very important additional role in extended family dynamics. Premature death is a frequent cause of the kind of upstream trauma to the extended family system that we are focusing on. In our earlier story of the 6 year old boy with OCD, death caused three of his grandparents to lose a parent. Sometimes, I have found that the death of a child is the crippling upstream wound. At other times, I have found that the crippling trauma was the permanent loss of family members due to separation. This is a frequent occurrence in the family histories of Americans, because most of our inhabitants are the descendants of emigrants, who left family members behind.

After the great Irish potato famine of 1849, many Irish immigrated to the United States. The extended families they left behind knew that they would never see the departing member again, so they would hold wakes for them. The departing member's leaving, never to be seen again, was just like a death for them. Death, the danger of death due to severe illness, or prolonged or permanent separation make up the majority of the core causes of the upstream traumas to extended families. So this theory rests on three universal anthropologic sex markers and a final universal anthropologic death marker.

When one has a theory that enables you to predict something as complicated as the timing and character of marital discord or the timing and character of symptom formation in children and adolescence, then you are struck with how orderly the natural world, and human nature in particular, can be. What is more, with this theory, it becomes clear that the symptoms that family members struggle with, in a very real sense, do not belong to them. Their symptoms are merely manifestations of the extended family's attempt to remember unintegrated upstream wounds. The extended families are using an enactment mode to remember, and the symptomatic member is at the focal point of this enactment. If the two extended families complete an integration of their upstream traumas, the offspring or the spouse's symptoms disappear. And this happens without any need to discuss the details of the particular symptoms or marital problems.

It is like the little boy with his finger in the dyke. Once the extended family who owns the dyke collectively sets about to fix it, the boy who had been bound to the dyke, trying to keep it from leaking, is released from his symptomatic role. He can now leave his burdensome role of being attached to the broken dyke. And he can now go about catching up with the activities of his age mates. The precise details of how he had to stand, which finger he used, or of how he had to alternate his fingers when one or the other got tired become irrelevant.

This is what happened in the first case of the 6 year old boy with the sudden onset of OCD. By working with the mother's and father's extended families to integrate the upstream wounds, the two groups moved out of enactment mode. The boy was no longer at the focal point of the families' enactments, and he suddenly became free of his symptoms. In subsequent chapters, I will present many additional examples of the application of this theory to the solving of important people problems.

In the history of science, when a theory emerges that makes hitherto unintelligible and unpredictable data predictable, then Mother Nature has finally graced us by revealing a little more of herself. The development of this new theory of extended family dynamics is part of this process. And with this new knowledge comes great power. For it frees us from victimization by certain cryptic processes of the natural world. It is similar to finally understanding the role that bacteria play in the causation of infectious disease.

The knowledge of bacteria, so long in coming, made it possible for mankind to protect itself from infectious scourges. It also allowed us to begin to make use of the incredible power that understanding and working with bacteria affords us. We can now not only make better wine; we have also moved to being able to make synthetic medications, using bacteria as our factories. As Pasture said in his famous quote:

"Science and Peace will triumph over Ignorance and War, nations will unite, not to destroy but to build, and the future will belong to those who have done the most for suffering humanity."

This theory has been a very long in coming. I have been privileged to play the role of running the last small leg of this great relay race, to understand and tame human emotional afflictions. Once this theory is understood and applied, it will bring great boons to those who utilize this understanding. I now turn to the practical applications that have occurred to me and that can be made use of immediately.

Part Two   Practical Applications

Chapter 13

Emotional Problems

Many families struggle with emotional problems in one or more of their members. Those family members fortunate enough to have mild or moderate problems often achieve success and relief using therapy that is readily available. For those with bipolar disorder, OCD, severe depression, eating disorders, severe anxiety disorders, early symptoms of a psychotic disorder, or other severe emotional disorders, the chance for success and relief often feels more like the myth of Sisyphus. Sisyphus was a character in Greek mythology who was condemned to forever try to roll a large boulder up a hill. When he would get it near to the top, it would roll down again and he would have to start all over. His task never ended.

The families of individuals with a severe problem often ask themselves what they have done to deserve such an affliction. The parents are hard working, good people who have tried their best and yet they have a child, adolescent, or young adult with one of these severe emotional disorders. In spite of their best efforts and in spite of searching for the best therapeutic alternatives, there seems to be no help in sight that will rescue their offspring.

Mother Nature guards her secrets jealously. Only a few hundred years ago, the average lifespan was under thirty years, with most people dying of infectious disease. Yet before the 1880's, people didn't understand the true causes of infectious disease and therefore often could not protect themselves or their loved ones. In my experience, it is the same with the more serious emotional disorders. Individual therapy, hospitalizations, medications, and even regular family therapy are often ineffectual with these afflictions. They help some, but like the myth of Sisyphus, the problems keeps coming back over and over. And they often grow more severe with each returning bout.

When these problems are looked at using the Extended Family Adaptation Theory that we delineated in the previous chapters, it becomes clear that the problem doesn't even belong to these symptomatic individuals. They are merely caught at the focal point of long-term stress patterns that have been present in the two extended families to which they belong. If the Extended Family Adaptation Theory is correct, then it would make sense that individual therapy and other approaches aimed at removing the individual's symptoms will most likely fail when the situation is severe. For the wrong problem is being attacked. It is like trying to bail a rowboat with a hole in it. You work and work and work but your efforts are in vain. The water keeps coming in. On the other hand, if you approached the problem by finding the hole and fixing it first, you can have the boat dry in no time.

The central problem with the above mentioned emotional afflictions does not reside with the individual. The individual as symptom bearer is merely the unlucky family member at the focal point of the two extended families' long-standing stress. In my experience, only the extended family as a whole has sufficient power to change the situation in these severe cases. For, it is the extended families' need for integration of previous survival-threatening experiences that has gone unmet. It is the two extended families who need a change in their status quo, in their family culture.

If the two extended families come together in a series of retreats to do the needed integrative work, then the stress that was burdening the system will be alleviated. And the symptomatic individual will no longer be at the focal point of the groups' stress, because the stress will be gone. The integration of the old traumas will be complete and the system will have no more use for their internal enactments as a way to remember.

Once freed of the chronic stress burden, the previously symptomatic individual finds that they are now imbedded in an extended family matrix of non-verbal communication that activates their healthy circuits. The "use it or lose it" rule of synaptic plasticity[1] takes over. As we see with all skills and patterns, we retain the patterns we practice over and over again, and we loose the patterns that we stop practicing. In this case, the old dysfunctional emotional and behavioral patterns, and their associated brain pathways that were activated because they were central to the emotional dysfunction, fall into disuse and are slowly eliminated. At the same time, the previously burdened family member is now continually involved in new healthy non-verbal communication patterns within their extended families. These communicative experiences provide the neuronal stimulation needed to activate the pathways that will allow these previously burdened individuals to function normally.

What is more, all individuals seem to keep normative (normal or healthy) maps of what a healthy developmental configuration looks like for each of their developmental stages. They don't seem to need to "re-learn" the healthy developmental configuration. They don't seem to need to be taught how to act more developmentally appropriate. They just seem to grow into acting more developmentally normal. What the newly unburdened patient experiences and their family sees is a gradual healthy maturing process taking over. It is like the gradual healing of a broken bone that has now been properly immobilized and allowed to set. The unburdened member's symptoms gradually go away as the extended families go through the integrative process.

To repeat, the unburdened member's brain circuits that were related to the misconfigured developmental stages and that were causing their symptoms gradually get remodeled. And soon, the brain systems for those developmental phases become properly reconfigured. They now are able in all of life's situations to function normally. And what is more important, the extended families have now achieved integration of their old wounds. The extended families' perpetual enactment process that has been claiming victims in each generation since the inception of the upstream wounds now ceases. The pattern of internal victimization is now over.

It is my experience that grandparents are in the best position of all family members to appreciate the great victory that the family has thus achieved. For, they have seen first hand through several generations the toll that the previous enactment process has been extracting, even if they did not understand its nature. Now they see that tragedy has been replaced by comedy; that repeated misfortune has been replaced by emotional health.

This has been brought about by the extended families' coming to appreciate and making use of their inherent powers and capabilities, with the help of suitable professional leadership.

The Bipolar Disorders

I now want to give you some examples of families where a specific family member was at the focal point of chronic unintegrated stress and was exhibiting severe symptoms. The first example that I want to present is a problem that is being diagnosed more and more frequently in children and adolescents; Bipolar Disorder, either Type I or Type II. Bipolar Disorder is characterized by symptoms which may include: periods of "abnormally and persistently elevated, expansive or irritable mood"[2] that last 4 days to a week or more. Irritability is the mood abnormality that is frequently seen in children and adolescents. The person may exhibit inflated self-esteem or a grandiose manor or behavior. The person may show a decreased need for sleep or be incessantly talkative. They may seem to have ideas racing through their mind in rapid succession. They may be very distractible or show an increase in purposeful or non-purposeful behavior. Finally, they may show an excessive involvement in high-risk activities such as indiscrete sexual activity, unrestrained shopping, or flashy business deals that have not been thoroughly checked out.

If they have enough of these symptoms, and if the symptoms are severe enough to cause serious impairment to their occupational or social functioning, or if the person requires hospitalization for safety purposes, or if there are also psychotic symptoms present (loss of touch with reality), then a diagnosis of Bipolar I Disorder is made. Bipolar I Disorder may or may not include severe depressive symptoms that are mixed in to the overall picture. If the person's episodes of "elevated, expansive, or irritable mood"[3] are not severe enough to cause a marked decrease in the social or occupational functioning, and if these symptoms are not severe enough to require hospitalization and are not associated with psychotic symptoms, then a diagnosis of Bipolar

II Disorder can be made. Symptoms of serious depression also need to be part of the picture to make a diagnosis of Bipolar II Disorder.

These two diagnostic categories, Bipolar I Disorder and Bipolar II Disorder are clusters of symptoms that have been found over time to be useful ways to categorize the person's emotional disturbance. These diagnostic categories come from the DSM-IV-TR diagnostic manual. The DSM-IV-TR is a descriptive system that delineates conditions based on groups of symptoms that are frequently found together. It is not a system that groups conditions based on cause. With this in mind, the DSM-IV-TR system is useful to facilitate communication between clinicians and mental health facilities, but since it is not based on underlying cause, it is not necessarily the best classification system for the directing of treatment.

As a comparison, there was a descriptive diagnostic category of "consumption" that was commonly used in medicine in the 17th to 19th century. Consumption was a descriptive diagnosis based on the symptom of the wasting away of the body. Originally, this diagnosis was used to classify any wasting disease; so tuberculosis, congestive heart failure, and the wasting and emaciation due to recurring malaria were all grouped together, because the presenting symptoms of bodily wasting were all the same. This descriptive disease classification was useful at the time, because it helped convey the patient's condition. But from a treatment point of view, the descriptive diagnostic system left much to be desired, because it is not based on the actual cause of the condition.

In medicine, once the cause of tuberculosis, congestive heart failure, and malaria were determined, the descriptive diagnostic system with terms such as "consumption" was abandoned in favor of a diagnostic system based on cause. So "consumption" due to the tubercle bacillus became tuberculosis. No one talked about "consumption" as a term for tuberculosis once the tubercle bacillus was identified as causal.

If we move beyond the descriptive diagnosis of Bipolar I and Bipolar II Disorder provided by the DSM-IV-TR, we can look at the Bipolar conditions from a developmental perspective. A developmental perspective allows us to focus on which brain-emotional-behavioral system the child is having trouble with. If you make a developmental diagnosis instead of a symptom based DSM IV diagnosis, what you see is an individual who is unable to regulate his emotions. Instead of being able to keep himself in relative emotional stability, he is subject to continual bouts of mood swings. He is like a geographic area that is continually experiencing hurricanes with all of the associated disruptions of normal activities.

If you go back to look at the development of children, you see this very condition as a normal state of affairs in children under the age of 2 ½. Young children generally cannot calm themselves. If they get upset, they need a parental figure to assist them in calming themselves down. From about the age of 6 months, children very gradually acquire the ability to increasingly self-soothe. By the time they are about 3 ½, they are generally pretty good at calming themselves after they have been upset under most normal circumstances. Then, when they are adolescents, they revisit this theme again, from about age 12 ½ to about age 15 ½. During this 3 year period, they gain additional capacity to regulate their emotions which is needed, now that their biological system has become "supercharged" so to speak, under the influence of sex hormones. Children or adolescents with Bipolar Disorder do not have the brain system that is responsible for emotional regulation properly configured yet. They go through their daily lives with their emotion-regulation system unable to do the proper job for them. As they get older and the social and emotional demands on them naturally increase, their relative inability to regulate their emotions causes them more and more difficulties. Pretty soon, they are unable to function socially and occupationally.

When you look at the histories of the two extended families that this kind of child or adolescent comes from, you invariably find massive wounds upstream. These wounds, furthermore are very specific in the timing of their occurrence. On both mother's and father's side, the wounds invariably occurred to the ancestors when they were at the age where emotion regulation was one of the prime developmental themes they were working on. So, the individual ancestors who sustained the wound upstream were between either 6 months to 3 ½ years of age, or between 12 ½ to 15 ½ years of age. Often, an individual ancestor was working on the childhood phase of this theme on the mother's side and another ancestor was working on the adolescent phase of the theme on the father's side when their wounds occurred. While this kind of staggered upstream picture is common, one can see any of the four possible variations of upstream wounding patterns to ancestors: childhood- childhood, childhood-adolescent, adolescent-childhood, or adolescent-adolescent.

Frequently, one can find evidence of multiple wounding events occurring over several generations on each side. A constellation of multiple upstream wounding events, on either parent's side, or on both sides, has the effect of intensifying the degree of stress in the extended family system, related to the unintegrated wounds. Whether the wound to the developmental phase of emotion regulation resulted from a single severe upstream wound to each side, or from the accumulation of multiple serious wounds that added to each other, the effect downstream is the same. The current burdened family member suffers by being continually stimulated in precisely the right ways non-verbally by both extended family system, so as to maintain his circuits is a steady condition of misconfiguration. His circuits, in this misconfigured state, are unable to provide him with the needed age appropriate emotion regulation that is so critical to his normal functioning.

If the two extended families are fortunate enough to get an opportunity to go through the needed integration process, their burdened family member gradually gets put out of a job. The two extended families, by completing the integration of the old upstream wounds, are fixing the "family dike" so to speak. Their burdened member, who was previously stuck in the two extended families' wound memory processes, gets put out of a job, like the boy with his finger in the dike, once the dike gets fixed. As that happens, the misconfigured brain circuits in the burdened member gradually fall into disuse. As these brain circuits associated with dysfunction fall into disuse, they are replaced, thanks to the miracle of brain plasticity that we all possess, by new functional brain circuits. These new functional brain circuits are configured properly to do the job of emotional regulation successfully.

In order to achieve the integration of the old upstream wounds, the two extended families must meet separately, taking turns. Mother's side attends an integration half-day retreat on even months and father's side attends the half-day retreats on odd months. As this process of wound integration gradually gets accomplished over a period of months, the burdened individual gradually needs less and less of the mood stabilizing medicines that they may be on. They typically end up no-longer needing any medication about half way through the process.

The depressing and overwhelming emotions that were associated with the original wounding experiences of the ancestors gradually get dissipated as the wounds get integrated. It is like draining the two extended families' emotional swamps. And because the burdened individual had been at the focal point of all of this unintegrated upstream stress, with its associated depressing and overwhelming emotions, a tremendous emotional weight gradually gets lifted from this burdened individual. So not only does the burdened individual gradually get better and better able to regulate their emotions, the perpetual emotional burden that they seem to have been carrying gets gradually lifted.

When we look at extended families with a member that has been diagnosed with Bipolar Disorder, we frequently find that an uncle or aunt on each side has had similar sorts of difficulties. Because one finds family members in previous generations that have had the same kinds of symptoms, it has led some medical researchers to conclude that the Bipolar conditions have a genetic origin. But in fact, the ability of the two extended families to complete their needed integration, and have it result in the gradual return to normality for the burdened family member, shoots a big hole in the genetic theory. A condition such as sickle cell anemia, which is caused by a genetic mutation that results in a misshapen hemoglobin molecule, does not get resolved by holding monthly extended family meetings. On the other hand, Russian, as the language of a particular extended family, could look genetic to someone from another planet. After all, it clearly runs in families. But once our space traveler observed that an extended family, by working together, could switch over from Russian to English, they would know that Russian was not genetic. Genetically caused conditions don't get changed by the extended family changing the way they interact with each other.

So, to re-summarize, the emotions from the old wound gets processed and resolved. In other words, the extended family's wounded "emotional swamp" gradually gets drained. The system integrates the emotions from the old trauma and transforms them into a useful alteration in the family organizational culture, which is the original purpose behind the whole extended family adaptation mechanism. The burdened individual is thus eased out of their dysfunctional role as they become unneeded. The burdened individual's brain system that is responsible for regulating emotions is no-longer overwhelmed, by being at the focal point of the chronic stress. His brain circuits gradually get transformed to a well-functioning configuration and he is all better. And the two extended families have each succeeded in creating great value for themselves. Not only have they released their shared burdened individual from his dysfunctional bondage, but in the process, every other member's emotion-regulating brain system has gotten a simultaneous tune-up. But the biggest victory or gain is that the two extended family systems have gotten themselves out of enactment mode. They have now changed their futures. They will no longer be unconsciously selecting new members in each generation to carry the wound memory forward, awaiting the vital integrative experience.

So much for Bipolar Disorder. While I have obviously not worked with all possible cases of Bipolar Disorder, all the ones that I have worked with have turned out this way. And it is easy to tell from the beginning whether or not a particular Bipolar situation has the potential to be resolved. One just needs to examine the upstream history of both extended families. One needs to see if the right wound patterns exist to explain the current Bipolar symptoms in the burdened family member. If the right wound patterns are present, then I have found that it is always a case of unintegrated extended family wounds, and the situation can be completely resolved.

I should let the reader know that I have had the opportunity to gather upstream wound information on over 600 cases of severe emotional dysfunction in children and adolescents in the last 5 years. The conditions usually came from the following symptom-based diagnostic categories: Bipolar Disorder, symptoms of an early psychotic disorder, OCD, Oppositional Defiant Disorder, Eating Disorders including Bulimia and Anorexia Nervosa, Major Depression, and Severe Anxiety Disorder. In all of these cases of severe emotional dysfunction, I have consistently found that there are patterns of severe upstream wounds sufficient to explain the burdened individual's symptoms. And all of the extended families with members suffering from these conditions, who have completed the extended family integration process, have succeeded in resolving the dysfunction of their burdened member.

Early Psychotic Symptoms

I have gathered data on fewer families who have had a member with early psychotic symptoms; compared to the number of families I have seen with members with other diagnostic categories. However, in those families with a member with early psychosis that I have seen, I have found that the upstream wound patterns are consistently present. In such cases, the developmental phase that is wounded is always the Basic Trust phase and the wounding is always massive. I estimate that the level of stress that such families are dealing with is at least 10 times as high as the level of stress involved with other serious diagnoses. The wounds involved have occurred to ancestors either during their first year of life or during their first year of adolescence, from ages 12 to 13. Again, the wound pattern is always present in both mother's and father's extended families.

In cases of early psychotic symptoms where I have worked with the extended families to integrate the emotional wounds, the psychotic symptoms have gradually shifted to more obsessive symptoms as the integrative process progressed. As the work continues, the obsessive-compulsive symptoms gradually subside completely as sufficient integration of the upstream wounds is accomplished. This is interesting because many previous psychiatric researchers from decades past have made an association between OCD and psychotic symptoms.

I have not had the opportunity to do a large number of extended family integrations where early psychosis was the presenting symptom. Consequently, I cannot say that the resolution of the psychotic symptoms always progresses by first shifting to obsessive–compulsive symptoms, and then to complete resolution. However, this progression makes sense, in terms of there being a wound to the same Basic Trust system in both cases. The difference between the histories in these two kinds of extended families; where early psychosis is the presenting symptom in one and OCD is the presenting symptom in the other, seems to be a difference in the degree of upstream woundedness.

I have always observed, no matter what the presenting symptoms, that as the extended family integration progresses, the degree of symptom manifestation gradually decreases until all symptoms are gone. So, if the psychiatric researchers from previous decades were right, then one would expect to see a shift from the more severe psychotic symptoms to the relatively less severe OCD symptoms as the upstream wound integration progresses.

To summarize, I have concluded that early psychotic symptoms and OCD symptoms are on a continuum, from massive woundedness of the Basic Trust developmental phase to less severe woundedness of this phase. With this in mind, I find it very encouraging that my observations and my theory are consistent with the observations of a host of earlier psychiatric researchers who also considered these two diagnostic categories to be part of a continuum. I find this especially encouraging, since in my experience, the extended families that complete their integration process have the power to completely resolve their difficulties even when the presenting symptom is early psychosis.

Obsessive-Compulsive Disorder

We have looked at one case of OCD earlier that involved a six year old boy. Another case where OCD was the presenting symptom involved a 12 year old boy named Bill. His parents, Fred and Edith, said that he had always had OCD type symptoms from early childhood. He had trouble using the bathroom outside the home for fear of germs, and he showed frequent hand washing behavior. His symptoms had become worse during third grade. He also showed trouble with Autonomy-Control issues in his dealings with his parents at home.

In OCD, there is a wound to the Basic Trust phase, but I have often observed that the wound was indirect. By that, I mean, ancestors upstream were wounded at other non-Basic Trust developmental phases, but the character of the wound involved a deep disruption to the Basic Trust phase at the same time. In the previous case of the 6 year old boy, each of the wounded grandparents had completed a normal Basic Trust phase from ages 0 to 1 years, only to have their sense of Basic Trust devastated later by the death of their parents when they were 6. This may partially explain why extended families with OCD symptoms are on the less severe end of the continuum compared to extended families with psychotic symptoms. In the latter type of extended family, the wounds to the ancestors more often occur directly during the Basic Trust phase for 0 to 1 years of age.

OCD also has an Autonomy-Control component. This means that the child's ancestors had attempted to compensate for the severe disruption to their Basic Trust configuration by attempting to over-control things and situations in their environment. In this second case of the 12 year old boy, Bill, his father, Fred was two years old when Fred's mother was killed in a car accident. Because of the severe nature of the emotional trauma, Fred would have had his Basic Trust phase, which he had previously completed, severely disrupted. What is more, because Fred was 2 years old when the trauma occurred, he would have had additional disruption to his Autonomy-Control phase.

This indeed happened and it left Fred with an over-controlling configuration to this phase. Edith experienced trauma in the form of her parents divorcing when she was eight. Because she was eight when the divorce occurred and she remained living with her mother, she was spared the disruptive influence of losing contact with the same sex parent during the Industry phase. But the wounds that cause the OCD came from further back on her side. Edith's mother Gertrude grew up in a household where she was the object of significant ongoing childhood physical and emotion abuse. The unsafe nature of Gertrude's childhood constituted the disruptive trauma that damaged her Basic Trust system.

Gertrude's daughter Edith grew up learning about trust from a mother whose Basic Trust during childhood had been continually compromised. Thus, Edith's Basic Trust phase ended up being misconfigured as well. Maternal grandmother Gertrude had coped with the continual insecurity and trauma of her childhood situation by developing an over-controlling approach to life. She had married a man, Henry, who had a drinking problem (wound to Basic Trust) and who was overly compliant (wound to Autonomy-Control). When this couple interacted with their daughter Edith during the Autonomy-Control stage, Edith adopted a complementary style to her mother by being over-compliant. It was a given that she would have trouble with the Autonomy-Control stage since both of her parents were misconfigured for that stage. Since she spent most of her time with her over-controlling mother between the ages of 1 and 3, it made sense that she would be configured to the complementary position.

In each interaction with her mother that involved control themes, Gertrude would be over-controlling in the relationship, leaving an under-controlling response as her daughter Edith's only option. When Edith and Fred married and had a son, the son Bill got input from both extended families leading to his being misconfigured for his Basic Trust phase. In addition, he got input from both extended families which misconfigured his Autonomy-Control system. His exhibiting OCD symptoms from early childhood reflected the fact that he was misconfigured for these two developmental phases, while being at the focal point of stresses for these two themes.

As Bill's two extended families gradually integrated their upstream wounds, Bill's OCD symptoms gradually disappeared. His trouble with Autonomy-Control issues also gradually disappeared and that paralleled a marked improvement in the way each of his parents handled these relationship themes. His father Fred gradually became less controlling and subsequently more effective as a parent and also, more effective at work. His mother Edith gradually became more controlling in an appropriate way so that she was no-longer overly compliant in her relationships with others.

This case goes to show how the burdened family member may exhibit problems with more than one developmental phase. This frequently happens in OCD. For, as I mentioned previously, the wounds that originally caused the disruption upstream frequently occurred at an age that was different than the Basic

Trust age range itself. The wound to the Basic Trust system occurred because of the trust-disrupting nature of the trauma, and at the same time, there is a wound to the developmental theme that the child's ancestors were working on when the trauma occurred.

We also see something else in comparing these two cases. In some situations, such as that of the 6 year old boy, the disruption is severe and sudden on both sides. In other cases, such as in that of the 12 year old boy, the disruption is sudden and severe on one side and protracted on the other side. We see the protracted pattern of Basic Trust disruption with the maternal grandmother Gertrude's prolonged traumatic experience as a child.

As I said earlier, in my experience, OCD always involves a disruption to the Basic Trust system. And it is frequently but not always associated with a disruption and misconfiguration of the Autonomy-Control system. Depending on the age of occurrence of the upstream trauma to the child's ancestors, other associated developmental phases may also be affected. In the case of the six year old boy, there was a problem with the transition to the Industry phase, which is what is being worked on at age six. In any case, once the extended family integration is completed, the symptoms resolve and the affected developmental phases gradually revert to a normal adaptive configuration. I have found a pattern of upstream disruption to the Basic Trust system in all of the OCD cases that I have had a chance to examine. And a gradual resolution of the OCD symptoms has always followed the gradual integration of the extended families' unintegrated wounds.

Oppositional Defiant Disorder

Oppositional Defiant Disorder is a condition where the child or adolescent is having trouble with the Autonomy-Control phase of development. This phase of development occurs between the ages of 1 and 3 years old. The themes of this phase get revisited again in adolescence from the ages of 13 (12+ 1) to 15 (12 + 3). Children or adolescents having trouble with this theme are members of extended families where there were traumatic experiences to this developmental phase upstream. The following clinical example serves to illustrate the pattern.

Colleen was a bright attractive 7 year old who was in second grade. She had recently been suspended from school because of a pattern of behavior where she was refusing to follow direction and was continually getting into angry disagreement with the teacher. She was also getting into fights with the other students whom she was kicking and biting. Because she had become unmanageable in the classroom, the school asked her parents to seek help for her. In addition, the school requested that she remain out of school until the right alternate placement in a class for socially and emotionally disturbed students could be determined. The parents brought her to me for a psychiatric evaluation with follow-up family therapy treatment.

Colleen was clearly a bright, inquisitive, verbal child. However, during the evaluation, it became clear that she had a number of issues related to trouble with the themes of autonomy and control at home. She had trouble with these themes with her parents and with her younger sister, age 5. Colleen always tried to get her way. In general, she showed many of the behaviors that are related to problems with the sharing of power that one would more likely see in a two year old child in the middle of the "terrible twos". As I assessed her functioning in the family, it became clear that her parents also had some trouble with control issues. Her father was a very uptight professional who attempted to control all sorts of features of family life, large and small. Her mother was also controlling in many ways. While father tried to micromanage many issues, he routinely deferred to his wife whenever there was a power struggle between them.

Rather than proceed using regular family therapy, I followed Dr. Whitakers advice and arranged a subsequent extended session with the grandparents. The extended family adaptation theory would predict that there were wounds to the Autonomy-Control phase upstream on both sides that had never been integrated. In the first extended family session, the father's parents joined the nuclear family. In gathering history, it was revealed that grandfather was 2 years old when his mother contracted tuberculosis and had to leave the family for the next two years for inpatient treatment in a sanatorium. He was right in the middle of the Autonomy-Control phase when his development was severely disrupted by his mother's absence. It also came out that paternal grandmother's father was working out of state away from the family for most of the time when she was between the ages of 1 ½ and 4. She said she had heard that this was a very hard time for her mother, trying to care for the four children alone. So, paternal grandmother also had significant disruption to her Autonomy-Control phase because family life was very disturbed during this period.

In a subsequent session, we met with the mother's mother. Mother's parents had divorced when she was 14. This is again a severe disruption to the Autonomy-Control phase as it is re-visited during adolescence. Maternal grandmother related that her father's father had run off and left the family when her father was about two. So at one more level upstream, the wound was again to the Autonomy-Control phase. By the time we had collected all of this data during three extended family sessions, mother and father were reporting that Colleen's behavior had improved greatly at home. She seemed now to be handling control issues and the sharing of power in age appropriate ways. Her play with her sister at home had also changed. She was no longer getting into repeated conflicts and power struggles. All the kicking and biting behavior at home had ceased.

I consulted with the school psychologist and informed her of the progress Colleen had made. The psychologist agreed to let Colleen return to school for a trial period on the basis of my recommendation. Colleen's teacher was very surprised at the changes in her behavior. She was now handling peer interactions in an age-appropriate manner instead of getting into constant power struggles. There was no repeat of her biting or kicking behavior.

I have had a chance to collect the upstream data from over 30 cases where the presenting problem is Oppositional-Defiant Disorder. In every case that I have examined, there are upstream wounds to the Autonomy-Control phase of development present in both the father's and the mother's extended families. In each case where I have had the chance to work with the extended family, the child or adolescent's problems have completely resolved as the extended family completed the integration process.

Eating Disorders

Another very common and troubling set of disorders are the Eating Disorders, including Anorexia Nervosa and Bulimia Nervosa. These patients are typically adolescents, more frequently girls than boys. When one makes a developmental diagnosis of an eating disorder, one sees large problems with control issues, very low self-esteem, and frequently significant issues with emotion regulation. One also sees that these patients have trouble with their parents in terms of issues of separation-individuation. Frequently, the symptoms become so severe that there is risk to the health or even life of the adolescent. When one finds that the health or life of the adolescent is at risk, it indicates, from a developmental diagnosis point of view, that the theme of Basic Trust is also involved. When one does an extended family upstream assessment for wound patterns, one typically finds severe trauma to the 1 to 3 year age range. The following example will illustrate the kind of trauma that one usually finds.

Alice was referred to me together with her family. She had experienced persistent treatment failure. She was 27 years old, bright, with a college degree, and presently living with her parents. She began to have symptoms of anorexia nervosa at age 13 ½ which eventually shifted to bulimia nervosa. She had been in therapy continually since that time. She had been hospitalized twice and had been in day treatment programs for eating disorders on three occasions, each program lasting several months. She had been treated with a variety of medications. Over the course of her treatment, she had worked extensively with seven different therapists. Her involvement in treatment had been successful in keeping her from dying and she had only been hospitalized twice. But her eating disorder pretty much ruled her life. She was fairly isolated socially and was often depressed. She also suffered from disruptive mood swings. She had trouble advancing in her career due to the interruption that her affliction constantly caused her. She had not been particularly successful at dating and had a very poor body self-image, even though others found her to be attractive. Because of all her difficulties, she had not been particularly successful at leaving home and was still living with her parents.

When her family contacted me, they asked if I would accept her for treatment. I said that I would work with her but only if the entire family participated. Young adults who have an eating disorder and who have had treatment for years without much success are notoriously difficult to treat successfully. Because Alice's situation was so severe and of such a longstanding nature, I asked that her entire three-generational family participate. I wanted her parents who were now grandparents, her adult siblings, their spouses, and all the nieces and nephews to attend.

Her brother Robert, who had contacted me on behalf of Alice, thought that my demands were outrageous. He wanted me to see her alone in individual therapy. But I replied: why did he think that I could be successful when seven other therapists and several hospitals had failed with her? I told Robert that it would be hard enough to be successful with everyone helping. What is more, I liked winning and therefore I liked to stack the odds in my favor. I was firm that I would not get involved unless all of these family members came to help.

I didn't hear from the family for about 10 months. Then Alice's father, Hank, called. He said that the family had been talking it over and that they wanted to give it a try. They would all come for one meeting. However, he said that one of his other daughters had a 6 month old baby and would be traveling to the session by car from three hours away. Surely, I didn't expect that this baby would need to be present. I told him that I needed everyone. If they didn't want to bring the baby, that was ok with me. But in that case, I didn't want to meet. Hank felt I was being unreasonable and said that if I was going to be that inflexible, they might as well forget it. I said that the baby was part of the system, just like a pawn is part of a chess game. And no chess expert would sit down to a game with one pawn hidden from view, and try to play the game. Hank was not satisfied with my requirements. He said that I was asking too much and that they wouldn't be coming.

Then, a month later, I got a call from Alice's mother,

Beatrice. She said they would all come and that they would bring the now 7 month old baby. We ended up holding a series of half-day retreats with this group over a period of months. It came out in one of the retreats that Alice had been 1 ½ years old when her mother Beatrice gave birth to a child after a difficult pregnancy. The child did very poorly at birth and died after a month. Hank revealed that he had been dreading the birth of this child because he was extremely apprehensive about its chances for survival, since the pregnancy had been so difficult. Consequently, he had actually avoided being around for the delivery by arranging to be out of town on a business trip when the baby was due. When we went back into Hank's history as a child, he shared that his mother also had lost two children. A sister died soon after birth and a brother died before his first birthday. Hank related that he was 2 years old when the girl died and 4 years old when his infant brother died. It was clear that the death of his own infant son had provoked strong unconscious memories of the devastation that pervaded his family when he lost two young siblings. No wonder he was so apprehensive about the birth of this child following such a medically difficult pregnancy.

When we got to Beatrice's story, she revealed that she had lost three infant siblings before she reached the age of six. One can only imaging how much pain and mourning pervaded her early childhood. So for both Alice's parents, the death of their own infant reawakened the loss of five other infant siblings between them, and the associated devastation in their childhood families. It was "Déjà vu all over again" as Yogi Berra said. With such childhood losses accentuating the loss of their own child, the emotional trauma was overwhelming. Alice's happy family was thus devastated when she was 1 ½ years old at the time her infant sibling died. This created a huge emotional trauma for her at this age. The presences in the session of the 7 month old grandchild served as a living reminder of these losses. Beatrice also revealed that she felt she had never really been able to mourn properly and get past the death of her baby. She told the group that she had been secretly visiting the grave of the dead baby each week for the last 25 ½ years.

By the time we had held six retreats over about a six month period, Alice's anorexia-bulimia symptoms had completely gone away. This is the first time she had been symptom free since the onset of her anorexia at about 13 ½. Notice that the onset of her symptoms exactly coincided with her developmental clock being 1 ½ years into adolescence. This is just the age at which we would expect that she and her family would revisit the death of her infant sibling during her adolescence. When she was 13 ½, her dead sibling that died at 1 month of age would have been 12 years old. 12 years old is the beginning of adolescence, just as birth is the beginning of childhood.

The devastation to Alice's development at age 1 ½ years cut across several of her developmental phases. First of all, the loss devastated her sense of Basic Trust as she attempted to cope with her family's emotional devastation. Secondly, she was six months into the Autonomy-Control phase so the trauma would surely affect the way her Autonomy-Control brain circuits were configured. The loss would have thrown all of the normal family interaction patterns out of whack, so that she would have received very skewed Autonomy-Control interactions from her parents. Children at age 1 ½ years have very few issues to struggle over with their parents. One of the few issues that they can struggle over is eating. Alice was still perseverating over this eating control issue 25 years later.

The third developmental phase that was affected was self-esteem. Alice at age 1 ½ years, was early into the process of configuring her Self-Esteem phase. So, one would expect her self-esteem to be very adversely affected, which it was. Her distorted body image fits into her pattern of low self-esteem. One can think of the Self-Esteem phase as consisting of three parts: "being" self-esteem, "appearance" self-esteem, and "performance" self esteem. The first two start getting configured at the same time, beginning in infancy, although there is more emphasis on the "being" self esteem at the start of infancy. The third part primarily gets configured a few years later.

The fourth developmental theme that was affected was her developmental phase of Emotion Regulation. With the introduction of so much irresolvable sadness as a result of the death of her sibling, Alice's Emotion Regulation phase was severely disrupted. This resulted in her brain system for Emotion Regulation being misconfigured, with inevitable resulting mood swings. With her

Emotion Regulation system being poorly configured, she had never been able to regulate her moods in an age appropriate manner.

Finally, Alice was into step 3 of her Separation-Individuation developmental phase. During this step, she would normally be differentiating from her parents with the onset of her ability to walk at about age 1 year. Her family's trauma devastated the progress that she otherwise would have made at individuating from her parents at this stage. Her brain system for Separation-Individuation ended up being misconfigured. Consequently, when she became an adult, she would have great difficulty individuating from her parents in an age appropriate manner, which is what occurred.

As the family continued to do the needed work of integration, the young woman's other symptoms gradually resolved. Her mood swings leveled out to normal. She started to develop a normal body image and her self esteem slowly rose to a normal level. She began to date again. Her career started to pick up now that so much of her emotional energy was no-longer being consumed by her affliction. With her career on the upswing, she was anticipating being able to move out of her parents home successfully.

Major Depression

Major Depression is a symptom that is not specific to any particular developmental phase. Rather, it can be associated with a sudden current traumatic event, or it can be associated with major upstream emotional trauma to any of the developmental phases. However, as with the other diagnoses, if the upstream wounds lead to depressive symptoms, then matching wounds are always present on both the father's and the mother's side. If the symptom is present in a spouse, then the responsible upstream wounds are always present in the extended families of both spouses. I will present two cases to illustrate these mechanisms.

Alan was a very bright, shy boy who did well in school. A few months before he turned thirteen, he became very depressed. He was so depressed that he couldn't go to school. He had lost all interest in seeing friends or engaging in any of the activities that he normally enjoyed. He complained that he had no energy and he could not concentrate. His parents reported that he was sleeping excessively. His pediatrician referred him to me for an evaluation.

I saw him together with his parents and his brother, age ten. In getting an upstream history from his father Eli, it was revealed that Eli had been thirteen when his own father Isaac had died of cancer. For Eli, this was a severe trauma to his Basic Trust developmental phase as he revisited it during his adolescence. Remember, the Basic Trust phase gets worked on primarily between 0 and 1 years of age, and again, during the first year of adolescence, from 12 to 13 years of age.

In taking Alan's mom Frieda's history, she didn't reveal any particular traumas that occurred during her childhood or adolescence. However, in getting the history of her parents' childhood, it was revealed that her mother Mira was about a year old when Mira's father died in a work accident. Mira and her sister, together with their mother, moved into the maternal grandparents' house where Mira was raised.

After scheduling a series of integrative retreats with each extended family, the boy's symptoms gradually resolved completely. On mother's side, the wound was a generation further upstream than on father's side, and was directly related to the first period of the Basic Trust phase, from age 0 to age 1. On father's side, the wound was related to the second period of the work on Basic Trust, in Eli's adolescence. The wounds on both sides match however, because the wounds both occurred when the theme of Basic Trust was being worked on, even though one was in infancy and the other was in adolescence. Depression makes sense as the presenting symptom that occurred because the wounds on both sides represented huge loss.

The second example of depression in a family member is that of a somewhat older adolescent. Mark was 16 when he was referred to me by his pediatrician. He first came to see me with his father Owen, a university law professor, his mother Alicia, a librarian, and his sister Elizabeth, a freshman is college at a prestigious private school about 1 ½ hours from home. Mark agreed with his family that he had always been moody, but beginning about six months ago, he had become severely depressed. He had frequent thoughts of suicide and had asked the family to hide the large kitchen knives because they made him nervous. He had trouble getting to sleep, he frequently awoke at night, and he usually woke up at 5:30 am and could not get back to sleep, even though his schedule required him to get up at 7:00 am. He complained that he could no-longer concentrate on this school work. His grades had fallen off to the point where he wasn't sure he was going to pass all of his courses. He had previously been a nearly straight "A" student and was seen as very bright. His appetite had decreased significantly and he had lost all interest in doing things other than riding his bicycle. When he wasn't feeling depressed, he would often feel extremely angry and he would take his bicycle out for ten to twenty mile rides to try to work off his rage.

Both he and his parents were concerned about his suicidal ideation. Mark was also worried about his grades but his parents thought that he was such an exceptional student that he could catch up if he could only get over his depression. Psychiatric hospitalization had been suggested by his pediatrician as something that might be necessary, but both Mark and his parents very much wanted to avoid that. They felt there would be a stigma attached to a hospitalization that could hinder Mark's future career choices.

In getting the father Owen's family history, it came out that his father George, Mark's paternal grandfather, had come to the United States alone from Hungary when he was sixteen years old. At the end of WWII, George's father arranged to have his sixteen year old son George smuggled out of the country. George made it to Switzerland, where he was taken in by a distant cousin and her family. This cousin however was elderly and not well, so she sent George to the United States to stay with another distant relative.

The relatives George moved in with lived in Brooklyn. They were somewhat educated and kindly but quite poor. George finished high school in Brooklyn but then had to go to work to help contribute to his own support. Because of the political situation in Hungary, once the Russians took over, and because of the subsequent "Iron Curtain" that separated Hungary from the rest of Europe and the world; George was not able to contact his parents after he left Hungary until the Hungarian Revolt of 1956, when he was 25. During that brief window of Hungarian freedom, George managed to exchange quite a few letters with his family. But soon, the revolt was crushed and George's father dropped dead on the street one evening from a heart attack. George's mother died two years later of cancer in 1958, when George was 27, but he did not find out about it until six months after her death. George lost all contact with his younger sister after his mother died.

George married the same year that his mother died and his son Owen, Mark's father was born a year later in 1959. George was very bright but was unable to finish college for financial reasons. Instead, he apprenticed as an electrician and eventually owned his own business and did quite well. Owen was the eldest of three children. George and his wife Louise were still alive and lived on Long Island.

Alicia, Mark's mother, was from Kansas. She was the eldest of five children. Her father Eric was a farmer who owned his own farm. He was quite prosperous, and had many farm hands working for him. When Alicia was 15, her father was severely injured in a farm accident. While working high on a ladder repairing a silo, Eric fell a great distance and broke his back. Thereafter, he was paralyzed and confined to a wheelchair. At first, Eric was determined to walk again, but as the months of rehabilitation dragged on past a year, he became very discouraged. One Saturday afternoon when his wife and the children arrived home from the weekly shopping trip into town, the second child, James, discovered Eric dead in the barn. He had shot himself. Alicia was sixteen at the time.

Six months after the funeral, Alicia's mother Josephine sold the farm and moved the family in with her parents, a two hour drive from Wichita. When Alicia graduated from high school, Josephine told Alicia that she could afford to send her to college away from home. Wishing for some adventure and a chance to start a happier chapter in her life, Alicia applied and got accepted to New York University, where she met her future husband Owen when she was a junior majoring in library science.

Owen was a second year law student at Columbia when they met at a school dance. After they married, they settled in Hartford, Connecticut. Owen had been offered a job at a Hartford law firm as an associate. Alicia got a job at a local college as an assistant librarian. Owen started to think about teaching and got a job teaching law part-time in an evening program. After working with the firm for eight years and teaching part-time for five, he was offered a faculty position at a law school in the area, where he eventually became tenured.

The two families decided to do extended family work together to try to resolve Mark's problems. Owen's parents drove up from New York for sessions when we worked on his extended family. Alicia's mom Josephine was in the habit of coming to visit her grandchildren for extended stays, so by extending the length of a few trips, she was able to attend the sessions to work on their extended family. As the two extended families did their work, Mark's depression gradually resolved. His grades became even better than before and he found that he could socialize more effectively than ever.

In Mark's case, depression again made sense as the symptom because the underlying theme on each side was the issue of overwhelming loss. Mark's paternal grandfather George lost contact with his whole family when he left Hungary at age 16. Alicia lost the happy family she had known after her father was injured, and then the loss became devastating when her father committed suicide. It also made sense that the two extended families would revisit their losses when a grandchild turned 16. Mark's arrival at that age provoked the unconscious revisiting of that developmental stage for both extended families, and the parallel tragedies associated with that age.

Severe Anxiety

Like depression, anxiety is a symptom that is not tied specifically to any particular developmental phase. Rather, it is a kind a warning signal that something in the here and now is amiss and danger is present. Or, it is sometimes a signal that something at the developmental phase that the symptomatic individual has arrived at was amiss previously, either for the individual themselves, or for members of the extended families upstream.

Catherine was nine when she was referred to me by her pediatrician. She had been troubled by severe chronic anxiety and worries for about the past year. Her parents had brought her to individual therapy for about six months after her symptoms started, but it had not helped. Catherine was very bright but her constant state of anxiety made it almost impossible for her to concentrate in school. Her schoolwork was suffering to the point were she might have to repeat the fourth grade. The pediatrician had prescribed anti-anxiety medication which helped somewhat, but left Catherine feeling "doped up". Neither she nor her parents were happy with this side effect, so the medication was stopped. Since nothing was working and her progress in school was at risk, the family was referred to me.

Catherine's father Alex was a business consultant with a nationally prominent consulting firm. He specialized in business turn-around situations. Her mother, Evelyn was an internist. Catherine was the eldest of three children. She had a sister age six and a brother age four.

I first saw the nuclear family for an evaluation. In taking a careful history, there were no immediate problems in either her life or the family's life that might be a current cause for Catherine's anxiety. When I took a careful upstream history, I found out that Alex's father Clifford was from an old New England family. Clifford had met his wife Elizabeth, Alex's mother, when he was stationed in Germany while serving in U.S. Army Intelligence as a Lieutenant in the late fifties. Elizabeth had been born in England but had attended University in France and had found a job in Paris. Clifford had met Elizabeth while on leave in Paris in 1957, and they were married in 1958. The couple moved to the United States when Clifford's tour of duty was up.

I asked about where and when Elizabeth had been born. Alex told me that she had been born in London in 1931. I asked him where his mother had been during the war. He said that her family had stayed in London during the bombing. She was nine at the time. Alex said that his mother rarely spoke about that time in her life. Here was the first match of an upstream traumatic experience with the current presenting symptom. The revisitation of this upstream wound by Alex's family when Catherine was nine would have engendered a large degree of anxiety.

Evelyn, Catherine's mother, grew up in Connecticut. Evelyn's father Bill was nine when his father, Sam, was shipped overseas in 1944 to fight in the Pacific theater as a Marine. Sam returned home in September of 1945 when Bill was 10 ½. Evelyn's mother Doris was nine when her mother Grace, Evelyn's maternal grandmother, was found to have TB. Grace had to go into a sanatorium for two years starting in 1949. The availability of some of the first antibiotics to successfully treat TB enabled Grace to return home by the time Doris was 11 years old. Both Evelyn's parents' families had to endure more than a year of high anxiety related to whether or not a parent would be able to come home. So in Evelyn's extended family, as in Alex's extended family, age nine coincided with a time of great anxiety.

Both Alex's parents and Evelyn's parents lived in Southern New England. The two extended families decided to do extended family integration sessions. Since Alex's sister and brother lived nearby, they and their families attended when Alex's extended family met. Evelyn's sister Elise, and her family lived in Boston and were able to attend when Evelyn's side met. By the end of the extended family consulting process, not only had Catherine's anxieties completely resolved, but emotional issues related to anxiety and depression in two of her cousins, one from each extended family had also resolved.

Because I am just one practitioner, my sample of completed extended family integration cases is limited. However, I have found in every case that if the two extended families work in tandem to resolve the abnormally high levels of stress that they have been carrying, the burdened child or adolescent with one of these severe emotional disorders always gets completely well. What this means is that the extended family in each case has the capacity, working together, to integrate the old upstream wounds, no matter how severe they were. Once the upstream wounds and their downstream repercussions have been integrated, the extended families move out of enactment mode and the burdened child or adolescent's emotional difficulties resolve completely.

Chapter 14

Wealth Preservation and the New People Technology

Or,

How to Avoid

"Shirtsleeves to Shirtsleeves in Three Generations"

It is a worldwide, long observed fact that it is very difficult for a family to hold on to its money from generation to generation. The above quote, "Shirtsleeves to shirtsleeves in three generations" has its variation in every culture. And this tendency for the wealth that was built up by the founding generation to be dissipated occurs, in spite of all sorts of legal means devised to try to preserve it. Adam Smith wrote, "riches, in spite of the most violent regulations of law to prevent their dissipation, very seldom remain in the same family". The problem, as James E. Hughes Jr. asserts in his book <u>Family Wealth, Keeping it in the Family</u>, boils down to a problem of human behavior. Acquiring money is a skill, and keeping it is also a skill, a part of a successful family's way of operating, a part of its organizational culture.

For each new generation to be successfully enculturated to the ways and means necessary for the family's preservation of its wealth, the up and coming young members must arrive at adulthood as well-functioning family members. If the new members are functioning poorly, it bodes ill for the fate of the family team and its finances. The new members, in concert with the rest of the family, need to be functioning well both physically and emotionally. With these two areas of health as a basis, they then need to eventually function reasonably well in the other five areas of family wealth: spiritual, intellectual, social, financial, and contextual (relating to the environment the family is in).

One of the areas of family wealth that James E. Hughes Jr.[1] talks about in his book, <u>Family Wealth, Keeping it in the Family</u>, is spiritual wealth, which he believes is an essential prerequisite to a family being able to preserve itself and its financial wealth. He does not discuss this aspect in his book, because he feels that it is outside his area of expertise. He says, however, that if a family is weak in this area, then they should pursue strength in this area first and then come back to his book, where he provides guidance on how to set up the family governance structures that he believes are necessary to achieving a family's goal of wealth preservation. I think he is correct that a family needs a strong spiritual aspect to their family culture, in order to thrive and persist. However, it is my experience that after physical health, a family next needs good emotional health. The family needs to be in good developmental shape in order to be able to successfully achieve and maintain any of the other 5 types of family wealth, including spiritual wealth.

The tradition of yoga observes that in order for humans to achieve, they first need to have sound bodily health. A famous yoga master, B.K.S. Iyengar states: "Unless freedom is gained in the body, freedom of the mind is not possible".[2] Just as we all need bodily health as a foundation is order to pursue other aspects of life freely, we also need to be emotionally well functioning members of our extended family in order to succeed in life. This means that we need to have all of our developmental phases in good functioning order. For families to preserve wealth from one generation to the next, they need to have all members of each new generation as emotionally healthy as possible. Otherwise, these new members of the next generation will not be able to function well enough to behave in the ways that are needed to contribute to the family's wealth preservation and growth efforts.

Raising emotionally healthy children can be a particularly difficult challenge for wealthy families. There are three types of reasons for this.

Past Family Wounds Served to Empower the Founder

First, wealthy families often have great unhealed wounds, which were part of the original motivating circumstances that lead to the founder's tremendous drive to succeed. In virtually every case, severe challenges or wounds to the family system upstream, or to the emotional development of the founder, eventually led the founder to respond to these wounds by making a Herculean effort to acquire great wealth. The founding member often pairs with a mate who has an equally great and equally family determined motivation to acquire wealth. The couple, both energized by previous upstream family wounds, makes a matching long-term Herculean effort to accumulate great wealth, and they succeed. While upstream wounds act as the rocket fuel to get the founder and mate into the realm of great wealth, there is usually no chance along the way to finish an extended family integration processes of these upstream wounds, so that they usually get in the way in the future.

In the case of the founder and mate specifically, the upstream wounds create the needed drive and motivation. This gets combined with great individual genius to create wealth, and results in a kind of "perfect storm" of financial wealth creation. It is somewhat like the launch of the space shuttle. The wounds in a sense fuel the large needed "booster rocket" that propels the founders, the space shuttle, into the financial stratosphere. The "rocket", that is, the effort, has to be extremely well functioning in order to allow for the "rocket-like" rise in financial status. But, the founder and mate give up a large portion of life's opportunities and pleasure in order to put so much of their energy into such a meteoric rise. There are exceptions to this general rule, and these founders are extremely fortunate, for they get the chance to create great wealth and still keep a fair amount of balance in their lives. What happens much more often is that the balance comes later, if ever, after the bulk of the wealth has been achieved.

By focusing on creating a fortune, the founder and mate get a tremendous energy boost from their family wounds. But the next generation is usually left to deal with the wounding nature of the previous traumas. It is this second generation that gets crippled by the previous wounds. Crippled as they are, the second generation passes their developmental wounds to the third generation. In the third generation, there are often several members who just cannot function. By the time the third generation takes over stewardship of the family fortune, they are primed to end up dissipating it or losing it. It is this sequence that leads to the notion of "shirtsleeves to shirtsleeves" in three generations.

Busy Schedules Leave Little Time for Childrearing

The second reason why it is so difficult for wealthy families to raise emotionally healthy children has to do with time allocation. The Romans said that one can either be a "man of letters" or a parent. They did not think one could do both well. Once the family has great wealth, the demands of looking after that wealth and all the opportunities, roles and responsibilities that go with it frequently take great amounts of time away from the time the parents can devote to the direct raising of their children. Kay Graham's family, of "Washington Post" fame, is a good example here. According to her memoir, Kay's parents were so busy with the lives they led associated with great wealth and great responsibilities that Kay never got much chance to interact with her parents until she began to work at the family newspaper.

Wealthy families often try to compensate for the parents lack of time by hiring nannies to make up for the parents relative unavailability. This can work adequately, if it is done very well. But frequently, the family does not have sufficient awareness and understanding of the essential issues involved in using nannies as substitute parents. Often, large parts of the nanny substitution scheme are done badly, and not because the parents don't care. Like all parents, they love their children deeply. Rather, the nanny substitution scheme is frequently executed badly because the parents don't know how to do it better. Having been so focused on the acquisition of great financial wealth and then on the use of all the opportunities that accompany this wealth, these parents fail to discover what it takes to develop healthy children. In essence, they are deprived, by fulfilling their wealth roles, of the moment by moment, day by day experiences that lead to the education of parents by the parenting processes.

The developmental phase of Generativity thus gets short shrift, and the wealthy parents end up relatively clueless about what is needed. They are subsequently ineffective at directing the nanny's effort, because they don't really know from experience what needs to be done. Winston Churchill's family is another great example of the effects of wealth on parental time, and thus, ultimately on the quality of the parenting effort. Winston's parents were at the very highest level of British society. With everything the accompanying roles require, they had almost no time to devote to the direct parenting of Winston. It was only in adulthood that Winston was finally able to make a direct connection with his mother. And as for Winston and his father, it was too late. Winston's father died before Winston had a chance to really develop a relationship with him.

Great Wealth is a Strange Environment

Finally, raising children in the environment of great wealth has some unnatural aspects. This makes it very difficult to avoid making some critical mistakes. Everything about human nature evolved in the context of extended families needing to "struggle for their daily bread". Great wealth takes the family members into a new terrain that they are not entirely equipped for, from an evolutionary point of view. It is a little bit like being on a spaceship where all the occupants are weightless. We did not evolve in a weightless environment, so many of our bodily mechanisms are not properly attuned to it. It is much easier to get around in a weightless space station, because we can just jump a little, and float to our goals. However, at the same time, it is much harder to stay put. The very gravity on earth that makes it such work it get around also operates to keep earthlings stationary when they want to attend to something. Also, weightlessness breeds weakness, because our muscles evolved in such a way that they need to be used in order to stay strong. In a spaceship with a weightless environment, one cannot do only what seems natural. Such a space traveler needs to arrange very deliberately and consistently to get the right kind of exercise, otherwise, their muscles will become very weak and even their bones will lose calcium and become weakened. In a like manner, in very wealthy families, one has to arrange things in a very deliberate way to make sure that the new generation gets the experiences they need in order for all the developmental phases to progress properly.

The New Wealth Paradigm

Wealth is a kind of new evolutionary challenge for more and more modern extended families. Never in the history of the world have so many families had to move forward in the highly unusual circumstances created by abundant wealth. A *Merrill Lynch-Capgemini Report* states that there are about 7 million families worldwide with financial asset wealth above 1 million dollars. And there are 70,000 families worldwide with financial asset wealth above $30 million. This paradigm of having to move forward under circumstances of great wealth will become a more and more common challenge for extended families as globalization increases, and as the whole world continues to move into the knowledge revolution.

In the pre-industrial agrarian societies, wealth was usually associated with land ownership or control. This meant that wealth was concentrated in the hands of relatively few families. With the rise of industrialized society, wealth flowed mainly to those who could control the means of production and distribution. Again, this amounted to relatively few families. Now, in the ever increasing knowledge society, wealth can be created from individual creativity and effort. Every relatively intelligent individual is a potential creator of great wealth. There has never been a time in history when wealth accumulation has been so far removed from the zero sum game of the agrarian and industrialized economies. In this new wealth paradigm, the percentage of wealthy families will start to increase more and more rapidly. There will come a time in the next few centuries, when a large percentage of families will have great affluence, that is, wealth far beyond their basic needs.

Wealthy families of the present, and those greater numbers to come, will need people technology mechanisms to move forward without suffering the detrimental effects of their affluent circumstances. Otherwise, their forward progression will falter and their descendants, many of them dysfunctional, will experience a regression to the mean, and will end up nearer the bottom of the economic ladder, fulfilling the promise of the "shirtsleeve to shirtsleeve" prediction.

What new people technologies are essential for modern extended families to acculturate successfully to the new environment of great wealth? What must all wealthy families succeed in doing in order to be able to retain their new fortunate circumstances on a long-term basis? They must, first and foremost, assure that all their members are raised emotionally, that is "developmentally" configured, in an optimal way, so that their new members can carry on and maintain the family's successful circumstances. If this goal is not achieved, then their "successful house" will come tumbling down in a generation or two.

One can gain great insight into this necessary process by looking at another successful growth phenomenon, the growth of trees. If a tree is healthy, it creates a new generation of outer cells that make up the new year's growth ring. The cells of previous growth rings die and become the structure that holds the tree up. The central heartwood is made up of the dead previous growth rings. Because the previous dead growth rings provide a structure that holds the new growth ring up in the air above the forest floor, trees maintain a huge advantage from year to year over other forest plants. They always have access to abundant sun (resources) that assure the best chances for good growth from year to year.

If the accumulated central heartwood becomes weak and rotten, then the tree will fall down. But this seldom happens. If you take a walk in a natural forest, you will see trees from time to time that are dead, but are still standing. The central heartwood usually holds the tree up after the tree has died. It is the outer growth ring whose faltering leads to the tree's demise. The new growth ring is the new generation. Everything depends on the success of this new generation. If this new generation of growth falters, the life of the tree is over. Then microbes can enter the central heartwood, and rot sets in. The tree soon falls. So trees have evolved mechanisms to foster the growth and success of the new growth ring. This mission is paramount.

Likewise, in a wealthy family, the new growth ring (new generation) protects the heartwood (financial assets). No matter how hard and strong the inner wood is; decay will set in rapidly if the outer growth ring becomes weak. It is the outer growth ring's vitality that protects the inner heartwood (financial asset structure). And every new growth ring (new generation) has the same developmental needs as the previous growth rings (previous generation) that came before, just as every new family member needs to learn to walk and talk, no matter how wealthy the family is. The tree has been programmed evolutionarily to develop the new growth ring in an optimal way, and each successful new year's growth gains more height (greater wealth). Just as with trees, successful wealthy families take care to ensure the physical and emotional health of the next generation as their highest priority. And a healthy new generation ends up adding to the wealth and advantage of the family.

But how is this accomplished. Trees have developed mechanisms to bring sufficient nutrients up to each cell of new growth, no matter how high up in the tree the new growth is. For wealthy families, the needed mechanisms are family cultural mechanisms or traditions. And mankind is still trying to develop these needed mechanisms. Just as the breakthrough in survival brought about by farming led to new family cultural mechanisms over time, mankind is still in the process of trying to develop these needed next generation nurturing mechanisms.

The New People Technology and Its Ancient Biological Origins

This is where the technology being discussed in this book comes in. In fact, this new people technology is a scientific elucidation and refinement of a very old people technology. Our ancestral primate extended families made great strides by taking a more organized approach to their team living back more that 700,000 years ago. They developed fire and hunting traditions involving tools. This approach was passed on as a cultural tradition within extended family teams. With each passing millennia, extended family team behavior became more advanced and effective. Eventually, the organizational culture of the extended family team became the most important survival mechanism humans had.

Then, about 100,000 years ago, genetic changes occurred

that lead to a change in the voice box of an ancestor, leading eventually to the capacity to make a wider range of sounds. This resulted in a new genetically based capability, the capacity for language. Many scientists believe that this change to the human voice box, making possible human language sounds, became the basis for the emergence of modern Homo sapiens. With this new genetically based capacity to make a wide range of sounds, the human brain started to change to make use of this increased sound making facility. Proto languages developed. These proto languages were of great benefit to any group's team effort, and any team that could develop a more effective one had a great advantage.

Remember the Tower of Babel in the bible? When the people working together could no longer communicate with the same language, they could no longer function together effectively. Just the opposite happened with the emergence of more and more effective proto languages. The better the proto language, the more effectively an extended family team could cooperate.

One can imagine the situation about 100,000 years ago. Homo sapiens now had the capacity to make a wide range of sounds, enough to develop a real language. Chimpanzees can make about 360 distinct sounds, each with its own meaning. That is a start, but it is nowhere near as effective as a capacity to make more than 1,000,000 sequential sound combinations, the number of words in the English language. Now that man possessed the voice box with the needed versatility, it was up to each extended family group to develop more and more effective language structures.

But the particular language developed is not genetically determined. Only the capacity to develop and use language is genetically determined. So language became part of the organizational culture of each extended family. Over thousands and thousands of years, those groups with better languages, which were more useful in coordinating the team's activities, were more successful in the environment.

Language also opened up the possibility to pass discreet knowledge from the older to the younger generation. Like drawing is to the external world of representation, language became useful as an internal brain schematic that a person could develop and later convey to others in the group. The Eskimos have at least seven words for snow. Each kind of snow has different properties and knowing about those is useful for survival. With the possibility of language development, the possibility to mentally classify the world in terms of facts and properties became available. It is as if language was a sort of increased hard disk space, which allowed for the storage of a greatly increased set of facts, observations, ideas, and concepts. The brain now had a better discrete internal storage system.

Synaptic structures (See Ch 20 The Brain) get built in the brain to correspond to the acquisition of facts, ideas, and concepts. So with the advent of real language, internal brain architecture began to better reflect the person's accumulated knowledge of the outside word. And this accumulated knowledge was passed on from older members to the younger members they interacted with. By giving the younger generation a language system, the older generation was giving them an auditory sound system of codification that could be used to store the knowledge being passed on, together with the associated experiences. The words became a sort of precise classification system.

One can see that language represented a huge advance in a group's cultural schema. Just as the corporation with the better organizational culture has a great advantage, the extended family team with the better organizational culture was better able to compete in the natural world, both with nature and with other family teams.

Important as language is, the developmental phases as a way of organizing extended family team life are much older and more fundamental than language, for they are essentially non-verbal. Early Homo erectus man, organized in extended family units, inhabited the earth as far as Asia, 500,000 years before modern Homo sapien man arrived on the world scene with his modern language ability. The extended family teams of Homo erectus man had an organizational culture that was for the most part non-verbal, for these teams pre-dated the appearance of modern language by about 500,000 years. If one thinks about it, the developmental stages are the fundamental themes governing the interactions of all primates within a primate group. Trust, power, separation, and rank within the group (what we would call self-esteem) have been the fundamental parameters of human primate interaction long into our early primate history. So these pre-verbal developmental stages have a very long lineage into our distant primate past.

A sense of trust gets built for the infant, not by the parents repeating "trust us" over and over like the multiplication tables, but by the ongoing non-verbal experiences that the infant is having in relationship to the mothering care-giver. The Chinese say, "The one who feeds the baby is the mother". This whole moment by moment set of experiences gets built up mostly non-verbally. In the Autonomy and Control phase, the toddler needs to have experiences with the caregiver that include allowing the toddler to do what she wants, and also blocking the toddler from doing things that are unwanted or harmful. Deaf parents who cannot speak can nevertheless give their children the right kind of experiences to enable them to configure their young brains to the family's culture. So the acquisition of this developmental phase is also essentially non-verbal.

The capacity for extended family behavioral interactions to lead to internal brain configuration changes developed very early. This capacity allowed for the "writing" of the essentials of the group's organizational culture into the brain configuration of the new members. This capacity developed as the internal brain process component of the emerging developmental stages. This was long before language came on the scene. Also, somewhere way back in our ancient past, most likely going way back into our animal heritage, the capacity for the extended family collectively to edit or alter its organizational culture slowly emerged.

What examples are there from biology, that support the idea that communication between members of a group can affect something as basic as the internal structure of group member's brain's? One example is the capacity of cod fish in a large group to excite each other to reproduce. Cod fish in small mixed sex groups cannot reproduce. The adult males and females within a small group are unable to reach the needed level of sexual excitement. In order for cod fish to become successful reproductively, they need to be part of a large school, of perhaps a million or more members. Only in such a large school can individual adult male and female cod fish become sexually excited. It is the complex communicative interaction of an individual cod fish seeing a million others of its own kind that somehow excites its brain sufficiently to turn on its reproductive system. Here is one example of communicative interaction affecting basic biological processes.

Another example of communication between individuals affecting biological processes is that of the Grouper fish. Grouper fish are large reef fish that live in mixed gender groups close to a warm water reef structure. When the lead male fish in a group dies, there are changes in the communication patterns in the remainder of the group. Somehow, these changes to the communication patterns lead to the body of the oldest female of the group undergoing a transformation. Her whole body changes from female into male, thus replacing the lost lead male. It is the equivalent of a sex-change operation, accompanied by a complete physiological change, accomplished only with a communicative intervention. Science fiction writers could have a field day with this idea, yet, as far fetched as it seems, it actually happens routinely in the life of Grouper fish.

In Clown fish, the opposite of the grouper sex-transformation takes place. The death of the lead female results in altered communication patterns of some sort within the group. The body of one of the males of the group subsequently undergoes a complete physiological change and becomes a female. It is incredible, but it is part of the ordinary life of the reef dwelling Clown fish.

Within a pack of wolves, the lead female inhibits the reproductive capacity of the younger adult females by smell communication. The lead female wolf of the pack gives off a hormone in her urine. When the younger adult females of the pack smell this hormone, it inhibits their reproductive capacity. Here, the entire reproductive capacity of young adult female wolves is turned off, just by a smell signal.

With female college students, something a bit similar takes place. Researchers have found that female college students who live together as suitemates gradually affect each others menstrual cycle timing until all of the female suitemates menstrual cycles become synchronous. The researchers are unsure whether this effect is mediated by some sort of smell signal, or by some other behavioral communicative signal.

In a certain species of Tiger salamander, researchers have shown that biological communication is family specific[3]. In this particular species of salamander, jaw development can proceed in either of two directions for any juvenile individual. Either a large jaw can develop, or a smaller jaw can develop. Salamanders of this species are noted to practice cannibalism if they happen to develop a large jaw. This is not the case if they happen to develop a small jaw. Sibling salamanders raised together develop a small jaw and do not attempt to eat each other. Young salamander offspring from different parents raised together develop large jaws, useful for eating each other, which they proceed to do. The more aggressive ones eat the less aggressive non-relatives and survive. Researchers do not yet know how family relatedness is communicated and how this communication ends up determining the course of jaw development, but the experimental fact that this routinely occurs has been established. This could be the ultimate form of nepotism.

During the Second World War in London, the community had to care for many babies that were orphaned by bombing raids. Initially, they were placed in well organized orphanage nurseries. The orphanage nurseries were kept very clean and the infants were kept warm and well fed. However, the death rate of these infants was extremely high, sometimes as high as 90%. Some psychiatric researchers who had been studying infants raised in an institutional setting began to suspect that the infants were dying because they lacked sufficient maternal stimulation. To test their idea, the doctors in some of these orphanage nurseries decided to change the nursing schedules so that the same nurse took care of the same few babies on a daily basis on each eight hour shift. This allowed the babies to develop a relationship with a particular day nurse, evening nurse, and night nurse. The nurses were also instructed to spend time playing with, holding, and talking to "their" babies. The response to this change in the communicative environment for these infants was a fall in the death rate to below 10%. The only change was that the babies now received a reliable, warm, emotional connection and adequate stimulation from a constant set of caregivers. This change in their communicative experience changed their physiological makeup in such a way that the death rate went down from over 90% to under 10%. This demonstrates the very powerful effect of the emotional communicative environment for infants. These results were subsequently repeated in many centers throughout the world. This knowledge is now at the heart of the planning for institutionalized infant care. In all of these biological examples, it has clearly been shown that communication can affect basic biological functions and even structures. The biological world is full of such examples. So there is more than enough biological evidence to support the possibility that extended family group communicative behavior could possibly result in corresponding brain configurational changes in its members.

The Ancestral Origins of the New People Technology

As the capacity for more and more sophisticated organizational structure developed in extended families, the parallel capacity to collectively modify that structure and the capacity to keep the new structure stable also developed. Eventually, what emerged was an extended family group capacity to modify its organizational culture. At the same time, the leadership role of an elder in the triggering and directing of the organizational change process also slowly emerged. What eventually resulted was the role of the elder or shaman as guardian and architect of the covert organizational structure of the extended family group. Since the extended family team's organizational approach to the environment, and the team's political direction, go hand in hand; it is likely that these two processes emerged in parallel. Since political behavior can be seen in modern chimpanzee groups, as observed by Jane Goodall, the emergence of these two capacities, the capacity for political group behavior and the capacity for synaptically encoded organizational culture behavior must be very old indeed. And the emergence of the role of the shaman as guardian of the extended family's covert organizational culture most likely paralleled in time the emergence of the role of the political leader as the guardian of the group's overt political structure.

Just as wound healing is a very old mechanism that plastic surgery has built upon, I believe that this new people technology presented in this volume builds on a very old extended family group capacity.

"Alone we can do so little; together we can do so much".
                                                    Helen Keller

Industrialized society tends to focus on the individual when it comes to health or achievement. Yet, there are many capacities that are group capacities, not individual capacities. The healing and enhancement of individual emotional and behavioral functioning made possible by this new people technology described in this volume is very much a group capacity.

Problems Ahead in Family Wealth Preservation

Getting back to the theme of helping families to keep their wealth from one generation to the next, I want to look at some of the problems that often show up in the new generation, which bode poorly for the overall continued success of the wealthy family. Clearly, if a new member has an identifiable emotional problem, it is going to hamper their ability to contribute to the wealthy family team's continued success. Severe problems with basic trust, self-esteem, and emotion regulation tend to produce severe emotional problems. Problems with separation-individuation, autonomy and control, initiative, and industry tend to show up later as an underlying component of a pattern of poor functioning.

Industry Phase Issues

For wealthy families who have been spared severe emotional problems in their members, the first indications that a young new member may be having difficulties often show up in their inability to accomplish and enjoy work. The developmental phase of Industry needs to be well configured for an individual to be a successful worker. People that have this phase well-configured are able to work steadily at something and gain a sense of satisfaction from doing so. They are also able to get a sense of satisfaction from the completion of a task or project.

Children enter this phase at about the age of 7, and complete the main work on this phase by the time they are 12 years of age. This is the time when healthy children are internally compelled to be good at things, whether it is baseball or soccer, math or reading. This is also the time when the child needs to bond strongly with and identify with the same sex parent. If a family has wounds related to this phase, the developmental experience offered to the child will be deficient.

A workaholic father or mother who is totally engrossed in their own activities and has no time for their same sex child will short-change their child's developmental experience with the Industry phase. The workaholic parent, besides having other developmental wounds, has distinct trouble with the Industry phase itself. They overuse its themes, like a broken record, going over and over the same ground. The workaholic cannot engage in or enjoy the other parts of life, because they are so preoccupied with working. Many founders have more than a touch of this problem.

The founder who is completely tied up generating success often has almost no time for their same sex offspring. The son or daughter then ends up neglected. They do not have enough of the needed same-sex parent's time. The overachieving parent seems impossible to identify with. The parent's achievements seem out of reach for the child. The child does not have the sense of how the parent has achieved such lofty goals, through hard work over a very long period of time. The child doesn't realize what Michelangelo was talking about in his quote: "If people knew how hard I had to work to gain my mastery, it wouldn't seem wonderful at all". The child just sees the end result, the superhuman parent, and cannot imagine how they will ever be able to measure up.

The Industry phase requires that the child be teamed up with an interested parent, who shows the child how to become masterful, and how to enjoy the process on the way to becoming masterful. The child needs to get the sense from their own parent (or other blood relative substituted, if the parent is deceased) that the process is enjoyable, worthwhile, and worth taking pains with. The child needs to come to learn experientially, through the interaction with their parent, that becoming good at something first requires the permission to be bad at it.[4] Or as Kenny Werner states in his book <u>Effortless Mastery</u>, about mastering a musical instrument, "there are no wrong notes". By practicing at something, and being given the permission to make lots of mistakes, one gains mastery.

In addition to not learning how to joyfully acquire mastery by working at something, children who have no access to the same sex parent during Industry phase end up with serious damage to their self-esteem.   The very inaccessibility of their parent gives the child a deep sense of worthlessness. The child feels, "if I were worth something, my father would make the time to spend with me". This child often finds it almost impossible to keep up any sustained effort in completing a project or in acquiring a skill. They just don't feel good enough about themselves; and they feel no joy in working. The absence of their parents' involvement with them is felt in every moment, like the absence of wind for a sailor, leaving the child literally "in the doldrums".   Children with this kind of damage to the Industry phase never succeed at anything unless this damage is undone at a latter time.

If one looks with a discerning eye, it is pretty easy to see that a particular child is having this sort of difficulty. The important point to remember is that a child who is not motivated to do anything or be good at anything is having trouble with the Industry phase. It is not a part of their character that isn't measuring up. They are not intrinsically a "ne'er-do-well" yet.

Children of wealthy families who do not complete the Industry phase in a healthy manner end up as liabilities for the long-term success of their family. They won't be able to master anything because they can't get that part of their "life software" to work. Thus, they may end up trying many things but never finishing anything. Because they are unable to "stick with it" and learn mastery, they often experience an undue amount of failure, even though they may be exerting great effort. And the emotional wounds they sustained by being cheated out of a good Industry phase leave them with an overwhelming amount of sad emotions to have to "work through", if they ever go back and try to fix this phase.

Often a wealthy family with a child who is wounded in this way helps the child cover up for this gapping hole in their "life software". The family uses its financial resources to make it appear as if the child is having successes. These children, as adults, are often good at getting projects started. They are perseverating in the Initiative phase, the last phase that may have been configured well for them. But gaining mastery over the project, and bringing it to a successful completion, is beyond them. And they often fail in a big way, sometimes over and over again in adult life. This is devastating for them personally, and it is no way for the family to build a winning team, by raising developmentally crippled members.

Wealthy families don't do this on purpose. Their previous upstream wounds that are still unresolved result in this phase going badly for new younger members. And the wealthy family often has no idea what is wrong, for the up-stream wound leaves them with a blind spot in this area.

Wealthy Families Often Get Very Poor Professional Guidance and Help

To make matters worse, wealthy families often get the worst kind of professional help. Great wealth often leaves outside professionals in awe of wealthy family members. As John Kenneth Galbraith said in his book <u>A Short History of Financial Crisis</u>, people tend to attribute intelligence to those who have acquired great wealth". While it is true that acquiring great wealth requires great knowledge and at least a certain amount of genius in some specific areas, it is by no means a given that the founders of great wealth have great knowledge in all areas, anymore than they are all world class violinists. Professionals in awe of the family they are working with often fail to communicate to the family the information that they need.

What is more, a large percentage of professionals are overly motivated, like all human beings tend to be, to please the customer. So, frequently they don't give the wealthy family the feedback they need. It is often easier to blame the child than to say that something is damaged in the "life software" of the wealthy extended family itself. Samuel Goldwyn, the great movie mogul, said, "I don't want any yes men around me. I want everyone to tell me the truth, even if it costs them their jobs." He was absolutely right to want that, but in this world, that isn't always easy to find in a professional.

Often, the professionals whom wealthy families consult don't even have a family oriented framework with which to conceptualize what may be amiss with the young person. So their advice can be very dated. Their advice may be as up to date as something given by one of Freud's pupils in the 1930's.

Tom Watson Jr., the son of Tom Watson Sr., the founder of the IBM Corporation, appears to have had marked difficulty with the Industry phase. He gives us a glimpse of what it was like for him growing up in his memoir, <u>Father, Son & Company, My Life at IBM and Beyond</u>, Bantam, 2000. As a boy, Tom Watson Jr. had some access to his workaholic father, but Tom Watson senior was so driven to succeed, that time preparing his son for life was in short supply when Tom Jr. was between 7 and 12 years of age. Tom Jr. had all the signs of difficulty with the Industry phase. He did poorly in school, in spite of superior intellectual ability.[5] He was often in trouble. And when it came time to decide on a career, he was at a loss. His father wanted him to eventually join and lead IBM, but Tom Jr. couldn't imagine being able to follow in his father's footsteps. Tom Watson Jr. was fortunate in having the chance to re-work his misconfigured Industry phase and his accompanying low self-esteem. During WWII, he was assigned to the staff of an American General, stationed in Russia, as the General's pilot. He got to spend a lot of time with this important General, who took a real interest in him. It amounted to a "corrective emotional experience", that allowed Tom Jr. to rework his Industry phase and Self-Esteem phase themes. By the time the war ended, Tom Jr. had achieved a real sense of competence as a pilot, and a real sense of his own value and ability to contribute. The interest the General took in him and the long duration and large amount of time they spent together was critical in allowing Tom Jr. to rework his misconfigured phases. Most young people from wealthy families with serious Industry phase and Self-Esteem phase wounds are not so lucky. This brings us to the next very frequent people problem that one sees in the young members of wealthy families, problems with the Identity phase.

"If your kids grow up living in fairyland thinking that they're princes and princesses, you're going to curse their lives"

Ross Perot[6]

If a child is to become a productive and fruitful member of an extended family team, they need to pass successfully through the Identity phase of development, from age 12 to about age 24. If the Identity phase gets configured properly for the adolescent, then she or he will be able to get a sense of who they are, and they will be able to settle on a career that feels congruent with who they are. They will be able to choose a career which is an outward manifestation of who they are, so that the community, by knowing what career they have settled on, has a sense of who they are as a person. Because their career fits their personhood, the community gets a sense of who this young adult is which is congruent with whom the young adult feels that they are. Without this sense of congruent identity, the young adult will not be able to achieve much going forward into adulthood.

Because the Identity phase has to do with whom this young person is, vis à vis the community, and because it needs to fit with who the young person is inside, it requires a revisiting of all the previous 8 developmental phases of childhood. But this time, as the adolescent revisits these 8 developmental themes, the focus is on their relationship to the community, rather than on their relationship to their family.

The Identity phase begins at 12 years old, the onset of adolescence. Now, the child's developmental clock has completed one revolution in 12 years, and is set to begin the second revolution. The entire second revolution will be taken up by the Identity phase, from 12 years old to 24 years old. And within this Identity phase, which takes up the entire second revolution, the adolescent will revisit each of the 8 developmental themes of childhood again. But this time, the revisited themes will be sub-phases of the overarching developmental phase of Identity, rather than discrete developmental phases unto themselves. This is because when the child first encounters a developmental theme in childhood, the goal of that encounter is to configure the child for that developmental phase for the first time. In contrast, in adolescence, the goal of the entire Identity phase from age 12 to age 24 is to achieve a workable identity. And to do so, the adolescent has to revisit the 8 developmental themes of childhood again, this time as sub-phases. And this time, each revisitation is subservient to the larger goal of Identity. The purpose of each component revisitation is now to further develop each theme, so that it now includes not only how the child relates to their family, but also how the adolescent relates to their community, vis à vis this theme.

The first sub-phase of this Identity phase is a revisiting of Basic Trust, from age 12 to age 13 years. This takes place during the first year of the second revolution of the child's developmental clock, the adolescent developmental clock revolution. As with the Basic Trust sub-phase, all of the previous 8 developmental themes end up being revisited as sub-phases in the same order in which they occurred in childhood. Also, each of the 8 developmental sub-phases gets revisited for the same length of time as in childhood.

While the emphasis during the Identity phase is on the relationship between the adolescent and the community, the adolescent is still embedded in the matrix of the two extended families to which he belongs. And his passage during this phase is regulated by his belonging to his two extended family matrices, as well as by the nature of the community to which he is now forming a deep relationship.

A boy raised in a headhunter extended family in New Guinea will be forming his identity vis à vie the large tribe to which his extended families belong. He will also be forming his identity vis à vie the other tribes in the environment which his own tribe has to deal with. In one particular society that Joseph Campbell talked about and that was featured in an exhibit at the University of Pennsylvania's Museum of Archeology and Anthropology, the male adolescent was expected to learn to cooperate as a hunter and warrior within his extended family and large tribe. He was also expected to conform to the expectations of his extended family group and tribe, with respect to how other competing tribes were regarded and dealt with. By the time he was an adult, he was expected to be a skillful warrior.

One of the rules governing his tribe was that after he married, the young man would have to successfully kill a male from a competing tribe and display his skull at the entrance to his hut, in order for he and his new bride to be allowed to get pregnant and have a child. If he could not successfully kill a male from a competing tribe, he was not allowed to father a child of his own. Killing a competing male for this young man was akin to getting a drivers license here in the US. No drivers license, no driving; no skull of a male from a competing tribe in front of your hut, no offspring.

Furthermore, each time this young man wanted to father another child, he has to kill another male from a competing tribe, and again hang the skull in front of his hut. This system in effect amounted to a kind of intertribal birth control, since competing tribes in the area practiced the same system. In was a brutal but effective way to keep a cap on the population in the area.

To operate successfully in this system, the young male warrior had to learn in adolescence to trust his fellow warrior teammates fully with his life; his survival, as well as his chance to have children, depended on it. This is like the trust that needs to develop between members of an Army platoon in combat. But the young male warrior also had to learn to distrust completely the male members of competing tribes, for he was out to kill them and they him. Everyone's chances to pass on their genes in the next generation depended on who won out in this deadly competition.

So Basic trust got revisited by the young warrior from age 12 to 13, but the nature of that revisitation was determined by the extended family to which he belonged and by the tribal environment that his extended family was in, as well as by the nature of the competing tribal environment.

A middle class American adolescent also goes through this same revisiting and further configuration of the Basic Trust sub-phase as part of the Identity phase. But the ways this theme gets reconfigured during the revisitation are vastly different. He has to learn a much more flexible combination of cooperation and competition with extended family and community members. At the same time, he has to learn that there are some elements of the community whose values are more like that of the headhunter. He may have to learn to stay out of certain neighborhoods, lest he be robbed or killed by gang members, who have an enemy orientation toward him. He also has to learn to abide by the laws of the community that forbid him to actively seek and kill gang members lethal to him. His extended family expects it of him, and the community environment expects it of him.

Let us contrast a hypothetical politically oriented extended family with a hypothetical mob family, both of the 1930's, to see how a young male member of each group might go through forming his Identity, while keeping that formation in line with his extended families "game plan" (how they go about making it in the environment). In the political family, the son is urged to get a prestigious education and to make as many useful connections a possible. While he may be permitted to indulge in alcohol and pre-marital sexual relationships, he is certainly massively discouraged from committing murder to achieve his goals. He would be shunned or "excommunicated" within his extended family if it became public knowledge that he gunned down a fellow student football team member in order to eliminate him, so that he could get the position of starting quarterback. Such behavior on his part would greatly harm his family's prestige in the community. If his father was a U.S. senator, his being known as a murderer would ruin his father's chance of getting re-elected.

By contrast, in the mob family, a young male might be seen as wasting his time if he tried to go to a prestigious college, especially if he was the eldest son and expected to take over the "family business". If on the other hand, he successfully planned and executed the murder of an important rival gang member, while having the approval and "go ahead" from his family's leader, he would most likely be seen as showing great promise, and the murder would be seen as a source of pride by his father and uncles and others in the "family business". Notice, in both cases, the young man is developing, during his Identity phase, a sense of who he is, vis à vis the environment. In each case, he is working to establish himself in a congruent career. But in each case, the nature of that career by necessity needs to conform to or be compatible with the overall organizational culture of his extended family. Allegiance to the nature of one's extended family system is paramount. The adolescent is not forming an identity in a vacuum.

This is nicely illustrated in the movie "The Godfather". The eldest son comes home from military service with a girlfriend who knows nothing consciously about what business his family is in. The eldest son's initial idea is to build a career that is outside of the mafia way of life. But circumstances change and his family needs him within the "family business". Even though he was initially headed into a life path that did not involve crime, the requirements of his family to maintain their collective way of life pulled him back to the basic "family crime business".

One is programmed or configured during the Identity phase to play the game that one's extended family is involved in, within the environment in which your extended family exists. An analogy would be to look at different sports teams as if they were extended families. If one is a member of the New York Yankees baseball team, one attends training camp to become a better baseball player. If one is a member of the New York Giants football team, one attends training camp to become a better football player. And if one is a member of the New York Philharmonic, one attends the summer training program to become a better orchestra member. All three of these teams (extended families) are working to make it in the environment, but they are going about it in unique ways. As a new member gets enculturated to any one of these teams, they find their niche, but it is within the culture of that team.

Failure of Functional Identity Formation

In all extended families, a poor outcome to the Identity phase for one of its young members represents a real loss for the group. After all, the family group has nurtured and raised this young member from infancy and has made a large investment of time and energy and resources. Identity formation represents the transition from a young dependant member undergoing a long period of formation to a productive adult member on whom the next generation will depend. The family's wealth position is only as secure as the level of functioning of its members. While its children represent the future, its young adults represent the present and near future, on which the family depends.

In ancient Roman society, a family could add to its functional adult members by adopting highly promising young adults. A wealthy family could seek and adopt an extremely promising young man that was coming from modest circumstances. This was a way to select part of the next adult generation, while knowing pretty well what the family was getting, assuming they exercised sufficient due diligence in selecting the young adult. For the Romans, often, "selection was better than formation", for it was a better guarantee of gaining a highly promising new adult member.

On the other hand, for wealthy families from modern industrialized countries, they have the custom of relying on the formation of their own children to furnish them with the supply of functioning adults that they need to carry on. If one or more adult members fail to develop a well functioning, useful Identity, then this represents a real loss for the group. If all the young in a wealthy family arrive at adulthood with poorly functioning identities, it amounts to a catastrophe for the extended family team.

In their book <u>Beyond the Grave, The Right and the Wrong Way of Leaving Money to Your Children (and Others)</u>, trust and estate lawyers Gerald Condon Esq. and Jeffrey Condon Esq. portray a couple who have founded a fortune. Mr. and Mrs. Perkins had become enormously wealthy. They had a fortune in excess of $30 million dollars. However, they had three adult children who had never found "their place in life". The Perkinses were still supporting these three children, who were in their twenties and early thirties. None of the three children had any sort of job. None had a career or any movement toward a career.[7]

The Perkinses came to Attorneys Condon looking for estate planning guidance, but what they ended up talking about was the real dilemma they were facing with regard to their three dysfunctional young adult children. This was a "shirtsleeve to shirtsleeve" transition in the making. The Perkinses knew they could leave their entire fortune to their three adult children. But since their children had never managed to acquire the capacity to settle on a career and get down to their life's work, these founder parents were pretty sure that their offspring would blow through all the money in 10 or 12 years. Then, there would be nothing to show for all of their years and years of effort. The Perkinses could try to set up some sort of Incentive Trust to try to motivate their children into achieving functional Identities. But these trusts have a record of very mixed or dubious results. It is notoriously hard to finish the raising of one's children from the grave. After all, the Perkinses had not been able to do it so far, while they were among the living.

If they had lived in ancient Rome, they could have hired an "adoption headhunter" to find them a few new adult family members to adopt, ones with real character and promise. But it is notoriously hard to embrace the customs of an ancient alien culture and feel comfortable and good about it.

In the case presented in the book, Attorney Condon eventually recommended to the Perkinses that they give almost all their money to charity, and let their three adult children and young families move back into the middle class. This would allow their three adult children to learn to fend for themselves through the "school of hard knocks". For the Perkinses, this was the most constructive compromise they could come up with. It held the possibility that their children would eventually become productive adults, ones with functional Identities. The Perkinses would essentially be leaving their adult children on their own, to struggle to work to "make their daily bread", like the rest of the middle class. But it also represented a compromise that included the giving up on their "dream". For, they had come to the Attorney's office hoping that there was something they could do to push their adult children to finally "do something useful with their lives".[8]

What this family was suffering from was a failure of the Identity phase to come together in a functional way for their offspring. This turns out to be a very common problem for wealthy families.

"Inherited wealth ….. is as certain death to ambition as cocaine is to morality.

Commodore Vanderbilt's grandson
Heir to some $60 million in 1885[9]

Why did things turn out this way for the Perkinses and so

many other wealthy families like them? And is it inevitable? It doesn't appear to happen in every wealthy family, so it must be possible to avoid this outcome under some circumstances. One prominent example of success is the Rockefeller family. But success like theirs is by no means the rule. Unfortunately, it is very common to have the children of the founders arrive at adulthood with poorly functioning Identities. These adult children end up in adulthood lacking productive, satisfying and personally appropriate careers.

If we look at the Perkinses example as described in <u>Beyond the Grave</u>, the authors tell us that the Perkinses had used their money to help their children get a good start in life. Almost all parents do this to the extent that they can. They provide their children with education and as many opportunities as they can, to help them on their way. But the authors tell us that the Perkinses "took their generosity to the extreme. Their attitude was that their checkbook was their children's checkbook. It started with toys and clothes. Now it was a complete subsidy of their (adult) children's lives, from houses and vacations to cars and credit cards".[10]

The Perkinses were the founders of great wealth. So by definition, as founders, they came from modest backgrounds. It certainly took them time to build their wealth, which they made in real estate. This slow acquisition of wealth gave them time to learn how to handle it. Wealth is like being given an airplane to fly. If you are a beginner, you start out taking lessons in a Cessna and gradually work your way up to more and more complicated aircraft. The military knows that it is a sure recipe for disaster to give a pilot who just got his flying license an F 21 fighter jet to fly. The flying of such a plane takes such skill and discipline that only a pilot who has been diligently training for years can be expected to fly such a plane safely.

Although they had the best of intensions, what the Perkinses did was the equivalent of giving their children rides in Cessnas (giving them all sorts of toys and clothing). They moved from there to giving their children rides in plush corporate jets (completely subsidizing their adult lives). And then the Perkinses ended up disappointed that their children had not "learned to fly", from a lifetimes of "rides". These were very intelligent people, but they failed to see that their children could never learn to handle responsibility, except by being given ever increasing responsibility to handle over years and years. You cannot learn how to fly a plane simply by watching. The Perkinses themselves had slowly increased their skills at making and handling money and responsibility by doing these things over many, many years. Why had they failed to notice that their children needed to have the same chance to "learn by doing"?

What I have seen operating in wealthy families over and over again is a mechanism whereby upstream wounds distort the family system and how the offspring get raised. These distortions, if left uncorrected, may initially fuel the drive by the founders to acquire great wealth.   But these same wounds often end up paralyzing the children's chances to go through the Identity phase with a good outcome.

The upstream wounds that lead to the acquisition of great wealth often involve a large violation to Basic Trust themes. Some events or circumstances leave the extended family members in very painful and precarious circumstances for an extended period of time. The drive for wealth is often an effort to correct this situation, so that this painful circumstance will not be revisited on the family, or will cease to be perpetuated on the family. So the founder makes a Herculean effort to acquire wealth as a hedge against such an extremely painful fate for the extended family. That motivation combined with the right talents and opportunities, lead to a particular family member becoming a virtuoso at acquiring wealth.

But what happens in the next generation. Remember what William Faulkner said; "The past is never dead, it isn't even past". Not only is the founder trying to prevent a terrible repeat of the extended family's past, but the devastating effects of the previous wounds are still in the system, wreaking havoc with the developmental phases of the founder's offspring. The offspring end up playing roles in the system to represent the old wounds. The extended family enters into enactment mode.   If you raise offspring, but never give them a chance to shoulder age appropriate, ever increasing responsibility, you are virtually assuring that they will be functionally crippled individuals. When they are adults they will be helpless to take care of themselves in their lives. Such extended family dynamics virtually assure that the past repeats itself, and that the downstream family members will end up victims in the world, unable to take care of themselves. George Santayana's famous quote comes into play here. "Those who do not remember the past are destined to relive it". Or as Yogi Berra said, "It's déjà vu all over again". By giving these children "everything", their terrible fate is virtually sealed. They are like infant wild animals, raised in opulent captivity, which are released into the wild at maturity, to fend for themselves. They won't last a week. They will end up being eaten by some predator who is a master of the ways of the forest.

So here we have another example of upstream wounds being unconsciously re-enacted in the downstream generations, leading to a repetition of a terrible outcome. The family system was sculpted for eons to re-enact wounds from one generation to the next, until the family has a chance to integrate the critical survival lessons inherent in the wounds. The accumulation of great wealth as a byproduct of the previous terrible wounding process does not protect the extended family system from entering into enactment mode, if the old wounds have not yet been integrated.

What if the Perkins family had been referred by their attorney to an extended family integration process? Imagine that Mr. Perkins brought his parents, if they were still alive, to meet with he, his wife, his children and the grandchildren for consulting sessions and that Mrs. Perkins did the same with her side in alternating consultation sessions. Now, imagine that both extended families' upstream wounds got revisited in this collective consulting process and that both extended families became liberated from their respective enactments. The two extended families' organizational cultures would now become fertile ground in which the three adult children could undergo a belated but effective configuration process in their Identity phases. These three young adults would then have started to dwell on their futures and their places in society.

One would not see results for the first few months. Instead, the three adult children would enter a kind of moratorium phase, like the caterpillar that makes a cocoon. But within the three adult children, great changes would be taking place, as the developmental integrative process of the Identity phase was again allowed to proceed, now that they were freed from the paralysis of their extended families' enactment. Gradually, these three adult children would emerge with newfound purpose and direction, which matched their talents and life experiences thus far. Nothing is wasted in the developmental process of forming one's Identity. Like tomato plants moved into full sun from their previously stunting place in the shade, these three adult children would "take off".

The Perkinses would then end up with very sound human capital in the next generation, to entrust with their hard earned wealth. They would be able to retire, seeing that the next generation was more than up to the task of preserving their wealth, while putting it to good use. And what is more, they would be able to rest comfortably, knowing that their children were well on their way to leading satisfying, productive, and enjoyable lives. And they would be spared the agony of turning their unprepared, highly vulnerable, offspring loose in a cruel world; hoping that the "school of hard knocks" would toughen them and force them to be productive, without killing them or inflicting terrible suffering on them first. The Perkinses would no-longer be the doting but ineffective parents, turning their pampered offspring into the wild.

In summary, whenever you have a situation where a young adult is "rudderless", having achieved no career or useful working role in life, you have a problem with the failure of the Identity phase of development. And whenever you have the failure of the Identity phase of development, you have a situation where the enactment of old upstream wounds is determining things, in spite of the parent's best efforts to try to correct the situation. Two well meaning and diligent parents are no match for an extended family enactment that draws its power from severe upstream wounds. They and their children will be tossed around like a bail of hay in a tornado. Such parents are not bad or neglectful or inadequate; they are just outclassed by a process that is much more powerful than they are. And there are no bad offspring; there are only inadequate developmental environments. You can't grow tomatoes in darkness.

Technology, when it is based on a more profound understanding of the natural world and our place in it, brings great benefits.   Look at the doctor in London who finally understood how a cholera epidemic operated.   "All the king's horses and all the king's men", couldn't bring an end to these epidemics before. The right knowledge, implemented in appropriate public health measures, changed everything. The same happened with universal education and literacy implementation. We are at the very infancy of the implementation of this new people technology explained in this volume. The first step in making use of this new knowledge is that its benefits have to be fully appreciated, so that it becomes clear to more and more of the society. Once its benefits are clear, the huge return on investment of implementing this new technology will be able to be realized.

Chapter 15

Marriage

For Better or For Worse

Once a young adult has achieved a workable Identity, they are ready for the next step in the developmental process, the Intimacy phase. This is where the stage is being set for the rest of the young adult's life, if things go well. The young adult starts to narrow down the range of choices and make commitments, and what he or she commits to are partnerships with people. Intimacy is about being who you are, in deep commitment with others. These partnerships include marriage, business and career partnerships and deep friendships.

In an interview of Jim Collins by senior Fortune writer Jerry Useem, Collins was asked to discuss the art of decision making.[1] When asked what was the most surprising finding from his research, Collins said it was the observation that the most important decisions are about "who", not about "what".

Collins said: "Fundamentally, the world is uncertain. Decisions are about the future and your place in the future when that future is uncertain. So what is the key thing you can do to prepare for that uncertainty? You can have the right people with you."[2]

Napoleon Hill, the author of <u>Think and Grow Rich</u>, found that the choice of marital partner is one of the most important decisions a person will ever make in terms of their chances for future success.

Any loving parent is acutely aware of this when they think about their adult child's marital future. There are few things that can make or break one's happiness like the nature of one's spouse. A nice young woman with a terrible husband is in big trouble. If she hasn't had a child with him yet and she has the wisdom to bail out, she can lick her wounds and start over. But if they have children together, then the equation becomes infinitely more complicated.

Some time ago, I was at a seminar being given by my mentor, Dr. Carl Whitaker. Someone in the audience asked him to share some of his thoughts on divorce. He answered, "I don't believe in divorce". The audience gasped and became quiet. After a brief pause, he said, "I don't believe in marriage either." At this point the audience collectively shifted in their chairs. Then he said, "I only believe in concretized orgasms. Once a man and a woman have a child together, they are connected for life, no matter what happens."

The phenomenon he was talking about was the factual biological connection that a child has to each parent and to their extended families. Once a child is born, she becomes a genetic member of two extended families. What happens in the development of that child is greatly influenced by the nature of the participation or lack of participation of the mother and father and their respective families over the course of that child's life. Once a young adult picks a partner to have a child with, the couple becomes indelibly intertwined, because each parent has a great impact on the outcome of that child's emotional development. The child as a member of the mother's extended family is highly influenced by the father and his extended family. And the child as a member of the father's extended family is highly influenced by the mother and her extended family. There are few things parents fear more than that their adult child might get "mixed up" (read conceive a child) with the wrong partner and his or her family.

Before about the twelfth century, with the appearance of the ideal of romantic love as a basis for marriage, families generally didn't take any chances with something so important as whom their young adult family members conceived children with. Marriages were arranged, so the family performed the due diligence on prospective spouses and their extended families. They knew that the fate of their extended family would be highly influenced by who they chose as spouses for their adult children. They also realized that the choosing of a spouse is really the choosing of a spouse together with his or her entire extended family. It was always a package deal. With the rise in the frequency of romantic marriage over the lasts eight centuries, this detail, that marriage involves marrying one's in-laws as well as one's spouse, has become conveniently ignored.

But once a woman or a man conceives a child, they rapidly become aware of how much influence the in-laws exert, both by their participation, but also by their possible absence. A man or woman without supportive relatives is often a weak team member. It is like a sandlot game of football where you are supposed to bring four players and your mate is supposed to bring four players to make a team of ten, to play the opposing team. If your mate shows up by himself, no matter how good a player he is, his contribution to your team will be weak, compared to if he had come with four other companions.

Because the extended family is so important to the emotional as well as financial success of the reproductive couple, arranged marriages made a lot of sense for many millennia. If the extended family was particularly influential and did not want to dilute their power, they often solved that problem by arranging for first cousins to marry. That way, they kept their assets in the extended family.

I remember participating in a discussion in a Sociology of the Family class when I was an undergraduate at Georgetown University. Several students were chosen to present their family trees. One exchange student from a third world country mapped out her family. Her extended family had been one of the ruling families in her country for more than a hundred years. In her genealogy diagram, she showed that there had only been one marriage that hadn't involved first cousins in the last eight generations. Her extended family kept their power and influence by having the family determine which alliances were made through marriages.

Many parents, faced with an adult child who is about to marry someone they consider "unsuitable", lament the passing of the arranged marriage. But it went out of fashion for a reason. If the young adult is fortunate enough to be able to choose a worthy mate, whom they love romantically, their marriage becomes much more satisfying and empowering. Modern societies have enough safety nets that almost all young adults feel safe enough to try to reach the "brass ring" of finding a worthy romantic lover as their marital partner.

But what can extended families do to hedge their bets? The family can try to actively determine the outcome in other important areas of their child's life. They can select the right schools and tutors. They can try to control which friends their child gets involved with. They can select the town and neighborhood they raise their child in, and the camps they send them to. They can even regulate the books that their child reads and the TV programs and movies their child is allowed to see. But in the choice of a mate, most parents feel helpless, while others are determined to break up what they see as bad matches. Any way you cut it, the parents' ability to influence a good outcome feels much less certain than is desired.

I was talking to one anxious mother in a very wealthy family about the young man her 24 year old daughter was currently dating. She said he was a college drop-out who had been working at a menial job for the last five years. He had no ambitions. He was covered with tattoos and the parents suspected that he used drugs. Grandfather described his objection to this young man by saying he was "an undisciplined person". I was saying to the mother that it was a shame that it wasn't the good old days. In those times, she could simply have packed her daughter off to Switzerland for a few years, until she forgot about this undesired suitor. Or better yet, have the undesirable suitor sent off to the Foreign Legion.

Because the parents are not blinded by the throws of the romance, they can frequently, but not always, see the real pitfalls in a budding romance. Nevertheless, they are usually helpless to convey their wisdom to their adult child.

In one extended family I was working with, the 25 year old daughter was engaged to a recently divorced thirty-eight year old man with a thirteen year old daughter and twin eight year old boys. The great grandmother in this extended family commented on her granddaughter's fiancé this way. "He needs help."

During the Intimacy phase, the young adult who has achieved a strong functional Identity starts to develop the capacity to make deep commitments, with all of the compromises and self-sacrifice such commitments may entail for the welfare of a team. This culminates for most young adults in the commitment to a marital union, hopefully a good one. Is there anything that this new science of extended family dynamics can tell us about what causes a young adult to seek out a good relationship vs. a doomed one? And is there any way that this new technology can be used to favorably influence the marital choices of young adult family members? Fortunately, the answer is yes!

It turns out that young adults whose developmental phases have been well configured, and whose families are relatively free of old unresolved wounds, and who are thus not perseverating in enactments, tend to make very good marital choices. In fact, I can go further and say that a marriage will only have serious internal trouble if the partners and their extended families have one or more seriously damaged developmental phases. What is more, one can predict what kinds of trouble a marriage will have by looking to see which developmental phases in the prospective spouses are poorly configured.

Take the example of the Basic Trust phase. We recall that developmental phases have to do with configuring the brain circuits that govern specific relationship themes. During the Basic Trust phase, brain circuits are being configured that govern how trust issues are perceived and handled in family relationships. From age 12 to 13 years, Basic Trust circuits are further configured, but now the configuration is centered on the circuits that govern Basic Trust issues in relationships with others beyond the family.

A very profound principle is at work in mate selection. People only chose mates that have the same degree of functional configuration for each particular developmental phase. So if Sara has well configured Basic Trust circuits, then she will only be attracted to young men who have equally well configured Basic Trust circuits. And if Catherine has poorly configured Basic Trust circuits, then she will only be attracted to men with poorly configured Basic Trust circuits. If a young adult is generally overly trusting in their relationship to others, they will usually gravitate toward a potential mate who is under trusting in their relationships. What is true of the Basic Trust circuits is true for all of the other developmental circuits as well. People only pair romantically with those with matching developmental wounds or matching developmental degrees of health. The matching is precise for each developmental phase and its degree of functionality or woundedness.

You may ask; how this is possible? The answer is that all the developmental themes are the building block elements in the transactions of each human relationship. Taking the Basic Trust theme again as an example; the manner in which one relates to others has imbedded in it how one trusts or mistrusts. Now look at the Autonomy-Control themes. How one relates to others implicitly includes how one handles interpersonal control and autonomy issues. And so it goes for each of the developmental phases.

If you speak French, that fact becomes immediately evident when you engage in a conversation. And if you relate in a controlling way with others, that also becomes immediately evident as you begin relating to another person. Unconsciously, each of us picks up the developmental styles of other people as we relate to them. At the same time, we use our own developmental styles (the way we relate with regard to each developmental theme) as we enter and engage in any relationship. It is evident to us, unconsciously, which developmental styles another person is using in relating to us, just as it is obvious to us whether a person is speaking to us in our own language.

People only get along romantically with others whose developmental phases each have the same degree of functionality. People with well configured functional Basic Trust circuits only get along with similar individuals. And people with poorly configured Basic Trust circuits only get along with others with the same poor Basic Trust configurations, although frequently a mistrustful person will be attracted to an overly trusting person. They both have equal misconfiguration and poorly functioning Basic Trust circuits, but the nature of the misconfiguration is complementary. One is overly trusting and one is mistrustful.

Let me give you an example of how this works to make it clearer. Suppose that George comes from an extended family where there is a wound to the Autonomy and Control phase. When he was 1 to 3 years old and working on the Autonomy and Control phase, his parents would have had trouble raising George, because they and their extended families have trouble with this theme. So George would emerge at age 3 with this phase misconfigured. Let's say that when George emerged from this phase, he was primarily over-controlling. Now, George is 26 years old and is starting to date seriously. He asks Denise out on a first date. On the date, he tries to control what Denise wears and where they will go. He takes her to a movie and tries to control which movie they see, instead of working it out mutually. He then takes her to dinner and tries to control what she orders and what they talk about. Would Denise be likely to accept another date from George? Hardly! If she is reasonably well configured for Autonomy and Control themes, she would most likely find George's over-controlling style oppressive. She would be glad to be finished with the first date and couldn't stand another date with him. This will happen to George over and over until he dates a young woman who also comes from a family with misconfiguration of Autonomy and Control themes. Let's say he now asks out Suzanne, who is also misconfigured for the Autonomy and Control phase, but in a complementary way. She is primarily under-controlling.

Remember, one can be misconfigured for Autonomy and Control themes by being either under-controlling or by being over-controlling. Both extremes are complementary forms of misconfiguration for this phase. And one usually finds both forms of misconfiguration present within an extended family with wounds to this phase.

So George asks Suzanne out on a date and he employs his over-controlling style. Suzanne is used to this. Undoubtedly, both of her parents also have problems with Autonomy and Control themes. Usually, one parent will be primarily over-controlling and one parent will be primarily under-controlling. Thus, Suzanne has had years of experience with both of these misconfigured Autonomy and Control styles.

On the date with George, Suzanne is a master at adapting to his over-controlling style. First of all, she grew up with one parent, who she loved, who had the same over-controlling style as George. Secondly, George's over-controlling style dovetails with her under-controlling style. So she is much more in her comfort zone with George, than she would be with a young man who is well configured for this phase. In addition, while she grew up adapting to one parent with an over-controlling style, she grew up identifying with and emulating her other parent with the under-controlling style. She is also likely to have at least one sibling who was over-controlling whom she learned to adapt to in a peer relationship. So she finds George's over-controlling style to be acceptable for now.

At a deep level, she and George already understand each other in a very profound way, even on the first date. They both know from a young lifetime of experience how hard it is to grow up with and try to function with a misconfigured Autonomy and Control phase. They both know unconsciously how much each of them is hampered in all of their interpersonal relationships by having Autonomy and Control problems. They know just what this chronic misconfiguration has cost each of them. So they have deep empathy for each other, based on direct personal experience.

Denise, the previous woman mentioned, would never get to the point of feeling that way for George. She would be so put off by his style, that she would never get a chance to get to know him. Denise would never personally understand, as Suzanne does, how crippling it is to live with a misconfiguration of the Autonomy and Control themes. Suzanne on the other hand has lived with an under-controlling misconfiguration. Thus, she has lived her whole life, loving and observing and adapting to an over-controlling and an under-controlling parent.

Because George and Suzanne have major trouble with the same developmental theme, they will be able to get along on this dimension. This will allow for the possibility of second and further dates. If they find each other attractive and suitable in a myriad of other ways, they will be able to marry. If not, George will continue to date, but he will only find success with young women who have misconfigured Autonomy and Control circuits as he does. No matter whether he prefers blonds or brunettes, tall or short, a city girl or a young woman who prefers the suburbs, he will only end up with a young woman misconfigured for the Autonomy and Control phase. Those young women who do not share a misconfiguration for this phase will not be able to stand him, and will never go out on a second date with him. In the end, he will invariably marry an Autonomy and Control misconfigured young woman.

Birds of a Feather Flock Together

This basic dynamic of mate selection operates not only

for the Autonomy and Control phase, but for each of the other 8 preceding developmental phases. A person marries a spouse who carries the same wound pattern to their developmental phases as they do. And not only do the wounds match, the spouses are a match for the degree of severity of misconfiguration for each developmental stage.

One could develop a rating scale to quantify the degree of misconfiguration for each developmental stage. If 0 designates a well-configured developmental stage and 1 up to 5 designate increasing degrees of misconfiguration, then the profile of marital partners always exactly matches. I have come to this conclusion based on over 600 interviews with families where I was able to trace these patterns.

Couples need to match on a whole host of dimensions in order to be able to fall in love and take the romantic relationship forward to a marriage, but they will always match exactly in terms of which developmental phases are wounded and to what degree, phase by phase. Their developmental wound-health profiles will be identical. This is both a curse and a blessing. It means that a young person will always end up with someone who is equally healthy and equally damaged, and in precisely the same ways.

Parents with an adult child who is damaged, but for whom the damage is not recognized because they, as parents, are too close to it, will see that their adult child will keep choosing wounded partners to date. It also means that sooner or later, their adult child will marry a wounded partner. And if their adult child has some rather serious misconfigurations, their future spouse will have equally serious misconfigurations, even if the parents don't recognize the matching quality of the wounds in the two young people. No parent wants a significantly wounded son-in-law or daughter-in-law, for it always spells trouble. So on the one hand, this matching pattern dynamic in mate selection is a curse.

On the other hand, if a family makes use of this new people technology to rapidly repair wound misconfigurations for the entire extended family, this reliable matching pattern dynamic in mate selection becomes a huge blessing. Never, since the days of the arranged marriage, has an extended family had so much control over the suitability of their adult children's future spouses. Parents and their extended families don't really care if their son or daughter marries a red-head or a blond. Just as they don't really care very much if a prospective mate for their adult child prefers tennis or bridge. But they care greatly that the prospective mate be well functioning and free of the predictable future problems that come with serious misconfiguration of one or two or three developmental phases.

If an extended family takes the steps to integrate their upstream wounds and the resulting downstream repercussions, they can virtually ensure that their adult offspring's developmental phases will be in good configurational shape. And then the parents can rest easy, trusting the law of matching developmental patterns in mate selection. Their adult child, who is now in good configurational shape for each of the developmental phases, will <u>only be able to get along with prospective mates who are in equally good shape.</u> They won't have to worry about whom their child will select, for it will now only be a good candidate. What an insurance policy! And the excellent results are all achieved without meddling. As sure as day follows night, the parents and the extended family will get a good result.

The underlying principles won't even have to be explained to the dating young adult. It all works on automatic pilot. If the adult child is well-configured, only those mating candidates who are equally well-configured will hold any appeal. I can imagine a time, long after I am in the grave, when bringing the extended family in for this kind of integrative consulting process, to ensure good results in adult children's mate selection, will be routine. Families will all want to integrate any lingering upstream wounds prior to their young adults reaching the stage of intimacy and mate selection. It will be as common as vaccinations, literacy, and indoor plumbing. By that time, maybe several centuries from now, it will become unimaginable to leave out such an important preventative step, because too much of their adult child's and extended family's future rides on good mate selection.

Examples of Re-writing Mate Selection History

When a sailboat skipper gets ready for the Bermuda Cup

Race, she or he starts months in advance to get their boat into excellent shape. They take the boats out on advanced shakedown cruises, hoping to discover weak, damaged equipment, so that it can be repaired in advance. They don't want be on the high seas in the middle of the race, when they find out that the fittings holding the mast in place are corroded and ready to break, or that a sail has a weak seam and will rip under enough wind pressure. The stakes are too high to leave the discovery of equipment problems to the race itself.

I will now tell you about two families who ended up using this extended family consulting process as a preventative "shakedown cruise", to help them avoid disaster in mate selection. The first family, the Greenwald's, came to me originally because their fourteen year old son, Aaron, was showing serious oppositional behavior in school and at home. He was an extremely bright boy who had managed to get himself expelled from two schools in the first five months of his freshman year of high school. The therapist who referred the family to me had been thinking that Aaron might need to go to a therapeutic residential school, and recommended the extended family consulting process as an alternative.

The family was very opposed to sending Aaron away to a therapeutic residential boarding school. They did not want to be separated from their son, for reasons that will soon be clear. Besides Aaron, the family had an older daughter, Rachel, who was 24 years old. Rachel had finished college 2 years earlier, and was working in advertising. Joel, the father, had made a fortune in real estate. His parents were both concentration camp survivors. Joel's father, Jacob, together with his whole family, was forced into the ghetto in the city of Lublin, when Jacob was 14. When the ghetto was liquidated, Jacob and all his family members were sent to a concentration camp. Jacob was the only member of his family to survive the war.

Hannah, Joel's mother was put into a concentration camp at age 14, after she had been in hiding since age 12. Her whole family perished. Joel's wife Judith, Aaron's mother's family had survived the war in Russia, where many family members died, including Judith's maternal grandfather. He was killed while serving in the Soviet Army, fighting the Nazis. The remaining members of both extended families made it to the United States after the war.

It was clear in working with Aaron's two extended families that the upstream wounds were the source of Aaron's difficulties. The unwillingness of the Greenwald family to send Aaron away was related to the history of so many painful losses in the previous generations. So the family was relieved to find that they could resolve Aaron's difficulties by working together.

Both Joel's and Judith's extended families had longstanding respect for each other. They were both members of the same synagogue for many years, and Joel and Judith had met through their family connections. Both extended families worked steadily in the integrative consulting process. By the time each extended family had finished six half-day retreats; most of their upstream wounds had been pretty well integrated. Aaron's situation had totally changed. His oppositional behavior was a thing of the past and he was now using his considerable energies and brilliance to place himself at the top of his class at his new school, both academically and socially. But since both extended families' upstream wounds had been so massive and so severe, and since both families had achieved such progress, they decided to stay in the consulting process for an additional year. It was the equivalent of the two extended families staying on for graduate school, where the first six half-day retreats for each side was like completing their undergraduate degree.

Rachel, Aaron's sister, had been engaged to a 30 year old man with an MBA who had a most promising career with a venture capital firm when the families began the consulting process. 7 months into the process, Judith called me between retreats to tell me that her daughter Rachel had broken off her engagement. I asked her what had happened.

She said that Rachel had started to ask her fiancé questions about his career. What she found out was that he wasn't a young member of a venture capital firm at all, but a cocaine dealer. Rachel immediately broke off the engagement. Her parents have been thanking God profusely ever since. What if she had married him? What if they had had a child? The nightmare was too dreadful to think about. How had the engagement come about in the first place? Why hadn't Rachel known about his "career" activities earlier? Why had she been able to learn about them now, rather than after they were married? Looking at some of the upstream wounds that the Greenwald's had been integrating provides some possible answers.

When Joel first brought his parents in for the paternal extended family consultation process, he was adamant that they not be asked about their concentration camp experiences. Joel said that both his father and mother had been interned at Auschwitz, among other camps.   He revealed, during the preliminary evaluation that preceded the consulting process that his parents had never spoken about their concentration camp experiences. Because of the enormous pain involved, he made us agree to skip over asking his parents about the camps in the upcoming family retreats.   We agreed that with his extended family, we would restrict ourselves to asking about his parents' families and their lives before the war and after the war, leaving out their wartime and their camp experiences.

The Greenwald extended family started the consultation process as other families do. The grandparents talked about their families and their experiences growing up. Keeping to our agreement, we never asked about the camps. The paternal and maternal extended families alternated scheduling their half-day retreats. By the fifth month, the Greenwald's came in for their third half-day retreat. It began as the other half-day retreats had, but soon into the session, Jacob announced that he and his wife Hannah had decided that they were going to talk about the camps. A family fight ensued. Joel and his sister Ella, who was also present for the sessions with her husband and two young children, protested. They said that it was too painful for their parents to talk about. Jacob said it had to be talked about. He said that he and his wife had been silent long enough. Then Hannah spoke. With an authority that I had never seen coming from a person, she said vehemently that they had suffered enough and that it "would be talked about". No one said a word after that. She had spoken with all of the force of her three years in Auschwitz, and no one was going to oppose her.

We started by asking Jacob about his time during the war and ended up talking about how he survived the camps. He said that he had volunteered to work as a high voltage electrician even though he had absolutely no experience. He sensed that by volunteering for this dangerous job, he would be kept alive as long as he was useful. He also said that one had to become a master at associating with incoming prisoners who weren't going to make it. He said that he and the other Polish Jews would wait for the transport trains coming from Hungary. The Hungarian Jews were not used to much hardship in their prewar lives. Jacob and some of his fellow prisoners soon observed that the Hungarian Jews would only last at the most three weeks after they arrived. Jacob said he would befriend one of these incoming Hungarian Jews and stick with them night and day until they dropped. Then he would immediately search their body cavities for valuables, such as a diamond. He said that the diamond he would find would perhaps "buy" an extra crust of bread to keep him alive for one extra day. His wife told similar gruesome stories. She also said that as a child and adolescent before the war, her family was so poor that she often was half starved. She was convinced that surviving such hardship as a child had enabled her to survive the starvation of the camps.

Jacob said that when they were liberated, the Army doctors with the U.S. forces told them that they should put their camp experiences out of their minds and never speak about them. The American doctors said that their camp experiences were so horrific that they could never be processed. They needed to bury them. Jacob said they had kept their secrets for over forty-five years and that it had been a mistake. The Army doctors' advice had been wrong. They should have talked all of this out a long time ago. But it wasn't too late, and he could see that talking it out would do some good, especially for his grandchildren.

Two months after the Greenwald's fateful session, I got the call from Judith telling me about Rachel's broken engagement. Clearly, something dramatic had changed for Rachel. As I came to understand it, Rachel had known unconsciously about her fiancé Adam's underworld "career" and she had unconsciously chosen such a man for a purpose. Besides all of the damage to the Identity phase that her grandparents sustained in the camps as teenagers, the primary damage, their loss of all of their family members and their horrific experiences in the camps, was a catastrophic wound to their Basic Trust. This Basic Trust wound had pervaded the subsequent generations of the family, since it had never been integrated. Rachel, with her huge resulting wounds to her Basic Trust phase, had selected a fiancé whose family had equally devastating wounds to Basic Trust. In Adam's family, the extended family system had responded to the devastating upstream events by resorting to underworld activities, to even the score as they saw it unconsciously. They had somehow come to consider the society as having been responsible for inflicting their devastating wounds, or as guilty of being heartless bystanders. In either case, they had come to the unconscious conclusion that the society needed to pay to make up for what they had suffered. And they had come to see criminal activities as somehow justified in collecting their debt.

Rachel and her fiancé Adam had been a match in terms of the status of their developmental phases at the time of the engagement. But once Rachel's family had begun to open up and integrate their massive wounds to Basic Trust, her Basic Trust brain circuits had begun to reconfigure. The family was now moving out of enactment mode; and her brain circuits could now assume a much healthier and more functional configuration. With this change, the condition of Rachel's and Adam's developmental phases no-longer matched. It was now time for Rachel to ask about this glaring difference, which prior to Rachel's extended families' integrative work, had been a similarity between she and Adam. Adam could sense that he and Rachel were no-longer a match, so there was no sense in keeping up the façade of respectability. He told her the truth and they broke it off.

It was the integrative work done by the Greenwald's two extended families that set the granddaughter free. Nothing else could have done it. Rachel was no-longer massively misconfigured for Basic Trust, like she and her extended families had been. Because of the integrating of the upstream wounds, Rachel's built-in normative patterns for how Basic Trust circuits should be configured, in a balanced way, took over and self-corrected. Once that reconfiguration process was well underway, she no longer fit with Adam at all. Think of the value created by the Greenwald's through their integrative effort. By averting this marriage, they changed the whole coming history of their extended families. Even Joel and Judith's considerable fortune wouldn't have saved them from the agony they were in store for. Fifteen months after the Greenwalds finished their integrative consulting work; Rachel was married to a fine young man who was an up-and-coming investment banker.

The second family I will present is one I referred to earlier, in which the mother was wishing she could send her daughter off to Switzerland to break up an unsuitable relationship.

Clarissa was 24, her sister Anna was 16, and she had a 14 year old brother, John. The family had come to me because Anna was diagnosed with Bipolar Disorder. She was extremely moody, had recurrent severe depressions, and had been a treatment failure on five different medication regimens. The family was very wealthy on the father's side. Paternal grandparents, Ted and Louisa, had founded an extremely successful family business. Their son Ted Jr. was the father of the three children. He held the position of president in the business. His wife Nora was vice president of marketing. His sister Patricia was also married with two children, ages 8 and 10. She was an accountant and the firm's controller. Her husband was a very successful attorney who did some of the firm's legal work.

When I met with Ted Jr., his wife Nora, and the three children for the preliminary evaluation, it became evident that Anna was not the only child with severe difficulties. Clarissa was clearly having trouble with the Identity phase. She had finished college with a very high average. But since then, her life had been going nowhere. She would attempt to get some sort of a job, would hold it for two or three months, and then quit, at her families urging. The jobs were invariably not really suited to her. They paid 10 dollars an hour and were leading nowhere. She was basically directionless in terms of a real career. Her parents supported her with a generous monthly stipend. They were always on her case to identify a productive career direction, but so far, all efforts had failed.

Clarissa was very bright and personable, very outgoing. But she seemed to make very poor friendship choices. Her dating life was also going nowhere. She had dated casually in college and was now seeing a young man who sent shivers up her mother's spine. He was 24 and claimed he worked as an events promoter, that is, when he worked at all. Mostly he supported himself with menial jobs. He had dropped out of college after a year. As mentioned before, he was covered with tattoos and Ted Jr. and Nora suspected he used drugs. They were terrified that Clarissa would end up with him.

It was during a conversation, after the family had been engaged in the consulting process for about four months, that Nora remarked that she wished it were the "good old days". She would pack Clarissa up and send her to Switzerland for a year to do mandatory post-graduate work, and let this relationship with Lenny, her boyfriend, die on the vine. I told Nora that if the two extended families, hers and Ted Jr.'s, kept up their integrative efforts in the consulting process, she wouldn't have to worry. Lenny would become a distant memory and Clarissa would be dating someone who they felt really good about.

Nora wasn't so sure, and asked me why I was so certain. I explained how Clarissa's poor Identity formation made her attracted to similarly stuck young men. I told Nora that as soon as the family had finished integrating the upstream wounds that were responsible for the arrested development in her children, not only would Anna get back on track and without medication, but also Clarissa would start to make progress with her Identity phase. Then Clarissa would drop Lenny, and find herself attracted to young men with good motivation and career prospects. Nora wanted to believe me, but she felt that maybe it was too good to be true.

By the time the two extended families had each finished four half-day retreats, Anna was doing much better. She was now off all her medicines and her moods had stabilized. She was also much less depressed. She was seeing her friends and was doing B work in school, where she had been failing previously. And Clarissa and Lenny had broken up. Evidently, Clarissa had started to expect more responsible behavior from Lenny. She wanted him to keep the dates they made, and follow through with agreements. Lenny had not been interested in changing his ways.

By the time 14 months had passed, Ted Jr.'s family had completed seven sessions and Nora's family had completed six, Anna was a completely different girl. She was doing well in school and found herself becoming increasingly popular. Her depressions and mood swings were things of the past. In addition, her sister Clarissa had met a new boyfriend. He was 28, a graduate of the

University of Michigan Law School, and had passed the bar two years ago. He was practicing corporate law with a very good medium sized firm. Clarissa had enrolled in graduate school and was pursuing a master's degree in fine arts. She had tentatively decided to eventually set up her own art gallery in New York.

Nora and Ted Jr. were astounded by how much their two extended families had been able to achieve. Ted Jr. likened it to a "best ball" golf tournament that he had recently been involved in. He usually shot in the mid-eighties, but the team, using the "best ball" of the foursome at each hole, had finished the tournament at two under par with a score of 70, a score he would have expected from Tiger Woods. He said he saw the work the two extended families did in the same way. Collectively, the extended families were able to achieve "world class" results.

Since the extended family totally relies on the new generation to keep the "family game" going forward, and because the life partners the young adults choose have such a huge effect on the eventual outcome, the results that the integrative consulting process can achieve are invaluable.

As Any Smart Author Knows, the Point to End the Story is When the Couple is Riding Off into the Sunset.

Mark Twain

In the above section, we dealt with problems related to finding a suitable spouse. Would that finding the right spouse were the only hurtle to ensuring a long, productive and satisfying marriage. "But marriage brings troubles and problems begin"[3]. But why? After you have found the right mate who you love deeply, and who loves you deeply, why is marriage so often fraught with difficulties? Ask one hundred people these questions and you will get one hundred answers. You have heard all of these answers before. Does this mean that there are no underlying principles to the dynamics of marriage and how they go awry? Or does it simply mean that society's understanding of marriage dynamics and the inherent difficulties is simply inadequate?

In his book, <u>The Structure of Scientific Revolution</u>, Thomas Kuhn says that chaos in a field always precedes a major breakthrough[4]. We certainly have chaos in the field of understanding marital dynamics. Go into any bookstore and look in the self-help section. There are hundreds of books that have different answers about how to repair or strengthen a marriage. In contrast, consult any number of textbooks on electricity, from books for children to books for electrical engineers. They are all in agreement that electricity is the flow of electrons through a conducting material and they are all in agreement about the basic principles of electricity. When a field of study resembles a United Nations gathering of religions, all purporting to be the one and only way to God, that chaos indicates that there are principles at a deeper level that are not yet understood. These as yet undiscovered, deeper principles underlie all of the various opposing approaches.

When you look at marriage through the lens of the developmental phases in the context of the extended family, you begin to see patterns that start to make sense of the marital currents and eddies. When we are born, we enter our nuclear family, which is located within two extended families, our mother's and our father's. We become bonded to our parents, the people to whom we will be closest in our lives. We then proceed through the childhood and adolescent developmental phases. We develop or build our patterns of relating to other people, first to family members, and then to the community.

When we marry, we enter into a new intimate relationship. This is the second closest relationship most of us will ever have in our lives, second only to the deep relationship we had with our parents. Once we marry, what occurs is that we revisit all the developmental phases of childhood and adolescence again. But this time, instead of the focus being on the relationship with our parents and siblings as children, or on our relationship with the community as adolescence; the focus is on our relationship with our intimate partner. We revisit each of the developmental stages with our new spouse, in the same order that we went through them in childhood and with the same amount of time devoted to each one.

Thus, a newly married couple first revisits the Basic Trust phase with each other. During this time, each member of the couple adds new Basic Trust circuits to handle the brain communication traffic that is inherent in handling relationship themes of trust with their spousal partner. We revisit, at the same time, the Sense of Self phase of development; our brains become busy adding additional circuits that are needed to handle these themes with our spouse.

The Basic Trust themes get revisited for a year, just as when we were infants. The Autonomy and Control themes get revisited starting one year into the marriage and going to three years into the marriage. Sense-of-Self themes get revisited, starting at the beginning of the marriage, and they continue to get configured for the first seven years of marriage. Finally, they get solidified for the next five years, just as they did in childhood. And so it goes with all the developmental themes. This makes sense.

The developmental themes are the building block patterns for all of our human relationships. We had to build these patterns, starting from infancy, to conform to the patterns in our extended families. Then we had to build on these patterns to handle the way we relate to the people in our community, while still staying faithful to the overall game plan of our extended families. So it makes sense that as we enter an entirely new deep relationship, marriage, we need to add to these developmental patterns to handle the transactional aspects of our relationship with our new spouse. Again, as in adolescence, the patterns we build in relationship to our spouse remain in agreement with the general patterns present in our extended families.

What happens if our extended family has upstream wounds that have not yet been integrated? How does this affect the revisiting of the developmental themes with our spouse? The answer; it frequently causes havoc, and keeps divorce lawyers in business.

Take for example a hypothetical marriage between Cliff and Rebecca. Lets us begin with the revisiting of Basic Trust themes. If Cliff and Rebecca get married and each belongs to a family with unresolved wounds to the Basic Trust phase, then they are in for a rocky first year. Suppose that Rebecca is overly trusting for the most part. And suppose that Cliff has severe trouble trusting others. If he has trouble with Basic Trust themes of the childhood phase, then he will have trouble trusting Rebecca, because he had trouble trusting the intimates in his nuclear family. What is more, as he revisits these Basic Trust themes, he will simultaneously revisit all of the emotions that he experienced in association with the Basic Trust phase when he had trouble going through it in infancy.

There is a very important clause in the marriage contract which is in extremely fine print. In fact, it is almost always overlooked by the newlyweds. It reads, "I promise to be your target for all of the negative emotions that you have left over toward your family, related to each developmental phase, if you promise to be my target". This clause is always adhered to while the marriage is in effect, and frequently lasts well beyond the break-up point of many marriages.

As Cliff revisits all of his preverbal, powerful pain and rage related to the disappointments he experience in the Basic Trust phase as an infant, he will direct this barrage of negative emotions squarely at Rebecca. And she will do the same toward him. She likewise, will be busy directing at him all of her pre-verbal pain and rage related to her misconfiguring experiences as an infant in her extended family.

In addition, this is a time when behavioral breaches of Basic Trust crop up in marital behavior. Problems with money and how it is handled (read security issues – Basic Trust) and problems with sexual fidelity often emerge during this first year. Both breaches have as their underlying issue the theme of trust vs. mistrust. In cases of severe wounds to Basic Trust, the honeymoon bliss soon turns into a nightmare and the couple is off to the divorce lawyers. The marriage often doesn't last the first year.

Rebecca's mother and grandmother, if she is still alive could have predicted the outcome, although Rebecca would never have listened to them. They could see the evidence of the wounds to Basic Trust in that louse, Cliff. And Cliff's family could also predict the outcome. They could see all of the deficits in Rebecca's character. What neither family usually sees is that Cliff and Rebecca are a matched set. Cliff and Rebecca both have equal, although often complementary wounds. Since everyone in Cliff's extended families is affected by their own unintegrated Basic Trust wounds, they don't see Cliff's wounds. They have been living with these same wounds for so many generations that these wounds and their effects are the norm for them. It is as difficult as trying to recognize one's own regional accent. Everyone else has an accent, but not our family. Rebecca's family is similarly blind.

If the wounds to Basic Trust in the two extended families are not too severe, then Cliff and Rebecca have a good chance of making it. Like an episode of <u>This Old House,</u> they embark on remodeling and building additions to their Basic Trust themes during the first year of marriage. It may get a little messy at times. But if their Basic Trust circuits are in fair shape, then they can use what is sound in their configurational foundation of Basic Trust themes to relate to each other reasonably successfully. Like a developing child, their new experiences with each other add functionality to their Basic Trust circuits and this developmental phase ends up being strengthened for each of them.

Couples who make it successfully through the first year of adding successfully to Basic Trust, Sense of Self, Gender Identity, and Separation-Individuation themes enter the second year of marriage having to work on their Autonomy and Control themes. Here the issue is power and how it is to be shared and divided. Having successfully worked on the developmental themes of the first year, the couple has enough trust in each other to try to tackle the power issues. If their Autonomy and Control themes are pretty well configured, then they should weather this step and emerge with good functional patterns for handling power between them. If they both have serious wounds to Autonomy and Control, then they will have to revisit all of their negative emotions stored up when they were originally misconfigured when they were children; which they will direct at each other. In addition to the barrage of negative emotions related to the wounds, marital behavior patterns that reflect power struggles often emerge. If the marriage blows up at this point, the issues that the couple will each complain to their attorney's about will be power issues. Again, the problems will always be bilateral, and often they will be complementary. One spouse will be over-controlling and one will be a doormat. However, sometimes, more frequently in a second marriage, the battle will be between two titans or two doormats.

The revisiting process proceeds from one developmental stage to the next as the couple moves further along in the marital relationship. Theme by theme, the couple will either remodel and add to the strength of the themes, or the themes will become so problematic for them, because of upstream wounds, that they will blow the marriage apart.

Once we understand this underlying dynamic in the marriage process, it becomes easy to predict which couples will have problems.   If there are upstream unintegrated wounds related to certain themes, then the couple will have problems related to those themes when they reach the time to work on them. It is like trying to predict the location of future earthquakes. Once you understand the Tectonic Plate Theory and know the location of the plates and how they move in relationship to each other, it becomes fairly easy to predict the location of earthquakes. With this knowledge of earthquake prediction, the potential hazards involved in locating a building in Southern California on a site that straddles the San Andreas Fault become abundantly clear.

And Baby Makes Three

This picture of marital dynamics gains an added layer of complexity with the arrival of each child. Not only do the spouses revisit each developmental theme with each other, the couple revisits them again, even more powerfully, starting with the birth of each child. When a child is born, he or she comes home from the hospital and becomes immersed in the family, and in working on the Basic Trust phase. The parents are also working on the Basic Trust phase with the child, but this time from both ends. First, they are the ones providing the trusting environment for the child. Second, observing their child in the Basic Trust phase provokes a deep internal revisiting of their own infantile Basic Trust phase, the first growth ring of their developmental tree. "It's déjà vu all over again".[5]

When the spouses revisit the Basic Trust themes as part of the early marital process, they do so with an intimate peer, but not with an extended family member. Dr. Whitaker used to say that the voltage between spouses was 110 volts, but the voltage between the biological parent and their offspring was 220 volts. I agree with him, based on my observations over my 30 year career. The revisiting between spouses is intense, but the revisiting in a parent, triggered by the arrival of their biological child at a particular developmental phase, is much more intense. There is nothing that evokes the emotional revisiting of one's family past as strongly as seeing one's own child at the same stage. Usually, the revisiting is mostly below awareness, but it is extremely powerful just the same.

To recap, let's use the theme of Autonomy and Control as an example. To predict the timing of a divorce in a couple where each spouse comes from an extended family with severe wounds to Autonomy and Control, we will need to look at several characteristic points in time. First, we need to look at the period of time 1-3 years into the marriage, or 13 - 15 years into the marriage (1-3 years into the adolescences of the marriage), the periods of time when the couple revisits the Autonomy and Control themes. And second, we need to look at the periods of time when each of the children is between 1 and 3 years of age, or between 13 and 15 years of age. It is at these times that the couple will be under the greatest stress from old upstream Autonomy and Control wounds. And it will be these Autonomy and Control themes that will always cause the rupture of the marriage in such a couple.

In a family with three children, the couple will revisit each developmental theme twice as spouses and twice with each child, in their role as parents. That is eight revisitations of the Autonomy and Control theme before the children go off to college. When you add to this the fact that most spouses come from extended families who have trouble with two or more developmental themes, one can see how many danger points there are. And with so many danger points, one can see why an understanding of the precise timing of marital discord has remained so obscure. Also, with so many danger points, one can see how a couple whose extended families have severe upstream wounds is often doomed.

If an extended family integrates their wounds before the mate selection of their young adults, they change this whole dynamic. They avoid the considerable morbidity to everyone involved: parents, children, and grandparents. In addition, the extended family avoids the cost of expensive divorce settlements. The avoidance of so much pain and loss, both emotional and financial, makes an extended family's investment in completing the integration of their upstream wounds very sound indeed! Like learning to read, this is a case of a tremendous R.O.I.

Chapter 16

"If a House Be Divided Against Itself, That House Cannot Stand".

Bible, King James Version, 2000
Mk 3, 19-30

Creating and preserving wealth is a family game. Every family in the world is participating. And the most common way that families become affluent is to own a family business[1]. Once the founder has accumulated a great deal of wealth, the management of that wealth in the next generation usually becomes a family affair. Whether the "goose that lays the golden eggs" is a prosperous family-held business, or the family business has been sold and the family collectively owns real estate and other assets, preserving the wealth that the founder accumulated often becomes a family team sport. During this stage of trying to keep all the members of the team on the same page a family can falter badly.

Everyone has read stories about the family feuds inside large closely held corporations like U-Haul or Campbell's Soup. But few people realize that the majority of family owned businesses don't survive to the second generation.[2] In fact, only about 40% of family owned businesses survive the transfer from one generation to the next. Thus, about 16% survive to the third generation and only about 2.5% survive to the fifth generation. One of the main reasons that family-owned businesses fail to survive is a failure to keep the joint owners working effectively together in each succeeding generation. Keeping everyone on the same page is fraught with difficulties, whether it is with the siblings of the founder or the cousin offspring of the founder's children,[3]

There are many organizational issues that have to be successfully addressed in order to keep a sibling or cousin owned family business team functioning optimally. But the biggest challenges, the most difficult obstacles to keeping the team working together relate to the upstream wounds in the family of the founder and the founder's spouse. Just as the revisiting of a wounded developmental phase can wreak havoc on a couple and their family, the persistence of unintegrated wounds within the extended family of the founder and their spouse always results in real trouble.

Sometimes, upstream Basic Trust wounds get played out as lack of trust or unfairness among descendant co-owners. Sometimes Basic Trust wounds lead to down right fraud and theft, with family members playing both perpetrator and victim roles. Unresolved wounds to Self-Esteem themes can often play out as unbridgeable rivalries, which divide the team, leading to its demise. Wounds to Autonomy and Control themes can get played out on the family business stage by someone playing the role of a tyrant, making other family members in the business want to liquidate their shares and flee, or stay and fight an all-consuming battle. As a result, all the energy goes into the internal battles and little goes into beating the competition.

No matter how you slice it, a team needs to work together in order to excel in the business game. The only way to do that is to have a very effective organizational culture that keeps people focused, helps to develop the upcoming members, and divides the benefits fairly. This cannot be done if the extended families of the founder and spouse are still in the grips of powerful enactment modes.

Originating with Leon Danco, the field of family business consulting has grown to meet the needs of family businesses. The attempt has been made to combine the disciplines of finance and accounting, business management, law and governance, and the behavioral sciences with regard to family businesses. This combined approach has helped many family businesses and the families who own them to preserve the unity of the family and at the same time preserve and enhance the functioning of the business. The disciplines of finance and accounting, law, and management science have been around for decades. What is new in the field of family business consulting is the adapting of these disciplines to the unique situations that are part of the terrain of a family business.

But it was the inclusion of the behavior sciences, particularly systems theory and the knowledge base of family therapy, that unified and empowered the family business consulting field. Family businesses involve the dynamic dance of several powerful and interconnected systems, the business system with its organizational culture, the owner's system with its rules of governance, and the family system.

The family system of a family business is the context within which the other two systems are imbedded. Before family therapy began to shed some light on how family systems operate, the field of family business consulting could not get off the ground; having no way to understand the workings of family systems, which so mightily influence the other two subset systems. But the family systems theory relied upon today is for the most part 30 years old. This 30 year old family system theory originated by studying two generational nuclear family systems (families composed of parents and children).

Murray Bowen, MD. did some of the earliest work uncovering the intergenerational transmission of family dysfunction, in his work dating back from 1955 to 1972. In a paper written anonymously in 1972, he detailed his effort to help resolve issues in his nuclear family of origin that had come to a boil related to the family business that his parents were passing on to his generation. His approach was to work directly on the relationship between himself and his parents and siblings. He was still taking a nuclear family approach, since he was only working with two generations at a time. But he had come to believe that the unresolved issues in the two generations of his family of origin affected adversely the functioning in his own nuclear family (he, his wife, and his children). Thus, he believed that upstream dysfunction was adversely affecting a third generation, his children. While Dr. Bowen's work, as well as work by other pioneer family therapists, made it possible to begin to make some sense of what happens in families, and thus in a family business, the theories remained rudimentary. Employing these theories was often helpful in resolving mild to moderate problems, but there was still no understanding of the specific upstream origins of family dysfunction, or of why these dysfunctions persisted. To the detriment of the family and the business they might hold together, these theories fell short.

When Dr. Whitaker began to work exclusively with all three generations of an extended family the "whole chess board" was finally engaged. This was the genesis of the solution to family business dysfunction. My work, following in the footsteps of Dr. Whitaker, has allowed me to put all of the pieces together. With all of the pieces of the puzzle in view, I could finally make sense out of the dysfunctional patterns that chronically plague family businesses.

What is more, the extended family consulting process can lead the family through the integrative process, thus resolving chronic dysfunctions. Freed of their stuckness in enactment mode, the family business team members find themselves embedded in a new highly functional family system. In the transformed family context, they find it much easier to work together effectively. Problems now become much easier to solve, because the focus becomes resolving the actual business issues. The family business team members no-longer find themselves repeating the patterns of enactment that would perpetuate their old relationship dysfunctions. The family business team is now able to focus on retaining and building on their wealth.

In the future, I predict that wealthy families will never consider engaging in a wealth building team effort, without first making sure that they have no interfering unresolved upstream wounds.

Chapter 17

Leadership

"The quality of the business owner/manager is the single most important factor in explaining the organization's performance and, correspondingly, the owner's net worth."[1]

Dr. Thomas J. Stanley
Author
The Millionaire Next Door

Once a person finishes configuring the stage of Intimacy, he or she enters into the developmental phase of Generativity. During this phase, the focus is on "establishing and guiding the next generation"[2]. This is the time in adulthood of productivity and creativity. It is a time when the focus is on the building of institutions, culture, and the wider society. Enhancing the world and helping the next generation to get ready for that world becomes foremost in this phase. Whatever career a person chooses, his efforts will contribute to the wealth of his extended family and to the collective societal effort. No matter what she does, she will be involved in building the world and in getting the next generation ready. For a person to contribute maximally, they have to function well with regard to the Generativity phase. One important aspect of developmental phase dynamics is that each phase depends on the soundness of all of the previous phases. Major misconfigurations of one or more of the previous developmental phases will hamstring a person in the next phase. With regard to a person's career, misconfigurations of any of the previous phases greatly hamper their success and their ability to help the next generation get ready for the future.

I want to look here at leadership as an example of a career path. I want to examine what can go wrong and what can be done about it. I could substitute violin playing or law or any other career path, but since many people have been studying leadership and what happens when it goes awry, this is fertile ground for our focus. Also, leadership is a highly leveraged career path. Great leadership creates tremendous value because it has such a widespread effect. Also, the leadership roles within an extended family have great impact on the ability of the family to create and preserve long-term wealth of all kinds.

Noel Tichy, in his 1986 book The Leadership Engine, says that "The scarcest resource in the world today is leadership talent capable of continuously transforming organizations to win in tomorrow's world[3]. He writes, "Around the world, the need for leaders has never been greater. We are traversing terrain that weak or sleazy self-aggrandizers cannot take us across safely. We need smart, gusty leaders with vision and integrity to get us through the minefields. And, unfortunately, these leaders are in woefully short supply."[4]

In Tichy's, The Cycle of Leadership, he writes "The ultimate destination for all leaders is sustainable value creation"[5] for the organization that they lead. He says in The Leadership Engine that he believes that all of us have untapped leadership potential. No matter what level we currently function at, we can "make quantum improvements".[6]

While we all have leadership potential, it is recognized in the field of leadership study that it takes a long time to develop a really seasoned leader. In an interview on The Charlie Rose Show, General Fred Franks, former commanding General of the Army's Training and Doctrine Command said: "The longest development process we have in the United States Army is development of a commander. It takes less time to develop a tank--- less time to develop an Apache helicopter---than it does to develop a commander. It takes anywhere from twenty-two to twenty-five years before we entrust a division of soldiers to a commander..."[7]

People are usually not trusted with great leadership positions until they have built a long track record of success. While it is not usually articulated as clearly as General Franks stated it, people generally recognize that leadership potential takes a great deal of time to develop. Once a leader has built a very successful track record over years, if not decades, and has attained a position of great power and influence, his subsequent functioning has a great future impact on all of the stakeholders in the organization he leads.

Yet very frequently, leaders in high positions fail. In fact, according to David Dotlich and Peter Cairo in their book Why CEOs Fail, "two-thirds of the people currently in leadership positions in the Western World will fail; they will then be fired, demoted, or kicked upstairs."[8] These authors go on to say that they consider a leader's failure to have its roots in the leader's behavior. "Leaders fail because of who they are and how they act in certain situations. Especially under stress, they respond with a pattern of behavior that can sabotage their jobs and careers. They rely on a specific way of thinking, speaking, and acting that ultimately causes them to fail. Many times, they're not even aware that their behaviors have become reflexive."[9]

These authors define leadership in terms of the leader's capacity to lead a team. "Leadership concerns the capacity to build and maintain a high-performing team, and leadership should be evaluated in terms of the performance of the team."[10] In their book Why CEOs Fail, Dotlich and Cairo describe eleven types of dysfunctional dispositions that interfere with a leader's effectiveness and ultimately lead to failure. In the book, they discuss each of these eleven dysfunctional dispositions which they call "derailers". Early in the book, they state that the book's goal "is to help leaders of all types to understand their own derailers, determine under what circumstance they can occur, and learn ways to manage them."[11] They state that derailers most often become manifest during times of stress, but what is stressful is different for different individuals. The authors state further that a leader cannot eliminate their derailers. "They are part of your personality. They haven't suddenly emerged ten or twenty years into your career. They've been with you from the start, only they may not have had significant negative consequences earlier."[12] The authors go on to state that "most effective and successful leaders we know have multiple derailers. The average person has two to three derailers."[13]

I have listed below the derailers that Dotlich and Cairo discuss. In addition, I have added the developmental phase that I believe the particular "derailer" is related to. A few of the derailers are caused by more than one developmental phase being misconfigured. All of the "derailers" listed below[14] are ways in which the Generativity phase can end up going off track due to misconfiguration. Remembering that all the preceding developmental phases impact subsequent phases, it stands to reason that the Generativity phase might be distorted because of misconfigurations to previous phases.

One   Arrogance: You believe that your are right and others are not - Self-Esteem, Identity

Two   Melodrama: You want to always occupy center stage - Self-Esteem, Identity

Three   Volatility: Your mood often changes quickly and without apparent reason - Affect Regulation

Four   Excessive Caution: You have great difficulty making decisions - Basic Trust

Five   Habitual Distrust: You concentrate on other people's weaknesses and mistakes - Basic Trust

Six   Aloofness: You are removed and distant Separation-Individuation, Intimacy

Seven   Mischievousness: You treat the rules as though they don't really apply to you - Initiative, Self-Esteem, Autonomy and Control, Identity

Eight   Eccentricity: You often choose to be different, just for fun - Initiative, Self-Esteem, Identity

Nine   Passive Resistance: You often fail to speak up, and thus mislead others into thinking you are in agreement - Autonomy and Control Self-Esteem

Ten Perfectionism: You miss the important things while trying to make the small things perfect Basic Trust, Autonomy and Control, Self-Esteem

Eleven Eagerness to Please: You always try to please everyone, even if it means making bad decisions - Self-Esteem, Identity

These are all dispositions that adversely affect a leader's ability to build and lead a team. When you analyze each of the eleven "derailers" the authors have identified, each of them is a manifestation of a misconfiguration of one or more developmental phases. Since each of the developmental phases encompasses themes that determine how we relate to others, and since building and leading a team is about relationship skills, it makes sense that each "derailer" is based on one or more developmental themes.

Notice that almost all of the developmental themes preceding Generativity are represented in what makes up "derailers". If we look at a time line of the developmental phases again, we find all of the following developmental phases included, except for those noted.

Basic Trust   0-1
Sense of Self 0-7 and 7-12
Separation-Individuation 0-3 ½
Gender Identity 0-4   Not Mentioned
Affect Regulation 6 months to 3 ½
Autonomy and Control 1-3
Initiative 3 ½ to 6 ½
Industry 7-12   Not Mentioned
Identity   12 to Early Twenties
Intimacy Early Twenties

Notice that Gender Identity is not a component of the above list of derailers. In a different presentation of leadership "derailers", Gender Identity might be more prominently featured.

Some leaders become ineffective or get into trouble because of how they respond to females or males. Witness the commanding officers at the Air Force Academy who were fired because of their response to the gender issue problems of their subordinates. There are also many female leaders who self-sabotage because they have been trained to see themselves in a diminished way, due to their feminine gender.

Industry phase based "derailers" are also not mentioned in the above list, but could have been. All leaders have a strong or overly strong Industry phases. A strong Industry phase is an inherent part of the self-selection process in becoming a leader. However, many leaders are workaholics. Some leaders limit their effectiveness or get into trouble (including trouble with their health) because of "workaholism" which has a basis in heavy misconfiguration of the leader's Industry phase, combined with misconfiguration of their Self-Esteem phase.

Some leaders "need" their developmental phase misconfigurations in order to have the drive to get to the top of their field. Had they been better balanced individuals, they might not have achieved as much, having been more content with an ordinary level of success. But even these leaders (whose developmental misconfigurations, with the resulting distortions in their motivations and satisfactions, provided great drive) often come to desperately need the balanced, well configured, developmental phases that they have done without in their struggle to get to the top. In such leaders, misconfigurations of the right sort and right degree have helped them to get to the top. But once there, these leaders now need much more balanced and well configured developmental phases in order to lead their team effectively.

I now want to present two leaders who exhibited the presence of serious derailers, how these derailers affected their careers, and how they dealt with them. The two leaders I will present learned to deal with their derailers through painful experience. Like Dotlich and Cairo's clients, these two leaders succeeded in developing a skillful ability to manage their "derailers". Unlike Dotlich's and Cairo's clients, the first of these, Winston Churchill, had to learn to manage his "derailers" on his own, and his self-learning process was very tortuous. At the end of this chapter, I will discuss how leaders can efficiently rid themselves of their "derailer" limitations by making use of the extended family consulting process. This can result in a great savings to the extended family or organization, because it bypasses the "school of hard knocks" learning method, with its often extremely expensive associated failures.

Note: Readers whose primary interest is not leadership may want to skip this section. In order to examine Winston Churchill's leadership crisis adequately, this section needed to be rather long and involved.

Chapter 17 Part II

Winston Churchill

Winston Churchill was one of the most effective leaders of the twentieth century. We are fortunate to have access to a great deal of information about his life, his family, his successes and his failures. With this information available, it becomes possible to shed some light on how misconfiguration of certain developmental phases contributed to his great drive, underlies some of his greatest failures, and how he learned to manage these "derailers" and rise above their limitations.

Winston Churchill was born into two powerful extended families. On his mother's side, his grandfather Leonard Jerome was a very successful American financier. On his father's side, his grandfather John Winston Spencer Churchill was the 7th Duke of Marlborough. This grandfather came from a long line of illustrious British royalty. The Duke resided in a huge country estate, Blenheim Palace, which had 320 rooms and was set in 2700 acres of parkland. He was a Member of Parliament for many years, first in the House of Commons and then in the House of Lords. He also served as a cabinet minister in Lord Derby's and then in Benjamin Disraeli's government.

Winston's father, Randolph, was the second son of the 7th Duke. Before his marriage, he traveled in the highest social circle, that of His Royal Highness (HRH), the Prince of Wales. HRH had assumed all of the social duties of royalty after his mother the Queen had withdrawn from social events, following her husband's death. If you were close to HRH, your social standing was "made".

In 1874, Randolph ran for Parliament and was elected. The same year, he married Jenny Jerome and Winston was born. His star was on the rise. At first, the social life of the couple was extraordinary. They were in HRH's social circle, and were invited everywhere and attended everything. Randolph and Jenny lived for their social life. They had such a full social calendar that they had virtually no time for Winston.

It is well documented that in Winston Churchill's early life, his parents had little time for him. His father, Lord Randolph Churchill was becoming a prominent statesman with a good chance to become prime minister. His mother, Jenny Jerome, the beautiful daughter of Leonard Jerome, adored the attention she was receiving in the highest social circles.

When Winston was a small boy, he was taken care of by his nanny, Mrs. Elizabeth Everest. She began caring for him when he was a month old. According to William Manchester, one of his biographers, throughout his childhood, Winston's parents only found enough time for him each day to say a brief good night[1]. One can imagine the neglect he felt. He undoubtedly felt that he wasn't "important enough" to warrant his parent's attention.

As he was being configured for the Self-Esteem phase, he would have internalized the experience that his parents had time only for important matters, which did not include him. This would have left him markedly misconfigured for the Self-Esteem phase, and indeed he was. His "Being" self esteem was greatly diminished.

Heinz Kohut MD, the originator of the theoretical work on the Self-Esteem developmental phase, mentions Winston Churchill in his book, The Analysis of Self.[2] Dr. Kohut discusses how young children normally start out with grandiose fantasies about their capabilities. He states that as they mature, young children gradually admit to their imperfections and limitations. They gradually come to recognize the limits of their power and their grandiose fantasies about themselves gradually decrease and become more realistic. He states that this needs to happen as part of the precondition for health in the Self-Esteem developmental phase's configuration.

Dr. Kohut says however that there are exceptions to this rule, in that the persistence of a delusional grandiose sense of self may actually be of some benefit to certain individuals. He states that a "persistent active grandiose self with its delusional claims usually severely incapacitates"[3] a person of average abilities. But a gifted person "may well be pushed to the use of (their) utmost capacities, and thus to a realistically outstanding performance, by the demands of the grandiose fantasies"[4] of a poorly configured, immature, Sense of self. "Churchill may have been such a person. Goethe may be another example."[5]

Dr. Kohut goes on to say that people, who are misconfigured in the Self-Esteem developmental phase in such a way that their immature grandiose fantasies of greatness persist, have left over immature convictions of their omniscience. Such people "are often unable to ask for information and they are unable to admit a lacuna (holes) in their knowledge. When they are asked, for example, whether they have read a certain book, their grandiose (immature) self, with its persistent omniscience, forces them to say yes --- sometimes with the indirectly beneficial result that they now have to rush and quickly read the book (a good prognostic sign!) --- in order to pull reality achievement after the magical claim."[6]

If Dr. Kohut was right, and Churchill was misconfigured for the Self-Esteem phase in such a way that he had greatness fantasies about himself and was driven to try to fulfill them, it would explain a lot about Churchill's huge drive to be a world-class success. This tremendous drive to be great may serve individuals such as Churchill in propelling them toward greatness, but it leaves them vulnerable to trying to "fly too high", like the myth of Icarus. This persistence of immature grandiose fantasies about oneself and one's capabilities also leaves a person vulnerable to the first of Dotlich's and Cairo's derailers, Arrogance, the sense that they are right and everyone else is wrong. Or, it can leave them vulnerable to a sense that they are omniscient, even when they don't in fact have the knowledge they "believe" they have. I will show in the section that follows how Churchill's misconfigured Self-Esteem phase got him into some career destroying trouble. But first, let's look further at the picture of Winston's early family life.

In 1876, when Winston was as little more than 1 year old, a family crisis developed. His father's older brother George had been having an affair since the end of 1875 with a married woman, Lady Aylesford, whose husband was on a hunt in India with HRH. Having affairs with others in one's social circle was commonplace for the day; however trouble started when the couple decided to elope. While affairs were met, by societal consensus, with a blind eye, loosing one's spouse to an illicit suitor was an affront to one's honor. The husband hurried home and the woman's brother challenged Winston's uncle George to a duel. Then Randolph got involved.

He first asserted that his brother George could only be challenged to a duel by the injured party, the husband. Randolph then found out Lady Aylesford's previous lover had been none other than HRH. This was no surprise since HRH had a continuous string of adulterous affairs with other men's wives. HRH was however always discrete and those who knew him socially protected him to the utmost, for he was to be the future King. In this case, however, he was left potentially exposed. Lady Aylesford had given Randolph her old love letters from HRH as proof of their previous affair. Randolph then made the grave social misstep of going to Princess Alexandra, wife of HRH; asking her to intercede with the prince to quiet matters down. Randolph also let friends know about the love letters he now possessed. He boasted that he had "the Crown of England in his pocket".

HRH's mother, the Queen heard about this matter and was angry with her son for disgracing the family by allowing one of his numerous adulterous affairs to become public. HRH was enraged. He retaliated by refusing to see Randolph and his wife socially. He also refused to visit the home of anyone who entertained the couple. HRH thus completely exiled Randolph and Jenny from the social scene.

For Winston's parents, this was a catastrophe. They lived for the social scene. Randolph now realized that he had gone way too far in his attempt to protect his brother. He turned the letters over to a royal emissary and the letters were burned, but HRH was not satisfied. Randolph then wrote to Benjamin Disraeli, the wisest statesmen in England at the time, begging his advice. Disraeli wrote to Randolph's mother that the only way to resolve the matter was for Randolph's father, the Duke, to accept the Lord Lieutenancy of Ireland and take Randolph with him out of the country. Randolph's father, the Duke, was at first reluctant to leave his Blenheim estate and go to what was considered primitive Ireland. But he eventually accepted Disraeli's offer in the summer of 1876.

Winston was 20 months old when the Duke acquiesced to Disraeli's request. That winter, when Winston was just 2 years old, he, his grandparents, and his parents moved to Ireland in social disgrace. The Duke was afforded the consolation of a redeeming cover, accepting an important government post. Randolph resigned his current government post and accompanied his father as the Duke's unpaid secretary.

Winston's father's star had risen and crashed for the first time all before Winston was a year and a half old. As Winston later wrote about his father, "The fashionable world no longer smiled. Powerful enemies were anxious to humiliate him. His own sensitiveness and pride magnified every coldness into an affront .....A nature originally genial and gay contracted a stern and bitter quality, a harsh contempt for what is called 'Society,' and an abiding antagonism to rank and authority."[7] This humiliation and rupture in the family's social standing was a large violation to Communal Basic Trust for the family. Where before, the elite social circle had embraced them; now they were shunned.

Their fall from social grace had also cast a huge pale on the family's self esteem. Winston had just passed the age of concentration on Basic Trust and was now in the mist of the most sensitive part of the development of Self Esteem. His family's tremendously adverse social experience undoubtedly influenced how his developmental phase of Self-Esteem was being configured. Babies pick up the feelings of family members like a sponge. And while Winston was too young to cognitively comprehend what had just happened to him and his family, he was not too young to absorb the emotional tones of the social disaster. Researchers looking at infants have concluded that by the age of one, an infant is as completely fluent in non-verbal communication as an adult. And since 95% of our communication as humans is non-verbal, Winston would have picked up 95% of the experience of the disaster his family was undergoing including all of its emotional overtones. At such a tender age, it would have had a profound effect on how his Basic Trust and Sense of Self were configured.

The family stayed in Ireland for 3 years. While there, Randolph became seriously interested in Irish political problems. For him, the stay in Ireland was a time to become more serious, and his work there laid the ground for his stellar but brief political rise later. For Jennie, Ireland became another endless round of parties and social events. In the summer of 1879, Jennie became pregnant, probably not by her husband. That summer, she had been a guest on the 8700 acre estate of Colonel John Strange Jocelyn. When Winston's brother was born in Dublin on Feb. 4, 1880, he was named John Strange Spencer Churchill.

It is very likely that Jennie blamed Randolph for their banishment and fall from social grace. Having an affair would not only be an enjoyable distraction from her troubles, it would be her payback to her husband for his blunder. Also, affairs were commonplace among the upper class at this time. However, the current practice was to be discrete. Naming her child after her paramour was a major breech of etiquette.

Whatever the tensions in the family that led to or resulted from the affair, it surely damaged further any sense of security Winston had in his family life. One can imagine the strain it put on his mother to become pregnant by another man, have the child, and then have the audacity to name it after her lover. Jennie must have been furious with Randolph for ruining their lives, and what better way to let him know in no uncertain terms.

While Jennie was partying, Randolph had been busy laying the groundwork for his return. In 1880, he moved his family back to England, ran for Parliament as a Conservative in his home district, and won the seat. This was quite a political victory, since Benjamin Disraeli and the Conservative party had been overthrown by Gladstone and the Liberal party. Once back in England, Randolph attempted to re-open favorable relationships with HRH. Queen Victoria had forgiven Randolph and favored re-including him in court affairs. But it would take HRH another four years to make up with him. That finally occurred at a dinner which they attended together in March 1884.

Tragedy struck again in 1881 when Randolph suffered a paralytic attack brought on by third stage syphilis. At first, his speech and his gait were affected only a little. But things got worse and, in April of 1882, he left London for seven months. When he returned in October, he was gaunt and sickly looking. When asked by others, he was vague about where he had been and why.

Winston was just 7 years old at the onset of the paralytic attack. Randolph and, soon thereafter, Jennie knew that it was the beginning of a hopeless downward spiral in his health. Winston, however, was not told. But by now he idolized his father and would have been subconsciously aware of the sudden shift in the family's emotional tone toward hopelessness. Winston, at seven, was just at the beginning of the Industry Phase. Like all boys at this age, he was in great need of time and attention from his father. Unfortunately, the man that he needed to identify with was in the hopeless downward spiral of tertiary syphilis.

Randolph had known, according to his biographer, William Manchester, that he had contracted syphilis when he was twenty-three. He was the victim of a vicious Oxford prank in which he was drugged one evening during an informal college discussion and carried to the Red Light district. There he was placed with a sickly prostitute. He awoke from his drugged sleep beside her in bed. He found that he had evidently had sexual relations with her, although he had no recollection of it. He left in terror for the nearest doctor, for he knew only too well the lethal risk he had been exposed to. At the doctor's office, he was treated with a strong disinfectant. But three weeks later a characteristic syphilitic sore appeared, the first stage of the infection. Soon after, more generalized skin lesions appeared. He returned to the doctor at the first sign of a lesion and was treated with poisonous mercury medicine. He was told to abstain from alcohol and to keep his constitution strong, but that he had nothing to worry about.

This was overly optimistic. Mercury treatment for syphilis was the best treatment available at the time. It probably had some therapeutic effect with some patients, but it was certainly not a sure cure. Studies in the first half of the twentieth century found that about one third of patients who are infected with syphilis when on to develop tertiary syphilis, where the bacteria attacks organs throughout the body including the brain. Patients with tertiary syphilis die of their disease. While Victorian medicine did not know what percentage of secondary syphilis patients went on to develop tertiary syphilis, they certainly knew the signs of its onset and they knew the eventual certain outcome.

In 1881, with the onset of the paralytic attacks, Randolph knew for certain that he had entered the end stage of the disease and that it would eventually severely weaken him and then kill him. In December 1882, there was an announcement in the

London papers that Randolph was leaving for Algeria and Monte Carlo for health reasons. He returned in February 1883, looking much healthier. His illness had apparently gone into remission for the time being. By this time, Jennie knew the nature of her husband's illness, its dangers to her prohibiting them from having sexual relations ever again, and she knew its eventual outcome. One of Winston's biographers, Henry Pelling of St. John's College Cambridge, noted in his book that at this point in the couple's life, it was natural that Jennie start turning to other men. What began in Ireland as retaliation or diversion became a necessity at this point, if Jennie was to have a sexual life. Randolph was 32 at the time, and Jennie was twenty-seven.

Sadly, Winston's father was handed a death sentence just as Winston needed to begin a deep period of identification with him. This death sentence made Randolph even more remote from his son, if that was possible. And the nature of the terminal illness further broke the marital bond. For Jennie was a survivor by nature. While she never abandoned Randolph, staying with him until he died; she began what became a new lifestyle, a series of numerous affairs with powerful men. Jennie was not promiscuous. She had affairs with one man at a time and each man was carefully chosen. But Randolph knew many of these men. He would be playing cards with them and entertaining them in his club on some evenings, while on other evenings, they had in their turn been sleeping with his wife. One can only imagine how this must have hurt him.

Winston certainly would have been subconsciously aware of his mother's stepping out on his father in Ireland. Parents think that young children don't know of such things. But children are constantly in tune with the emotional topographic maps of their parent's lives together. And they are acutely aware, even if it is repressed and therefore subconscious, when major breaches in the fabric of their parent's relationship have occurred.

On March 20, 1882, Winston learned that his father was sick with a serious infection. But the catastrophic nature of Randolph's illness was carefully kept from him, so that he was still only aware subconsciously of the disastrous nature of his father's illness. Sometime soon after that, he became consciously aware that his mother was intimately involved with other men.

As he was trying to identify with a father who he barely knew, he was simultaneously identifying with a doomed man whose wife had become constantly unfaithful. Since this is the only father he had (we each only get one), he was proceeding to identify with his father's greatness in Parliament, but also with his disgrace by his wife, and with his doomed and taboo health situation. Thus, Winston's Self-Esteem phase was further seriously distorted as he identified with this great but "lost cause" father.

When Winston was 7 years old, he also confronted an additional crisis. As we have seen, Winston had no chance to join with his father to complete the developmental phase of Industry. Randolph was becoming more and more distant from the family. This distance put Randolph out of reach to his son for the remainder of Winston's life. To make matter's worse, Winston was packed off at age 7 to St. George's boarding school, which he hated. He did not want to leave home nor his only real sources of emotional support, his nanny, Mrs. Everest. But his parents insisted that he go.

Winston stayed at this school for two years. While he was there, he was in constant conflict with the sadistic headmaster of the boarding school, a Reverend H. W. Sneyd-Kynnersley. Instead of cowering to him, Winston was provocative and constantly misbehaved, evoking the constant physical wrath of the headmaster. At one point about two years into his attendance, when Winston could no-longer take the beatings, he ran away to home. His mother, who had been ignoring his pleas about his treatment at the school, saw the welts, crisscrossing his back and bottom, from the beatings. She removed him from St. George's and enrolled him in the Thomson Sister's boarding school in Brighton. There he found support from the two sisters who ran the school and finally started to perform better as a student.

Starting in about 1880, when Winston was 6 years old, Lord Randolph began to play an increasingly prominent role in parliamentary politics. By 1885, when Winston was 11 years old, Randolph had become recognized as the Conservative leader in the House of Commons. Even though he was ill and his health was doomed, remissions in his illness gave him some hope; and he valiantly pursued the one area where he could excel in spite of his illness, politics.

When the second Salisbury government was formed after the election of 1886, Lord Randolph was appointed Chancellor of the Exchequer, a cabinet post and the second most powerful position in the British government. He had been given the post by newly elected Prime Minister Salisbury after Randolph had engineered the upswing of the Conservative party and the defeat of Gladstone, placing Salisbury in power. Randolph at this point was very ambitious and was actually coveting Prime Minister Salisbury's job. Lord Randolph was also now the leader of the House of Commons.

Winston idealized his distant father, who was very effective as the leader of the House. But Prime Minister Salisbury had laid a trap for his political ally, Randolph, by giving him the job of Chancellor of the Exchequer. Salisbury knew that this financial position in the Cabinet did not suit Randolph's temperament or abilities, and so Salisbury appointed him, wanting and expecting him to fail. Prime Minister Salisbury did not want Lord Randolph to become too powerful and thus threaten Salisbury's own political position as head of the party. And Lord Randolph was a real threat, as the leading rebel within the Conservative party.

Randolph, who had never forgiven his fellow party member's for not supporting him when he was shunned by HRH, soon tired of financial matters in his new position. He also found himself in constant conflict with the other members of the cabinet. He started to give speeches directly opposing Prime Minister Salisbury's positions. Lord Randolph next submitted a budget proposing to reduce military spending and cut taxes, a budget that looked as if it had come from the Liberal party instead of his own party. Salisbury rejected it without fanfare. Lord Randolph decided to force Prime Minister Salisbury's hand.

In December 1886, Lord Randolph suddenly submitted his resignation as Chancellor of the Exchequer. Randolph expected his resignation to trigger the Conservative party to rise up in support of him. After all, he had been indispensable in the party's recent rise to power. He expected the party to oust Prime Minister Salisbury and his cabinet; and place him, Lord Randolph, as Prime Minister. Randolph came very close to bringing down Salisbury's government. However in the end, the outcome was very different than what Randolph had expected. The cabinet was reorganized;

a Mr. Goschen was appointed Chancellor of the Exchequer and Lord Randolph's career as a Conservative leader was finished. He would never hold office again. Winston was 12 years old at the time.

Because Winston had almost no connection with his father, and since Winston almost never saw his father after his father's illness, Winston had been following his father's political career in the news. Despite having hardly any contact with his father, Winston was always his fathers' staunchest supporter. In May, 1887, Winston was still writing his mother telling her of support he had stirred up among the youth at his school. He had not been told by his family that his father's career had ended the previous December, 1886. Winston had just turned 12 years old at this time. He was now working on Basic Trust themes again as an adolescent, but this time, as with all adolescents from ages 12 to 13 years, his focus was on Basic Trust themes in his relationship to community. At 12 years old, he would also have just started to intensely revisit Self-Esteem themes, again with a focus on his and his family's relationship to the community.

An adolescent boy of 12 years, who loved and idealized his very inaccessible father, would not have taken kindly to his father being "sacked", even if it was of his father's own doing. Idealizing his father as Winston did, he would have seen Randolph's fall from power as due to treachery on the part of the political community. Winston's Basic Trust in the community would have been greatly diminished by this experience. It would also greatly wound his Self-Esteem, for Winston was very identified with his distant and defeated father. For Winston, his father's political defeat and failure was Winston's own failure.

At the end of 1887, when Winston was just 13, his beloved nurse Mrs. Everest, whom he called "Woom", contracted diphtheria during the Christmas holidays and was very ill for months before recovering. Winston's sense of Basic Trust was getting hammered from all sides.

Four months later, in April 1888, Winston entered the Harrow School. He flunked the entrance exam and was accepted only because he was the son of a cabinet minister. At the time of his acceptance, he was last in his class academically. This was humiliating for Winston, and even more so for his father.

Winston's self-esteem received a real push downward due to his poor academic performance, in addition to his father's lack of support.

Keep in mind that the all important healthy entrance into Industry phase, and healthy identification with his father, was denied Winston when he was 6-7 years of age. Winston therefore didn't develop a solid Industry Phase configuration for a long time. Once at Harrow, Winston was a failure as a student, but the school did give him some chance to begin to heal developmentally. Winston became interested in fencing; and was taken under the wing of the school's fencing coach. Eventually, Winston would excel at fencing, thus beginning his reworking of his Industry phase wounds.

Because Winston was such a poor student, he was put into a class for "dunces" at Harrow. But fate was smiling. The "dunce" class was lead by a gifted English teacher who drilled the students endlessly in the structure of the English sentence. Winston was such a poor student that he remained in the class for three terms instead of one. His continued exposure to this gifted teacher gave him the fundamentals to become a good writer. In fact, Winston would go on to support himself financially for most of his life by writing; and would eventually win the Nobel Prize for Literature in 1953.

After graduating from the Harrow School, Winston planned to attend the Royal Military College at Sandhurst. He had to pass the entrance exam first. In the summer of 1892, at 17 ½ years old, he took the exam but failed badly. He went back to Harrow in the fall in an effort to continue to prepare. Mr. Welldon, the headmaster, realized the nature of his difficulties. He told Winston "I feel it is essential that in coming back to school you should come resolved to work not by fits and starts but with regular persistent industry."[8] Mr. Welldon could clearly see that Winston's Industry Phase configuration was in very poor shape, crippling his attempt to master the material needed to pass the entrance exam. His next attempt at the exam was on November 24, 1892. He was 6 days short of 18 years old. His father had been disgusted with his first failure, but not surprised. He never liked Winston and had always expected the worst from him since Winston began his school career.

Winston's fall term initially went well. He was one of the best in the School Rifle Corp; he made the swim team, excelled in boxing, and became the fencing champion of the school. He was even chosen to represent Harrow at the fencing tournament at Aldershot, the National Tournament for private schools throughout England. That day, he was victorious and he became the National Champion, a great achievement.

But his second attempt at the entrance exam had not gone well. The results published in December 1892 showed he had failed again. He was 18. He left Harrow, not triumphantly, but dejected. His father was so disgusted that he was considering farming him out as a commercial apprentice. In other words, his father would find him work, but he would not have a career suitable to his class. But Mr. Welldon, the headmaster, begged Randolph to give Winston another chance. He told Lord Randolph that his son needed tutoring to cram for the exam. At this time, seven out of ten boys who passed the exam did so with the help of rigorous tutoring or cramming. Mr. Welldon recommended Captain Walter H. James, as "the most successful 'crammer' for the Sandhurst Examination."[9] Randolph relented and an appointment was scheduled.

Winston was now 18 years old and beginning to revisit the developmental themes of Industry and the associated re-identification with his father. His first course of Industry phase and father identification had gone so poorly that one would expect a crisis as Winston revisited this same phase twelve years later at 18 years old. And a crisis indeed occurred.

Winston was very upset following his second failure of the Sandhurst exam. That winter, Randolph's sister-in-law had given his family the use of her estate. Winston stayed there with his brother and a fourteen year old cousin. Each day, Winston would plan daring games for the three of them. On one occasion, they were playing fox and hare with Winston the pursued hare. During this game, Winston found himself in the middle of primitive fifty-yard suspended bridge on the property, an opponent at either end moving in on him. The bridge traversed a deep ravine covered with fir trees. Winston considered jumping off the bridge into the ravine, catching a fir tree to break his fall, and sliding down the tree to make his escape. "In his words: 'I looked at it. I computed it. I meditated. Meanwhile I climbed over the balustrade. My young pursuers stood wonderstruck at either end of the bridge. To plunge or not to plunge, that was the question! In a second I had plunged, throwing out my arms to embrace the summit of the fir tree. The argument was correct; the data were absolutely wrong.' He tumbled twenty-nine feet to the ground and lay insensible."[10] This brought both parents running. Randolph had to return from a protracted wild party he was attending in Ireland. Winston was unconscious for three days and had a ruptured kidney.

It is interesting to note that his quote "to plunge or not to plunge" is very much like Hamlet's "To be or not to be". A youth of eighteen's taking such action over such trivial stakes should be considered a suicide attempt and a very serious one, even if the self destructive gamble was subconscious. Given that he was beginning to revisit the extremely painful failure of his Industry phase themes and father identification, this kind of crisis is not a surprise. It was triggered, or one could say, ushered in, by his father's utter disgust and distain for him after Winston had failed the second Sandhurst exam.

Winston's failure was due to his poorly functioning Industry themes, which were in turn caused by his inability to get that phase properly configured, due to his father's emotional and physical absence. While Winston was again attempting to configure his all-important Industry themes and father identification, he began, at the outset, with an important failure and his father, instead of bending to help him "get up and overcome his shortfalls", distained him. For a boy with such developmental shortfalls, his father's withholding of help was essentially a career death sentence. As a result, Winston decided subconsciously to toy with making it a real death sentence. The ill-fated maneuver was also fraught with all the overabundant poorly judged initiative of a 3 ½ year old. The choice was all initiative devoid of reason. It also had the hallmark of great grandiosity. Even in a game, Winston was willing to risk everything to be the winner, betting his life on extremely incomplete knowledge and judgment of the situation. It also betrayed Winston's very poor configuration of the Basic Trust phase, in that, in a simple game, he was unable to trust his own instincts for self-preservation.

The whole episode repeated itself six months later. Winston

tutored by Captain James all spring to little avail, began as the exam neared to apply himself just a little. He passed the exam in June but not by much. His score was too low to be admitted to the Infantry program his father had wanted. Instead, he was admitted to the Cavalry program which required a lower score. Winston was off on a hiking trip in Switzerland with his brother and another friend when the scores were announced. He immediately wired and then wrote his father telling him the good news.

Winston received congratulations from grandparents, aunts, uncles, and cousins but no word from his parents. Winston did not realize his father was banking on Winston getting a high enough score to get into the Infantry program. The Infantry program would have saved Lord Randolph the considerable expense of providing Winston with horses. Cavalry cadets had to provide for their own horses and related expenses and Lord Randolph was in a bad way financially. Further, Winston didn't know his failure to get into the Infantry Program had resulted in a social humiliation for his father. Lord Randolph's friend, the Duke of Cambridge, the Commander and Chief of the Army, had promised Lord Randolph that he would get Winston into the Sixtieth Rifles, one of the finest of regiments, once he finished his cadetship. Now Randolph had to tell his friend that "his boy was too stupid to become an infantry officer."[11]

Randolph eventually wrote his son a scathing letter. "Randolph was surprised that he had expressed 'exultation over your inclusion in the Sandhurst list' instead of being ashamed of 'your slovenly happy-go-lucky harum scarum style of work. ... Never have I received a really good report of your conduct in your work from any master or tutor you had from time to time to do with. Always behind-hand, never advancing in your class, incessant complaints of total want of application, and this character which was constant in your reports has shown the natural results clearly in your last army examination.' Thus 'you have failed to get into the '60th Rifles' one of the finest regiments in the army.' Furthermore, as a cavalry cadet, 'you have imposed on me an extra charge of some £200 a year.' It got worse: 'Do not think I am going to take the trouble of writing to you long letters after every failure you commit and undergo .... I no longer attach the slightest weight to anything you may say about your own acquirements & exploits.' Randolph predicted that 'if you cannot prevent yourself from leading the idle useless unprofitable life you have had during your schooldays & later months, you will become a mere social wastrel one of hundreds of the public school failures, and you will degenerate into a shabby unhappy & futile existence. If that is so you will have to bear all the blame for such misfortune yourself." He ended venomously: 'Your mother sends her love."[12]

Winston was shocked and depressed. He idolized his father and respected his judgment implicitly. He had failed again in his father's eyes. And what is more, his longed for rapprochement and joining with his father to redo his Industry themes was not going to happen.   Winston wrote him back a letter of apology. But it was clear that his father was showing Winston, this time in writing, that he had no use for him and never would. Because Winston idolized his father, it never occurred to him that his father's written tirade might be partly the result of an unbalanced and diseased mind. Randolph was only three years away from his death from tertiary syphilis. The disease had been affecting his brain since his first symptoms of paralysis in 1881, ten years before. By 1892, general paralysis had slowly started to set in and his speech was slurred. His behavior was also starting to be very erratic.[13] Winston never made the connection that his father's behavior and his father's illness might be connected.

Immediately after he mailed his apology letter to his father, Winston was again involved in an episode that almost killed him. Winston and a friend rented a boat on Lake Geneva and rowed out about a mile. They decided to go for a swim. They both jumped over the side at the same time, not taking the precaution to take turns swimming, the other minding the boat to make sure it stayed nearby. A sudden wind whipped up and blew the boat away from them. "Striking out desperately, Winston just managed to reach the hull, hoist himself aboard, and return for his friend. Afterwards he wrote that he had seen Death 'as near as I believe I have ever seen Him. He was swimming in the water, whispering from time to time in the rising wind."[14] Again a foolhardy thoughtless stunt had almost cost Winston his life. It showed all the judgment of a 3 1/2 year old. It was all initiative, devoid of thinking and sound judgment. In light of what has been explained in this volume about the predictable revisiting of wounds at precise developmental stages, the near catastrophe was also predictable. Winston's explicit rejection by his father had again thrown him into subconscious suicidal behavior. A similar occurrence befell John Kennedy Jr. but unfortunately had fatal results. (This will be examined later in the chapter on disaster prevention.)

In light of Winston's background (great wounds to Basic Trust, Self Esteem, and Industry themes, occurring in both childhood and in adolescence, this time with near lethal results), let us take up the issue of how this developmental background set Winston up for career failure.

The next two times Winston and his extended family system would revisit the Industry phase were when he had been married 6 years in 1914 and again when his eldest daughter Diana turned six in 1915. At these two periods, the above pattern, evident in the two near death experiences, persisted. But this time, it wasn't only Winston's own life he risked, but the lives of thousands of Allied soldiers at Antwerp, and later, the lives of hundreds of thousands of soldiers at the Dardanelles. The outcome of these disasters would abort his career and lead to over 265,000 WWI Allied casualties. The disasters were called the Defense of Antwerp and the Dardanelles Campaign.

The background leading up to his career derailment started with Winston's entry into the army. Winston began a daredevil army career in 1895. He intended to make himself famous by daring exploits that he would then publicize in his own writing. He hoped, by this means, to make a name for himself and enough money to support himself. By 1899, his efforts were successful. He had made enough money to be self-supporting and to start a political career. He planned to further aid his political career by making himself famous through writing. His plan was designed to gain him fame and money and give him access to power, and it succeeded.

Winston was elected to Parliament as a Conservative in October 1900 at a time when the Conservatives were in power. From the start, he took a very independent stand, often criticizing his own Conservative government. Continuing to speak and vote based on his own principles rather than on the basis of party allegiance, he eventually found himself ostracized by his party, the Conservatives.

On May 31, 1904, he "crossed the floor" to join the Liberal party, being in disagreement with the current policies of his own Conservative party and effectively having been shunned by them. This is "the riskiest move a British Parliamentarian can make. In doing so he forfeits all former political friendship, without any guarantee that he will find affection among his new fellows."[15]

But Winston's beliefs lay with the Liberals now and he found support among them. What is more, the Liberal party was ascending. On December 4, 1905, Mr. Balflour, the Conservative Prime Minister, resigned due to the weakening of his party's position and the King sent for Sir Henry Campbell Bannerman, a Liberal, to form a new government. Churchill's new party was now in power. As Mr. Campbell Bannerman formed the new government, Winston, one of the ablest young men in Parliament, was offered the government position of Under-Secretary for the Colonies. This was his first cabinet post. He was 31 years old.

His performance as Under-Secretary for the Colonies was a success.[16] In April 1908, Mr. Campbell-Bannerman resigned as PM for health reasons. He was succeeded by Mr. Herbert Asquith. Mr. Asquith offered Churchill a promotion to the cabinet position of President of the Board of Trade.[17] Again, Winston was successful in his position.

In 1910, general elections were held. Churchill had won "wide popular acclaim. ...It was clear that he deserved promotion."[18] As a result of the elections, Mr. Asquith remained PM. In the new cabinet he formed, he offered Churchill the post of Home Secretary. In Britain, Home Secretary is the Principle Secretary of State, a very powerful position. "Churchill was thirty-five. Only one Home Secretary had been younger – Sir Robert Peel at thirty-three."[19] His responsibilities were huge. They "included the welfare of seven million factory workers and a million miners, national security, England's police force, immigration and law and order. Every evening when the House was in session, Winston had to write a longhand report on its proceedings for the King. He was answerable for conservation, the censorship of stage plays, regulations governing automobile mudguards, the licensing of Italian organ grinders – everything, in short, which directly involved the people living in the United Kingdom."[20]

The job was extremely difficult but again, he did well under the circumstances. But by 1911, Churchill's thoughts were turning to the possibility of a war with Germany. In August, 1911, he submitted a memorandum to the Imperial Defense Committee offering his predictions about how a war with Germany might initially unfold. While his report was criticized by a prominent army general at the time as "ridiculous and fantastic"[21], it turned out in 1914, at the outbreak of the war, to have been extremely accurate.

In September 1911, Mr. Asquith, concerned about the growing threat from Germany, moved Churchill to the cabinet position of First Lord of the Admiralty. This is equivalent to the position of the U.S. Secretary of the Navy. Like the U.S. Navy of today, Britain's navy at the time was the most powerful naval force in the world. Mr. Asquith felt that he needed a strong First Lord presence and Churchill fit the bill. What is more, Churchill had become very interested in the possibility of a coming war and the preparations required.[22]

Churchill threw himself into the task of getting the British Navy ready, should war come. He initiated a needed reorganization of the Naval Staff. He oversaw the Fleet's conversion from coal power to oil. He started and developed the first Naval Air Corp. And he began an ambitious ship development and building program to put the Fleet in a very strong position. When the war came, he was widely recognized as having done a superb job of getting the Fleet ready.

For Britain, this Fleet was their ultimate safety shield against invasion and ultimate military force to exert world wide power by controlling the seas. Churchill's preparation had secured Britain's dominance of the seas.

On August 4, 1914, Britain declared war on Germany. She was required to do so by her treaty with Belgium to defend its territory, which Germany had already invaded. At this point, Winston had been married for just about six years (Sept. 10, 1908-Aug. 4, 1914). Due to his great developmental wounds to Industry phase, he and his family were destined to revisit these wounds six years into his marriage and again when his first child Diana turned six in 1915. Remember what happened when 18 year old

Winston and his family revisited this wound the last time? He initiated two extremely ill-advised episodes which nearly killed him, the 29 foot fall from the footbridge and the near drowning in Lake Geneva a mile from shore. In revisiting this wound again, he was now about to nearly destroy his career.

Once the war began, it would have been prudent for Winston to stick with his role as First Lord of the Admiralty, a very great responsibility. Winston however desired a wider scope for his activities. On August 16, 1914, just twelve days into the war, he organized the Royal Naval Division, composed of extra naval personnel. The Royal Naval Division was a land fighting force, to be deployed and directed by the Admiralty, something like a small Marine Corp in the United States.

By October 3, 1914, the German Army had invaded deep into Belgian territory. Antwerp, Belgium's largest port, had become surrounded by the German Army by Oct. 2. The Belgian Government warned the British that Antwerp was in danger of "falling" unless they received substantial help from the outside. The next day, Churchill, in a meeting with the Foreign Secretary, Mr. Grey and the Secretary of State for War, General Kitchner, offered to send his newly formed inexperienced fighting force, the Royal Naval Division, to assist Antwerp. In addition, Churchill offered to go himself to Antwerp to report on the situation to the cabinet.

The cabinet agreed to his proposals and off he went. When Winston arrived, he found that the King and Belgian Government had already initiated plans to evacuate the city. Winston convinced them to remain and fight. With approval from London, Winston took command and mounted a defense of the city.

On October 5, Winston took an extraordinary step. He telegrammed the Prime Minister and offered his resignation, in order to remain in Antwerp and lead the troops in the defense of the city. The Prime Minister, astounded by his offer, telegrammed his refusal, saying that Churchill was needed at the Admiralty. An Army General was sent to Antwerp from England to replace Churchill. The attempt to hold Antwerp was brave but ill-fated. The defending Belgian troops were exhausted. Churchill's Royal Naval Division was new, had little training, and was untried in battle. The German troops and artillery attacking Antwerp were overwhelming. The city surrendered on October 10.[23] Winston dejected at the failure, thought his efforts had been in vain.[24]

But although Antwerp was eventually lost, the attempt to defend the city, instead of letting it surrender a week earlier, on Oct 3, did serve an important purpose. The defense of Antwerp engaged a large segment of the German Army for an additional 7 days. This delayed the German Army from moving forward and occupying the Northern French ports. Keeping these ports in Allied hands became crucial to the subsequent Allied war effort. Delaying the fall of Antwerp also prevented the Belgian Army from being captured. The Belgian Army, saved, was able to fight with the Allies for the next four years. Lastly, the 7 day delay in the city's fall gave the British and French Armies time to extend their front to the sea, preventing the German Army from turning their northwestern flank. These were very important strategic results, even though the defense of Antwerp itself was a failure.

While the defense of Antwerp was a long-term strategic success, the public only saw that the defense had failed. Churchill received all the blame. The public saw it as a mad fiasco that had wasted the lives of young soldiers needlessly. They saw Churchill as unbalanced, given that he was willing to undertake such a futile defense. The public and much of the press accused Churchill of being unfit for office, incompetent, and wholly unable to stick to his current job of First Lord of the Admiralty. They saw him as overstepping his expertise in directing troops, leading to the disaster. And because all the details of the defense of Antwerp were under war secrecy, Churchill could not defend himself. He couldn't even inform the public that he had only acted with the explicit approval of the Prime Minister and War Office. The public and the press accused him of having undertaken the defense of Antwerp on his own.

In a larger sense, however, the public was right. Churchill's actions had been out of place. The British Government should have sent another Army General to Antwerp, instead of allowing Churchill to lead the expedition. And Churchill should have known better than to have volunteered. It was not his place to be a Divisional Commander of troops in the field. And while he was gone, the Admiralty was without its leader. Furthermore, Churchill didn't have the training and experience required, in spite of his having done a good job in delaying surrender.

Winston's poor judgment was a direct result of his poorly configured Industry Phase. Someone with a much healthier configuration would have known that to try to militarily lead the defense of the beleaguered city, having no high command experience, was beyond the scope of their expertise. Instead, Winston acted as if he alone could save the day – the derailer of arrogance. This arrogance derived from his very damaged Self-Esteem Phase. Winston was still stuck in the grandiosity of the 3 year old, thinking he was all powerful or nearly so. He acted, like a 3 year old, with an overabundance of initiative and very little industry.

As you will recall, when a child has trouble entering a particular phase, they tend to perseverate in the previous phase, like a broken record that can't get to the next song, playing the previous song over and over. If Winston had been a trained General with a well configured Industry phase, he would have known the defense of Antwerp was hopeless and thus only valuable as a delaying tactic. Winston jumped in where he didn't belong (way too much Initiative Phase), in a publicly viewed "lost cause" and got blamed. This weakened his reputation substantially, doing real damage to his career. People began to see him as unbalanced and of unsound judgment. Even Lloyd George, who knew the situation and knew that Winston had gone to Antwerp with the approval of the Prime Minister, said that "Churchill is too busy trying to get a flashy success to attend to the real business of the Admiralty". [25]

Churchill moved from this career failure, the defense of Antwerp, to his next serious failure, the appointment of a previously retired naval admiral named Lord Fisher as First Sea Lord. First Sea Lord was the position just below Churchill's position of First Lord of the Admiralty. While the First Lord of the Admiralty position was usually filled by a very senior civilian politician, the First Sea Lord position was always filled by a very senior admiral and was the highest ranking position for a naval officer in the British Navy. It will become clear later why the appointment of Lord Fisher to First Sea Lord was a serious blunder.

By the end of Oct. 1914, Churchill was under dangerously heavy criticism in the press due to his perceived role in the defense of Antwerp. The press was questioning his ability to perform the job of First Lord of the Admiralty. Winston was also being blamed for a number of other naval failures or disasters that had occurred prior to the Antwerp fiasco. First, the German cruisers *Goeben* and *Breslau*, sailing in the Mediterranean at the start of the war, had managed to elude British pursuit for a week and had escaped thru the Dardanelles strait into the Black Sea and had anchored off of Constantinople.[26] Second, on September 22, 1914, the *Aboukir*, one of several older cruisers on patrol in the area of the Dogger bank in the North Sea was torpedoed by a German submarine. Two sister cruisers, the *Hogue* and the *Cressy*, came to her rescue and were also torpedoed. All three ships were sunk, and over 1400 crew members were drowned.

Prior to their sinking, Churchill had heard this particular naval patrol referred to as the "live bait squadron" during a previous visit to the Grand Fleet. He had been told that some cruisers on this North Sea patrol were of a very old type and were particularly vulnerable to torpedo attack. On Sept. 18, he wrote to the First Sea Lord Prince Louis Battenberg, Lord Fisher's predecessor. Churchill directed him to move the three old vulnerable cruisers to a safer and more appropriate location; and replace them with modern ships that could patrol the area more safely. The order for this substitution had not yet been carried out when the cruisers were sunk. A Court of Inquiry was convened but before it could finish its investigation, a journalist published an article claiming that Churchill had been warned of the dangers these old ships faced but had refused to recall them until it was too late. This version became widely believed.[27]

When the Court of Inquiry finished its work, it found that Churchill had not been to blame. But Prime Minister Asquith decided to block the report's release, not wanting to allow details of naval operations to be made public. So Churchill's vindication did not become public; consequently, a large segment of the population blamed him for the losses. Antwerp's failed defense, detailed above, occurred about two weeks after the sinking of the three cruisers.

In addition, there was the matter of the German cruiser *Emden*. She had been cruising the Indian Ocean sinking or capturing British merchant ships and the British Navy had been unable to stop her. Churchill was blamed by much of the public for this failure to stop the marauding German cruiser. Finally, there was the sinking of the *Audacious*, one of the newest and best battleships of the British fleet. The *Audacious* had hit a mine in the waters off Northern Ireland. A passenger liner, *Olympia*, had witnessed the disaster. It came to her aid, rescued the crew and began to tow her to safety, but *Audacious* sank before reaching harbor.

In late October, after the naval failures of September and October, Lord Haldane, an assistant to the Prime Minister, recommended that Churchill bring back Lord Fisher to the post of First Sea Lord in order to restore the public's confidence in the Navy.[28] Churchill thought this was a great idea. Lord Fisher had been First Sea Lord from 1904 to 1910. During his tenure, he had completely modernized the British Navy. He had introduced the new "Dreadnought" super battleship and had begun a submarine service. He had overseen the building of 161 new large warships. He had also revamped the naval educational system.[29] He had retired from the Navy in 1911 at 71. Since Churchill became First Lord of the Admiralty, he had often consulted with retired Lord Fisher about further modernizing and building the Navy. Lord Fisher was a man full of ideas and experience. But by 1914, he was very old. He was also a very egotistical and ambitious man, desiring great power.

In 1914, Churchill and his family were revisiting the themes of the Industry Phase and the accompanying theme of a child's connection to the same sex parent. Triggered by Winston's arrival at the point of 6 years into marriage, these themes were further, more forcefully triggered by Winston's eldest child turning 6. Since these themes were in great disarray for Winston and his family, Winston was beginning a natural process of attempting to rework them. At the same time, he was, in his present role of First Lord of the Admiralty, attempting to carry out the enormous duties and responsibilities of a high minister.

In reworking the themes of the Industry Phase and the connection between father and son, it naturally followed that Churchill would seek out, unconsciously, a counterpart to play the "wounded father" role as he revisited the role of the wounded son. He found that "wounded father" counterpart in the person of Lord Fisher. Like Winston's father, Lord Fisher was extremely egotistical. Also like Winston's father, Lord Fisher, now 74, was emotionally unstable. Thus, Lord Fisher was going to be able to fit the part perfectly.

Churchill approached the Prime Minister at the end of October 1914, seeking to make Lord Fisher his new First Sea Lord. The Prime Minister told his mistress, Venetia Stanley, that "Winston has a grandiose scheme (entre nous) for bringing in both Fisher and Sir A. Wilson."[30] Even though he considered the plan grandiose, the Prime Minister decided to back Churchill's plan. The Prime Minister took the matter to the King. The King was opposed to the appointment. He noted that Lord Fisher was too old and had been the cause of much discontent among the officers when he'd previously been First Sea Lord. The King also predicted that Lord Fisher and Winston would ultimately clash, because both were extremely ambitious and both would want to be absolutely in charge. The Prime Minister heard the King's objections but eventually prevailed on him to give his consent. When the King finally agreed, it was with marked misgivings. The King was wise enough to foresee the trouble ahead for these two personalities as they attempted to work together.

At first, Winston and Lord Fisher got along famously. They were a mutual admiration society. Churchill, with his very damaged Self-Esteem phase, was still stuck in a grandiose mode. And Lord Fisher encouraged Winston's immaturities by fanning the flames of his grandiosity and by often heaping unconditional praise upon Winston. Children in the grandiose phase (a normal phase in the development of self-esteem) are at the same time in a parallel mode of idealizing the parental figures. Children who don't mature beyond these four year old themes will show both tendencies in adulthood. Both of these tendencies were evident in spades in Winston's relationship with Fisher. Churchill was full of grandiose ideas about how to win the war and, at the same time, idealized Lord Fisher and his contributions. Lord Fisher, himself stuck in the immature themes of the Self-Esteem phase, was full of grandiose schemes of his own, which Winston encouraged. At the same time, Lord Fisher was also in need of someone to look up to and idealize, and Winston fit the bill. Here were two very Self-Esteem wounded men who had created in their working relationship a mutually grandiose and idealizing admiration society. In addition, Winston was also about to try to rework the disastrous relationship he had had as a 6 year old with his father. Unconsciously, Winston was setting out to use his relationship with Lord Fisher as the vehicle to revisit his failed father-son relationship. It was a recipe for disaster.

Very soon the honeymoon between Winston and Lord Fisher ended and they tried to out-influence each other. Winston came up with one plan and Lord Fisher with another. Winston would argue unceasingly for his plan and wear Lord Fisher down. Lord Fisher would eventually consent, but later change his mind. The sequence repeated itself over and over. This dysfunctional relationship pattern became most acute, and finally disastrous, over the issue of attacking Turkey through the Dardanelles Straits.

As events unfolded, it became apparent after the outbreak of war that Turkey would likely eventually join Germany and Austria against Britain and France. Turkey, initially a neutral country, had been pushed toward the Central Powers (Germany and Austria) at the beginning of the war. A new battleship Turkey had commissioned and paid for, built by a British shipyard prior to the outbreak of war, had been confiscated by the British government. Before the war, Turkey had sought to be allied with Britain. As a would-be ally, she had ordered and paid for one of the newest super "Dreadnought" class battleships that the British shipyards were building. Just before the war began, the new battleship was almost finished. Not wanting anyone else to have such a powerful ship in this time of war, Churchill, with the approval of the Cabinet, had the ship confiscated. This angered the Turks and helped the pro-German factions in the Turkish government gain control and steer the country toward an alliance with Germany.[31]

By the beginning of November, 1914, Britain and Turkey were at war. By this time, the European front lines in France were well established between Germany and the Allies. Both armies were bogged down, neither side gaining. By the end of November 1914, the British and French had suffered more than a million men, killed, wounded, or missing in trench warfare on the Western Front.[32] Members of the British Cabinet, including

Churchill, were looking for a new area in which to pursue an attack on the enemy and break the stalemate that was leading to so much slaughter. An attack on Turkey through the Dardanelles Straits, the entrance to the Black Sea from the Mediterranean, was a logical choice.

The attack on Turkey through the Dardanelle Straits appealed to Churchill for a number of reasons. Churchill liked to think in vast sweeping terms (grandiosity) and the Dardanelles attack offered such scope. The Balkan countries, Greece, and Italy were still neutral at this point. Churchill and the Cabinet hoped that by attacking Turkey, they could bring these hesitant countries into a war alliance with Britain. They also hoped to persuade them to join in an attack on Turkey with the promise that, once the Allies were victorious, the countries that joined the Allies would be rewarded with parts of Turkey carved up in a post-war settlement. Turkey was also an enticing target because if the British Fleet could get to Constantinople, their large naval guns could bombard or threaten the city into surrender. Once Constantinople had capitulated, it was believed that Turkey would fall, since most of her factories for producing arms were in the capital's vicinity.

If Turkey fell, and several Balkan states with large armies joined forces with the Allies, then they could attack Austria-Hungary from the south. They believed that Austria-Hungary would then need to sue for peace, leaving Germany alone and surrounded. Finally, if Turkey could be conquered, the sea lane to the Black Sea could be reopened. When Turkey declared war, she closed the Strait of Bosporus at Constantinople to all sea traffic from the Mediterranean to the Black Sea. This had cut off Russia's main transportation route to the world. Russia was an extremely important ally to Britain and France. She was fighting Germany on the Eastern Front, and thus keeping half of Germany's army occupied. With the sea lane closed, most Russian exports could no longer get out, so Russia became starved for cash. She had trouble making loan payments to France, which was counting on the income. In addition, armaments could not be shipped to Russia, so the huge Russian Army was extremely short of military supplies. It was said that many of the millions of Russian soldiers didn't even have a rifle or ammunition. In light of these situations,

Churchill and many of his colleagues in the Cabinet found the Dardanelles to be a very attractive target.

Churchill soon became a strong advocate for the attack. Initially, he wanted it to be a joint naval and army operation. But Lord Kitchener, the Secretary for War, said he could not spare any troops. Churchill was initially pessimistic about a purely naval attack. But Lord Kitchener urged that a purely naval attack go forward. Lord Fisher wanted a grand alliance of the Balkan states and Russia to simultaneously attack Austria–Hungary, while Bulgaria and Greece joined the British Army in attacking Turkey at Constantinople and the Dardanelles, and he wanted the British Fleet to force their way through the Dardanelle Strait.

Lord Fisher's grandiose plan was unrealistic. Neither Russia, the neutral Balkan states, nor Greece could agree on how to collectively help the British. They generally wanted to lay back and wait to see if a British attack would be successful. Lord Kitchener was holding firm to his stance that he had no army to spare. Lord Fisher could dream big but his plans lacked a basis in reality. So Churchill consulted with Vice-Admiral Carden, the commander of the naval force at the Dardanelles, on Jan. 3, 1915 about the possibility of success with a purely naval attack. Vice-Admiral Carden's answer surprised Churchill and his staff. He replied "I do not consider the Dardanelles can be rushed. They may be forced by extended operations with large numbers of ships".[33] This marked the beginning of careful consideration of plans to try a purely naval attack on the Dardanelles.

At this same time, Lord Fisher unexpectedly told Churchill that he intended to resign. Lord Fisher was alarmed by two recent German air raids on Britain. In one of the raids, a German Zeppelin (blimp) had dropped a bomb. Lord Fisher was worried that a heavy bombing raid by German Zeppelins could wreak havoc on London. At the beginning of the war, Britain had no Air Service or Air Ministry. Because Churchill had shown an interest in air warfare and since this domain was uncovered, Lord Kitchener, as Secretary of War, asked Churchill if he would be willing to have the Admiralty assume responsibility for the air defense of Britain. Churchill, never one to limit his scope, agreed. Lord Fisher was terrified that he and the Admiralty would be to blame if successful catastrophic air raids took place. Lord Fisher wanted the British

Government to threaten that if Germany conducted air raids on Britain, the British would start executing German prisoners of war. Since the British Government had failed to comply, Lord Fisher wanted to resign.

Churchill responded to Lord Fisher that while he recognized his right to be concerned, Lord Fisher was not an expert on aerial defense. What is more, it was not up to the Admiralty to make decisions about the threat Lord Fisher had proposed. Only the Cabinet could decide such matters. Churchill persuaded Lord Fisher to withdraw his resignation. But these two incidents, Lord Fisher's scheme for a grand invasion of the Dardanelles with resources that didn't exist, and his notion that he could appropriately dictate Cabinet level policy, demonstrate the grandiosity and inappropriateness of his thinking and judgment. And this was just a preview of much more to come. Churchill really had found an unstable "father figure" with whom to revisit his Industry Phase wounds.

Churchill consulted Vice-Admiral Carden further as to what he thought would be needed to make a successful naval attack on the Dardanelles. The Vice-Admiral formulated a plan and sent it to the Admiralty on Jan 15, 1915. His plan called for a large group of older ships to bombard the Turkish forts on either side of the Dardanelles Straits. The Vice-Admiral thought his plan could be accomplished in a month. The War Council was presented with this information and within days reached a decision that the Navy should attack the Dardanelles alone in Feb. 1915.

Churchill worked with Lord Fisher and the Admiralty staff to work out the details of the Dardanelles attack. But even as Lord Fisher worked with the others on the Dardanelles plans, he voiced his objections to others of influence, including the Commander of the main North Sea Fleet, Admiral Jellicoe. In his communications to others, Lord Fisher complained that the Dardanelles operation would weaken the main Fleet, leaving Britain's sea defense deficient. Lord Fisher was personally afraid of making a mistake. Captain Richmond, a member of the Admiralty Staff, wrote in his diary on Jan. 19, 1915, "He is old & worn out & nervous. It is ill to have the destinies of an empire in the hands of a failing old man, anxious for popularity, afraid of any local mishap which may be put down to his dispositions".

Lord Fisher began to object to the Admiralty staff plans. When he couldn't get his way, he threatened to resign. Finally, on Jan. 25, he prepared a memorandum listing his objections to the Dardanelle attack which he wanted presented to the War Council. In his memorandum, he stated that taking Main Fleet ships needed for a Dardanelles attack would seriously weaken the North Seas Fleet, which had the responsibility of protecting Britain. Churchill prepared a reply and both were presented to the Prime Minister. Prime Minister Asquith decided not to allow either memorandum to be given to the War Council. He was in favor of the Dardanelles operation and he decided against letting Lord Fisher undermine Churchill's authority. And so, the planning for the attack on the Dardanelles continued, despite Lord Fisher's attempt to interrupt it.

Then, on Jan. 28, 1915, just before the War Council was to meet, Lord Fisher sent the Prime Minister a letter saying that he was opposed to the Dardanelles operation and that he was resigning and would not be coming to the War Council meeting. The Prime Minister summoned Lord Fisher and Churchill to his office and heard them both out before making his decision. As a concession to Lord Fisher, the Prime Minister agreed to abandon a planned secondary attack against a Belgian port held by the Germans, but refused to drop the Dardanelles operation. They then went on to the War Council meeting.

When the Council addressed the Dardanelles, Lord Fisher left the council table. Lord Kitchener got up, followed him, and asked him what was wrong. Lord Fisher said he was not in agreement about the Dardanelles, was not going back to the table, and intended to resign. Lord Kitchener proceeded to convince him that it was not up to Lord Fisher to determine policy and that it was his duty to continue as First Sea Lord. Eventually, Lord Fisher returned to the table.

After the War Council meeting ended, Churchill was worried about what Lord Fisher and Lord Kitchener had been discussing. He asked Lord Fisher to come and see him and they discussed again the pros and cons of the Dardanelles attack. He ultimately convinced Lord Fisher of its necessity and Lord Fisher agreed to give his full backing. When the War Council met again in the late afternoon, Churchill reported that, with the backing of Lord Fisher, the Admiralty was prepared to go forward with the Dardanelles attack.

Planning for the attack continued, but by mid Feb. 1915, staff members involved in the planning began to have second thoughts about the likelihood of success for a purely naval attack. Lord Kitchener, meanwhile, was starting to think that some troops might be made available. In a meeting of the War Council on Feb 16, it was decided, upon further examination, that troops would be sent to the Dardanelles to support the naval operation. However, three days later, after a "turf" struggle with Churchill in another theater of war, Lord Kitchener partially reversed his decision, insisting that his strongest, most experience troops be held back. Churchill was against this. He now believed that a large experienced army would be needed to help the naval attack succeed. Unbeknownst to Churchill, Lord Kitchener had also cancelled all plans to have the needed troop ships assembled and ready to transport the extra troops, should it be decided to send them. This resulted in a delay of the arrival of the troops, which were eventually assigned to the Dardanelles operation, by many weeks.

Meanwhile, the plans for a purely naval attack went forward. Vice-Admiral Carden began the bombardment of the outer forts defending the Dardanelles Strait on Feb. 19. Since the original plan called for a purely naval attack, all the naval resources for attack were at the ready. The initial bombardment of the outer forts was a success, but further bombardment had to be delayed until Feb. 24 due to bad weather. The following day bombardment was resumed and the outer forts of the Dardanelles were destroyed.

On Feb. 26, the War Council met. They struggled over disagreement about whether to send their most experienced troops, the 29th British Division, to aid the other troops already assigned to assist at the Dardanelles. In spite of Churchill's best efforts and support from some of his cabinet colleagues, Lord Kitchener's view prevailed. The War Council decided not to deploy the highly experienced 29th Division. Churchill strongly believed this was a mistake. He now believed that increasing the number and experience of troops would better the chances that the Dardanelles operation might succeed.

The troops that were eventually assigned to the Dardanelle operation had not yet arrived, as a result of Lord Kitchener's unilateral cancellation of the troop ship plan. As of yet, Churchill was unaware that Lord Kitchener had ordered the troop ship cancellations. Consequently, he was not aware of the resulting delay. Because there were no troops on the scene ready to assist, Churchill and the War Cabinet had only two choices; either delay the continuation of the naval attack, until the arrival of the supporting troops, or allow the naval attack to go forward, and let the army troops help when they eventually arrived. Churchill was so committed to the eventual success of the Dardanelles campaign that he was willing to go forward with a purely naval attack at this point, even though he now thought this plan was inadequate and might lead to a defeat. This was a critical mistake. His desire for a victory in this operation swayed his judgment about the likelihood of success. Agreeing to go forward first with the purely naval attack, against his better judgment, he was accepting responsibility for a possible disaster. Like a surgeon who agrees to do an operation even though he believes the patient is not sufficiently stable, Churchill was accountable for the disaster that he should have predicted.

By Feb. 27th, 8 days after the naval attack had begun; Churchill learned that Kitchener had earlier cancelled the order to have the needed troop ships assembled. He subsequently contacted Lord Kitchener and had the order reversed, but critical time was lost. As a result of the troop ship schedule disruption, all troop movements were delayed making it impossible to coordinate a naval and army attack on the Dardanelles, even though this was what Churchill now deemed necessary. Churchill, realizing the debacle of the arrival, should have called a halt to the naval attack and let the army catch up. Or, painful as it might have been, even called off the whole attack. Ideally Churchill, at this point, could have admitted that however much he desired success, the actual resources needed to achieve this success were not there. He could have concluded that given the lack of coordination between the Army and Navy, it was not prudent to take a foolish risk.

Churchill, however, was too enamored with this campaign. He had been pushing for it and now he and the War Council were counting on it. He had an abundance of Initiative Phase spirit driving him forward. He wanted this success badly. But he did not have nearly enough Industry Phase prudence to conclude: he did not have a workable plan in place that could be executed at this juncture. He should have decided to be patient, wait, and either delay the attack until a large Army force could be committed and made ready, or to give up the plan entirely. In accordance with prudent judgment, lunging ahead would only waste men and resources.

Had Churchill exercised the prudence to stop the naval attack at this point, asserting that he would not go forward unless and until an adequate army force was ready to participate in a coordinated way, he would not have left himself open for blame over likely failure. He was fully aware at this point that failure was entirely possible, since he and many others now believed a purely naval attack was inadequate. But his weak Industry phase configuration did not allow him to mobilize the needed prudence.

Foolishly, Churchill allowed the naval attack to proceed unaided. The naval attack began again in early May 1915. The War Council optimistically started to concentrate on foreign policies to be pursued after the attack was a success. They were counting their chickens before they hatched. At this point, Lord Fisher, who had earlier agreed to back the Dardanelles attack in spite of his misgivings, was beginning to have more and more severe doubts about whether it could be successful. But in spite of his doubts, he continued to support the campaign.

The possibility of success in the Dardanelles had caught the attention of the neutral regional states in the area as well as Russia. Greece had finally agreed to help support the attack with a large number of much needed troops. But Russia was insisting that Greece not be allowed to help. Russia feared that if Greece helped, she might try to take Constantinople for herself. Russia wanted Constantinople if Turkey fell, and didn't want Greece involved.

Churchill had been working hard advocating that the British accept Greece's help in spite of Russia's reluctance. Now, Mr. Grey, the British foreign minister, turned Greece's offer of troops down so as not to upset Russia. Since Greece's 11th hour offer of help, Churchill had been counting on her 60,000 troops to make up for Lord Kitchener's missing 29th Division. Churchill felt that the Greek troops could help assure a victory. Now, the plan was weaker still. This too would have been a good time for Churchill to halt the naval attack, asserting that given the dwindling troops available to help, the plan would fail. He didn't do it. It is true that he had the approval of the War Council to press on with the naval attack. But his agreement to go forward with a purely naval attack positioned him as the person to blame if the inadequate plan failed. This is exactly what eventually happened. Churchill's desire for a spectacular victory got the better of his judgment, and led to a huge disaster.

By the second week of March 1915, the Navy was within the Dardanelles Strait. They were trying to clear the mine fields that blocked the channel. They were also trying to destroy the bordering Turkish artillery positions. Progress which had been so rapid at the outset had slowed down considerably. It was very difficult for the British Navy to clear the mines under cover of night, the only feasible time to try. Turkish guns, aided by search lights, continually fired on the minesweeping operation. Turkish mobile artillery was also much harder to find and eliminate than the fixed gun emplacements that had been so easy to knock out at the entrance to the Dardanelles. And so, the naval attack went ahead slowly.

On March 10th, Lord Kitchener appointed Gen. Ian Hamilton commander of the Army forces that would attack the Dardanelles. By March 12th, Lord Kitchener had reversed his position and now believed that the Army attack could not be successful without the participation of the 29th British Division. Before, he believed that Turkish resistance would be weak; now he feared that it might be too strong. While Churchill asked that the Army troops presently in the area help with the naval attack, Lord Kitchener decided that the Army could not get involved until the 29th Division arrived. The Navy still had to go it alone, and Churchill allowed it, another decision demonstrating Churchill's lacking of Industry phase prudence.

On March 16th, Vice-Admiral Carden had to resign his command due to poor health. Rear-Admiral de Robeck was now placed in charge. The main naval attack was about to take place. Great benefits were hoped to be gained from a naval success, and these benefits were now almost expected. "For Churchill, the outcome of the attack would be decisive to his whole future. Despite his original strong preference for a joint military and naval operation, and his many anguished and at times angry efforts to obtain a large army to co-operate with his ships, he had nevertheless been willing to offer victory by ships alone. If the battleships assembled, at the mouth of the Dardanelles, could blast their way past the forts and mines of the Narrows into the Sea of Marmara, and thence to Constantinople, Churchill's impetuosity, his pushing, his petulance, his ambition, his youth, would find their vindication."[34]

The main naval attack began on March 18, 1915. The plan was to use a flotilla of small vessels to clear the mines. Then, the assembly of old battleships would blast the defending forts and get past the Narrows and on to Constantinople. Old battleships were being used because their removal from the main North Sea fleet would not weaken it. The battleships to be used were obsolete for high seas fighting and thus considered expendable ships. The plan assumed that if the Allies lost several of these old battleships but still managed to force the Dardanelle Strait, the losses would be more than worth the political and strategic war gains. Both British and French battleships were participating in the attack, the British in command of the operation.

The attack was initially successful and by two o'clock, all nearby opposing forts were silenced. At about the same time, there was an explosion and within minutes, the French battleship *Bouvet* sank, loosing more than 600 crewmen. Admiral De Robeck pressed forward and by four o'clock, almost all the guns up to the Narrows, the Strait's bottleneck and thus the most treacherous part, were silenced. Now that the enemy guns were quiet, it became possible to begin clearing the Narrows' mines so that a final advance could be made. Once the Narrows were cleared, the path in the Sea of Marmara on the other side was open to sail up to Constantinople and take the city. A few minutes after four, the British battleship *Inflexible* struck a mine. Three minutes later, the battleship *Irresistible* struck a mine. While the crews of these two strickened ships were attempting to survive, the battleship *Ocean* also struck a mine.

The British Naval Command now realized that there were

uncleared mines in the immediate area where their ships had been operating. By the end of the day, the British managed to save most of the crews from the strickened ships, but the *Irresistible* and *Ocean* as well as the *Inflexible* had been crippled and *Bouvet* had been sunk.

Admiral De Robeck ordered a halt to the operation. On March 19, Churchill received news of the outcome of the previous day. The matter was taken up in the War Council and it was decided at Churchill's urging that Admiral de Robeck be given discretion as to whether to proceed further or not. Admiral De Robeck decided that he needed a few days to make repairs in order to continue the attack. Churchill and Lord Fisher were both eager to proceed with the attack. They had intercepted secret German telegrams stating that the remaining forts protecting the Dardanelles were almost completely out of ammunition.

By March 21, Admiral de Robeck had decided that he should not resume the attack until the Army was ready to land on the Gallipoli Peninsula that formed the Western border of the Dardanelle Strait. He asked Gen. Hamilton to attack with his Army at once. Gen. Hamilton thought it was a good idea but said he could not attack because he had orders from Lord Kitchener to delay any army attack until the powerful 29th Division had arrived and was ready. He told Admiral de Robeck that his army would not be ready until the middle of April. Admiral De Robeck then telegraphed the Admiralty informing them he was stopping the naval attack until the Army was ready in mid April.

The Admiralty staff debated Admiral de Robeck's decision. Lord Fisher and the other two most senior members supported Admiral de Robeck's decision, because Admiral de Robeck and Gen. Hamilton had decided on a joint operation. In addition, Admiral de Robeck was the commander on the scene and the Admiralty needed to respect his judgment. Churchill wanted to proceed with the attack, particularly since he had secret information that the Turks were almost completely out of ammunition. Churchill took the matter to the Cabinet on March 23. The Prime Minister and Lord Kitchener were in favor of resuming the naval attack at once. But Lord Fisher and Churchill's other two top naval advisors were still opposed. The Prime Minister decided he could not go against the advice of the country's top three Admirals. So Churchill had to accept Admiral de Robeck's decision to halt the naval attack.

With the solo naval attack abandoned, the command of the Dardanelle operation passed from Churchill to Lord Kitchener. The operation would now be an army affair with the Navy playing a supporting role. The Navy would never again try to force the Strait. Churchill continued to strongly advocate for the Dardanelles offensive and he was frustrated that his department was no longer at the center of decision making.

With the proposed attack more than a month away, the Turks had ample time to heavily reinforce the Gallipoli Peninsula. By the time the army attack began on April 25, the Turks were more than ready. The British, along with Australian and New Zealand Commonwealth forces, landed at two points on the Gallipoli Peninsula. They were immediately bogged down in intense fighting. Military gains proceeded with agonizing slowness and at heavy cost in casualties. The Gallipoli offensive became another version of the paralyzed Western Front. Month after month went by with no progress made. The casualties for the Allies would eventually exceed 250,000.

Churchill had to leave for Paris on May 5, 1915. He was involved at the time in negotiations to bring Italy into the war on the side of the Allies. Lord Fisher was temporarily left in charge of the Admiralty, which turned out to be a great strain on him. While Churchill was away, Lord Fisher had lunch with Clementine Churchill, Winston's wife. They had a pleasant lunch but at the end, Lord Fisher told Clementine "You are a foolish woman. All the time you think Winston's with Sir John French (a British General) he is in Paris with his mistress."[35] Clementine found Lord Fisher's comment to be very hurtful but also delusional. Anyone could verify that Churchill was at the negotiations with Italy. There had never been any indication or evidence of Churchill having been unfaithful. Lord Fisher's comment appeared to be evidence that Lord Fisher's mind had become unbalanced, perhaps due to the strain of managing the Admiralty by himself.

With the Army now playing the leading role, the Navy was entrusted to make the landings possible and provide support. However, by May 10, Admiral de Robeck was again considering whether a naval attack forcing the Dardanelle Strait would assist the bogged down Army in its task to try to defeat the Turks and take the Gallipoli Peninsula. But there were grave concerns. Now, the Peninsula was heavily occupied by Turkish troops. It was possible that if the British Navy forced its way through the Narrows and the Army was not able to assist and gain control, the Turkish forces could close the Narrows behind the British Fleet. The Fleet would be trapped and cut off from resupply. But Admiral de Robeck and the Navy wanted to help the Army.

Admiral De Robeck asked Churchill for his opinion. Churchill agreed that the situation was now different with the heavy Turkish military presence on the Peninsula. What is more, Italy had been promised the assistance of 4 battleships and 4 cruisers that were to be pulled from Admiral de Robeck's fleet, thus weakening it. No ships could be taken from the North Sea Fleet, whose job was to protect Britain. The plan was to replace the eight ships, removed to aid Italy, with French vessels.

Churchill returned from the Paris Conference on May 10. On May 11, Churchill and Lord Fisher became involved in a caustic dispute over whether Admiral de Robeck should take up the offensive. Churchill was in favor of Admiral de Robeck going forward. As a compromise to Lord Fisher, Churchill recommended that Admiral de Robeck limit himself to clearing the mines and destroying the forts up to the Narrows without going through, so that his advance could not be trapped. Lord Fisher was against any role for the Navy beyond support.

At noon, with Churchill and Lord Fisher locked in total disagreement, Lord Fisher requested the help of Lieutenant-Colonel Hankey, secretary to the War Council, to prepare a memorandum to send to Churchill, outlining his strong opposition. In it, he laid out his formal disagreement with any action by the Navy other than support of the Army. Lord Fisher also asked Colonel Hankey to tell the Prime Minister that he, Lord Fisher, would resign if any offensive action was taken by the Navy. In an effort to sooth him, the Prime Minister, via Colonel Hankey, replied that "separate naval action would not be taken without Fisher's concurrence."[36] The Prime Minister's reply allowed Lord Fisher to believe that "he had received veto power over Churchill. But only the Prime Minister possessed the power to overrule a member of the Cabinet. As First Sea Lord, Fisher could never have been entitled to such power."[37] Lord Fisher should have recognized that he was not being granted veto power over Churchill, but his great egoism made him believe that indeed the Prime Minister had bestowed on him this power.

Churchill was unaware of this last communication between Lord Fisher and the Prime Minister. But he considered his disagreement, with Lord Fisher, to be serious. He wrote a reply to Lord Fisher's memorandum stating that the Navy was intrinsically involved with the Army's operation. He noted that while he had no immediate plans to authorize a renewed naval attack, Lord Fisher needed to accept that the Navy was committed to doing everything it could to assist the army operation, even if it involved a naval attack at some point.

Lord Fisher received Churchill's reply but would not accept it. He acted as though he had the upper hand, and believed that the Prime Minister would back him exclusively. He asked Colonel Hankey and Francis Hopwood, another member of the Admiralty staff; whether they thought he should send his own memo to the Prime Minister. Lord Fisher told Mr. Hogwood that if his views didn't prevail, he would resign. Lord Fisher then responded to Churchill's letter, stating that he would not endorse any further naval attack until the Army was in complete control of the Peninsula. Churchill knew that agreeing with Lord Fisher would tie his and the Navy's collective hands in being an effective partner to the Army in the campaign. And so he did not respond to Lord Fisher's letter.

Instead, he met with Lord Fisher on May 12 and tried to offer him a concession. Churchill agreed to have the *Queen Elizabeth*, the only new Dreadnough super battleship assigned to Admiral de Robeck's fleet withdraw and returned to England. Churchill knew that having this ship in Admiral de Robeck's fleet made Lord Fisher very nervous, for fear that submarines in the area might sink it, a terrible naval loss.

On the evening of May 12, Lord Kitchener, Lord Fisher and Churchill were having dinner at the Admiralty house. When Lord Kitchener heard that the *Queen Elizabeth* was being withdrawn, he went into a rage, accusing the Navy of deserting his Army in its time of need. Lord Fisher said the *Queen Elizabeth* must be withdrawn, or he would resign on the spot.

That same night, a Turkish boat equipped with torpedoes

managed to sink the British battleship *Goliath* at the mouth of the Dardanelle Strait. This confirmed Lord Fisher's conviction that the *Queen Elizabeth* must be withdrawn. Lord Fisher was still insisting that Admiral de Robeck be ordered not to take any offensive action. On May 13, he brought the matter to the Prime Minister. The Prime Minister placated him and Lord Fisher felt he was getting complete backing. Lord Fisher told Colonel Hankey that the Prime Minister had said "Rely on me. I will never fail you."[38]

The same day, Churchill was attempting to get Lord Fisher to agree to a joint reply Churchill had drafted to de Robeck's telegram of May 10, inquiring about whether to proceed with offensive naval action. Lord Fisher refused to endorse the joint reply to Admiral de Robeck, insisting they order him to stop all offensive action. Churchill eventually gave in to Lord Fisher. Churchill then sent a telegram to Admiral de Robeck telling him to limit the naval intervention to a supportive role. Lord Fisher, still not satisfied, now wanted complete control over naval affairs. Again on May 13, Lord Fisher wrote the Prime Minister, complaining that the Dardanelles operation, pushed by Churchill, was occupying all the Admiralty's attention, to the neglect of the North Sea Fleet. He again threatened to resign.

On May 14, Lord Fisher was still complaining, now to Colonel Hankey, about Churchill's unreasonableness. That morning, the press reported a "political bomb". The headline declared:

Need For Shells
British Attack Checked
Limited Supplies the Cause
A Lesson From
France

The article asserted that the reason for a recent Western Front offensive failure was a shortage of artillery shells. Gen. John French, the Commander of the British Army on the Western Front, was angry that needed supplies were being diverted to the Dardanelles offensive. Gen. French had initiated the publication of the newspaper article because he was fed up with Lord Kitchener, his superior, who was also the head of the War Office.

Lord Kitchener had been diverting vital supplies to the Dardanelles, while telling the Prime Minister and the Cabinet that the Western Front was adequately supplied. Gen. French had estimated that a recent offensive in his area had suffered three times the expected casualties because the Army was short of artillery shells. He was determined to expose Lord Kitchener's failure and reveal the truth. The newspaper article was damaging politically because it challenged the adequacy of the Prime Minister's leadership, as well as he and his Cabinet's pursuance of the War.

The War Council met the morning the damaging newspaper article appeared. Lord Kitchener had a list of bad news. He reported that the offensives on the Western Front and at the Dardanelles had been stopped by the enemy. He reported that Russia had suffered a defeat in Galicia, what is now Eastern Poland and Western Ukraine. In addition, he complained about the Army's abandonment in its hour of need as a result of the Admiralty's withdrawal of the super battleship *Queen Elizabeth* from the Dardanelles. Lord Fisher, who was usually silent in War Council meetings, interrupted Lord Kitchener to say "he had been against the Dardanelles operation from the beginning' and that 'the Prime Minister and Lord Kitchener knew this fact well."[39] The serious conflict between Churchill and Fisher was now out in the open and it was now obvious that the business of the Admiralty "was being conducted in an atmosphere of crisis."[40]

Lord Kitchener went on to say that Britain was in danger of invasion and that new troops should be kept at home to keep the homeland safe. Churchill, angry with Lord Kitchener's assessment, answered that the Navy was well prepared to block any attempt at invasion. Churchill said "The armies in France should remain on the defensive; the whole British military effort should be concentrated at Gallipoli."[41] Churchill further saw no reason for Lord Kitchener's degree of pessimism. He did not see any reason to believe the Western Front would collapse. Further, he saw every reason to believe that the Dardanelles operation could end successfully.

His words persuaded the War Council. They ended the meeting having decided that the Dardanelles operation should go on. Gen Hamilton should be asked what men and resources he needed in the Dardanelles to insure success. After the meeting, Churchill sent a note informing the Prime Minister that Lord Fisher's erratic behavior could not be allowed to determine policy and that he, Churchill, would need to make the decisions regarding the best interest of the Dardanelles operation. He could not conduct policy on the basis of Lord Fisher's level of comfort.

Churchill subsequently met with Lord Fisher to attempt to heal the rift. They discussed which naval reinforcements they could jointly agree to give to Admiral de Robeck. Churchill ceded to whatever Lord Fisher was comfortable with and the two ended the meeting in agreement and on a friendly note. Churchill stayed up late that night working on the naval reinforcement papers. Upon reflection, he decided it would be prudent to add two additional submarines to the reinforcements being sent to Admiral de Robeck. He added the subs to the naval reinforcement plans, and included a cover letter stating he hoped Lord Fisher would agree, and that if he didn't, they could discuss it.

The next morning, May 15, Churchill was informed that Lord Fisher had resigned. Lord Fisher's resignation letter revealed that he found himself constantly in the position of blocking Churchill's proposals and he was tired of this state of affairs. He said he was leaving for Scotland. Churchill looked for him and when he couldn't find him, went to see the Prime Minister. Prime Minister Asquith wrote a letter ordering Lord Fisher back to his post and the Prime Minister's secretary searched high and low in London until Lord Fisher was found.

Lord Fisher returned to the Prime Minister's office, and informed Prime Minister Asquith that he was resigning. The Prime Minister persuaded him to stay in London but he couldn't persuade him to withdraw his resignation. The Prime Minister and Churchill knew that Lord Fisher's resignation would create a political crisis for the government. The political opposition would use Lord Fisher's resignation as evidence that the Prime Minister's government was not in control with regards to the pursuit of the war effort. A famous Admiral's resignation would indicate the government's Admiralty was in disarray.

The Prime Minister asked Churchill to write Lord Fisher a letter, believing a letter would get him to reconsider. After all,

Lord Fisher had resigned a total of eight times in the past nine months, and each time had come back. Churchill sent his letter beseeching Lord Fisher to return and included a plan for he and the Prime Minister to placate Lord Fisher. Lord Fisher received Churchill's letter late that evening. He declined. He replied to Churchill's letter: "You are bent on forcing the Dardanelles and nothing will turn you from it—nothing—I know you so well!"[42] He said he would not reconsider because though he had been loyal to Churchill, he had cooperated "in this Dardanelles business up to this last moment against the strongest conviction of my life."[43] He continued, "You will remain and I Shall Go—It is better so."[44] This was the final rupture of their relationship. Churchill was being abandoned by Lord Fisher at a critical juncture, just as he had been abandoned by his father when Winston most needed him. Winston, revisiting his failed Industry phase, repeated the pattern with Lord Fisher, the man who was playing the "wounded father" role in Winston's revisitation of these Industry themes, and who further abandoned him.

Churchill wrote again begging Lord Fisher to reconsider but his answer was still "no". Lord Fisher didn't want to be begged to come back. Instead, Lord Fisher intended, by force of his resignation and the threat to the Prime Minister's government he knew his resignation would create, to force those in authority to give in to him. "He wanted complete control over naval policy." Similar to Lord Randolph's resignation almost 30 years before, Lord Fisher was attempting to gain full control through his threat to resign. And like Lord Randolph before him, those in authority did not give in to his threat.

Lord Fisher did not achieve his grandiose plan. However, his resignation totally derailed Churchill's career. That night, Mr. Lloyd George, a member of the cabinet and the War Council, told his secretary that "if Fisher's resignation is accepted, Churchill would also have to leave the Government." He said 'It is the Nemesis of the man who has fought for this war for years. When war came he (Churchill) saw in it the chance of glory for himself, and has accordingly entered on a risky campaign without caring a straw for the misery and hardship it would bring to thousands, in the hope that he would prove to be the outstanding man in this war'. These were harsh sentiments; many people shared them."[45]

Winston's ambition, his excessive Initiative, and his poor grounding in the themes of the Industry Phase (i.e. appreciation of the slow work needed to bring about something of significance) had sunk him. Winston's re-creation with Lord Fisher of the failed relationship with his father, had delivered the final irreversible blow. And Winston's family's timetable, marking the precise time for this reworking of Industry Phase themes, had determined the timing of his career failure.

Churchill, hoping to solve the crisis before it became public, went to his Admiralty staff to ask for their support and to suggest Sir Wilson as his new First Sea Lord. Winston's Admiralty staff agreed to stand behind him and to support his proposed appointment of Sir Wilson as the new First Sea Lord. Winston then went to the Prime Minister to inform him that he could form a new Admiralty Board. Prime Minister Asquith concurred.

Meanwhile, as if to insure that his dagger thrust was fatal, Lord Fisher secretly contacted Bonar Law, the leader of the Conservative opposition on Sat, May 15. Bonar Law, subsequently consulted with his followers on Saturday and Sunday. On Monday, May 17, early in the morning, he went to Mr. Lloyd George to ask him if indeed Lord Fisher had resigned. Once Mr. Lloyd George confirmed the resignation, Bonar Law warned him that his supporters were extremely unhappy with the government in the present situation. He said there was great party dissatisfaction over the shortage of shells and the failure of the Dardanelles operation. In light of Lord Fisher's resignation, he warned that should Churchill remain at the Admiralty, his opposition party would try to force a change in the government. Bonar Law remarked that while he could understand the desirability of keeping the present government, changes needed to be made to avoid a Parliamentary fight for governmental change. Mr. Lloyd George understood the seriousness of Bonar Law's threat.

Mr. Lloyd George went immediately to the Prime Minister to inform him of the threat to the Liberal party's power. He advised the Prime Minister to allow some Conservatives to enter his Cabinet in order to form a coalition government. Prime Minister Asquith could have rejected Mr. Lloyd George's advice and fought this threat. Churchill had a new Admiralty Board lined up and had the ability to explain Lord Fisher's resignation in Parliament.

The Admiralty was likely to run much better in Lord Fisher's absence. But Prime Minister Asquith was not up for a fight. He had received very disheartening personal news. His much younger mistress, with whom he was deeply in love, had told him she had decided to marry another. He received the heartbreaking news on Friday, May 14, and had no energy at the moment to fight. So Prime Minister Asquith accepted Lloyd George's advice.

Churchill was summoned to Prime Minister Asquith's office before the scheduled Parliamentary session, where Churchill was scheduled to speak explaining matters. The Prime Minister told Churchill he was going to form a coalition government and that Churchill would be out of office. Lord Fisher's dagger had reached its lethal mark. Having failed to exert complete control over the Navy, he lashed out at Churchill in a manner fatal to Churchill's career. His timing was impeccable. Had he waited a few more days before his subversive disclosure to Bonar Law, Churchill may have been able to save himself.

Lord Fisher didn't give him the chance. If Lord Fisher couldn't have his way, he would make sure that he destroyed Churchill's career. Some friend he turned out to be! Lord Fisher turned out remarkably similar to Lord Randolph in his destructive effect on Churchill. Lord Randolph had lashed out at Winston in such a painful way that Winston almost killed himself. Now Lord Fisher, the father figure during Winston's revisitation of Industry themes, had killed the figurative son's career.

Churchill was crushed. He tried in vain to retain his position. Meanwhile, Prime Minister Asquith had not yet formally accepted Lord Fisher's resignation. In fact, Lord Fisher thought that, once Churchill was gone, he would be retained at the Admiralty and placed in complete control. On May 19, Lord Fisher submitted his "six conditions under which he could 'guarantee the successful termination of the war".[46] His first condition was that Churchill be dismissed from the Cabinet so that he was no longer a bother to him. Lord Fisher wanted the entire Admiralty Board replaced, he wanted Sir Wilson, who intended to accept First Sea Lord on Churchill's new board, banished from the High Naval Staff. He demanded complete and sole control of the entire Navy as well as sole power to appoint officers of any rank. He wanted the First Lord of the Admiralty appointee to be restricted to the role of bureaucratic policy and the interfacing with parliament. Finally, he wanted to have complete and sole control of all naval construction and dockyard work and to have complete control of the Civilian Naval establishment.

Lord Fisher sent his "terms" to the Prime Minister on May 19. He also disclosed them to Colonel Hankey, who subsequently wrote in his diary "Lord Fisher madder than ever". The Prime Minister thought Lord Fisher's "terms" indicated that "his mind is somewhat unhinged; otherwise his conduct is almost 'traitorous!'"[47] The Prime Minister believed that Lord Fisher's wish for total control "indicates signs of mental aberration".[48] Churchill was never told the extent to which Lord Fisher had turned against him. He thought their disagreement was over details and hoped it could be bridged. He still saw Lord Fisher as a friend and hoped he could influence him through friendly persuasion. Churchill was blind to the dysfunction in Lord Fisher's style of relating, as he had also been to his own father's dysfunctional relationship style with him.

When the Cabinet was reorganized, Churchill was offered, and accepted, a powerless, peripheral position, the Chancellorship of the Duchy of Lancaster. His most important duty, in this position, was to appoint County magistrates. He was allowed per the Prime Minister to attend War Council meetings, but he no longer had any power and no one needed to listen to him. This summation of events in his career threw him into a deep depression. Clementine Churchill, years later, told his official biographer Martin Gilbert "The Dardanelles haunted him for the rest of his life. He always believed in it. When he left the Admiralty he thought he was finished .....I thought he would never get over the Dardanelles; I thought he would die of grief."[49] The family developmental clock had again struck the 6-7 year themes. When Winston was seven in 1881, his father suffered a paralytic attack that signaled the onset of tertiary syphilis. Now Winston's daughter Diana, by her arrival at the same age, was triggering the family to revisit the dual tragedies of the onset of Lord Randolph's lethal disease, and the failed connection between father and son, which had doomed Winston's Industry Phase to grave misconfiguration.

As the family developmental clock revisited these two tragedies, Winston could not understand his grievous misfortune.

He felt the Prime Minister and Mr. Lloyd George had sold him out to political expediency. He could not recognize how he had changed; how his derailers had surfaced in a major way. "Churchill's contemporaries found themselves making frequent and caustic reference to his ambition, which, they felt, overrode consistency. Asquith and Lloyd George, whose respective patronage had been essential to Churchill for him to remain in Government or return to it, both felt that the imaginative, constructive, hard-working colleague of pre-war years was being eaten up by personal ambition, and that his judgment had been impaired."[50]

Winston's performance had completely fallen apart. Dotlich and Cairo's Why CEO's Fail refers to derailers emerging during times of stress. I have elucidated in this book that the "times of stress" are as predictable as the movement of hands on an extended family's developmental clock. When the small hand comes around to strike the year marking a developmental wound, the derailer becomes manifest. The characteristic themes of each derailer are determined by the year the extended family's wounds correspond to. The patterns are clear and yet hard to see until we know what to look for.

Churchill went on to recover his career and compensated, as best he could, for his derailer themes. In Nov. 1915, he resigned his Cabinet post as Chancellor of the Duchy of Lancaster. Feeling increasingly useless in this minor position, he accepted a command in the Army and proceeded to fight in the trenches in France. After being on the front lines for five months, he resigned from the Army in May 1916 to return to his Parliamentary duties. In July 1917, Mr. Lloyd George, having been appointed the new Prime Minister of an all-party Coalition seven months earlier, invited Churchill back into the Cabinet as Minister of Munitions. Churchill accepted. There was much protest from Prime Minister Lloyd George's Conservative colleagues, who still blamed Churchill for two disasters, the folly of the defense of Antwerp and the failure of the costly Dardanelles campaign. While Churchill resumed a Cabinet role two years after his fall, his career derailment continued to haunt him politically. In fact, in 1940, when giving a speech, he faced jeers from the audience "What about the Dardanelles?" And he was not entrusted with another Cabinet post with war responsibilities for another 20 years.

Chapter 17   Part III

George Soros

The next leader we will examine who had a struggle with derailers and also rose to greatness is George Soros. At Oxford University, when asked how he wanted to be introduced, Soros replied "George Soros, a financial, philanthropic and philosophical speculator."[1] He was described by the British press as the "man who broke the Bank of England"[2] after he made more than one billion dollars on a single currency trade.

George was born in Budapest, Hungary on August 12, 1930. His father, Tivadar, was born in Hungary in 1893 and his mother Erzebet, was born in Hungary in1903. To understand his experience with derailers, we will again look at his parent's background, since his experience is, as we have seen with Winston Churchill, an extension of his extended family's experience.

Tivadar, George's father, was the second eldest of eight children born to an Orthodox Jewish family. Tivadar's father, a merchant, recognized early that Tivadar was gifted. He made a financial sacrifice to send his son to an elite private school and then to university. There, Tivadar studied law. In 1914, when he was 20 years old, World War I began. Like many of his age mates, Tivadar enlisted in the Austro-Hungarian Army. He was still a university student at the time of his enlistment. Like most Europeans, Tivadar expected the war to be short; he had enlisted so as not to miss this once in a lifetime adventure. He was commissioned as a lieutenant in the Austro-Hungarian army and stationed on the Eastern front.

At first, the war in the Eastern trenches was boring. But by the end of 1914, the fighting had become dangerous and some of Tivadar's men were killed. In Jan. 1915, his army unit was overrun by the approaching Russian army. Tivadar was taken prisoner along with thousands of other soldiers and transported to a prison camp in Vladivostok, in Southeastern Russia. There he was imprisoned with men from all different ethnic groups who had been fighting in the Austro-Hungarian army. The prisoners included Germans, Czechs, Slovaks, Croats, and Magyars,

Hungary's main ethnic group. At times, the prison camp housed up to 20,000 men. Tivadar lived in a crowded barracks with about seventy men, many of whom were sick.

In 1917, Russia, engulfed in a revolution, made a separate peace with the Central Powers. But although Russia was no longer participating in the war, nothing changed at the prison camp. Tivadar came to call the camp "that unhappy graveyard". In November, 1918, World War I ended. The country, for which Tivadar had fought, Austria-Hungary, no longer existed, and Tivadar remained a prisoner. The Russians eventually transferred administration of the prison camp to the Americans and later to the Japanese. Still Tivadar remained a prisoner.

Tivadar tried to keep busy during his internment in the prison camp. He learned Russian and Esperanto, a synthetic international language. He also published a prison newspaper called the *Plank*. In addition to these activities, he just tried to stay alive. And he learned the value of keeping a low profile. On one occasion, he turned down an offer to be appointed Prison Representative. Soon after, an outbreak of violence occurred among the prisoners over poor living conditions. The camp administrator gained control of the uprising, and executed the appointed Prison Representative as a lesson to the other prisoners. Tivadar had saved his life by keeping his head down.

On March 3, 1920, Tivadar and twenty other fellow prisoners escaped and started to make their way toward Moscow. Russia was now in the midst of the civil war that followed the revolution. The Red Communists were battling the Whites (Monarchists). This made parts of Russia very dangerous and Tivadar and his group had to move slowly. After many survivalist adventures, Tivadar arrived in Moscow in December, 1920.

Still, Tivadar couldn't make his way back to Hungary. The Soviet government presently in charge in Moscow did not want to allow a former Hungarian army officer to travel to his native country. Hungary, after a brief experiment with communism, was now ruled by a virulently anti-communist government. This government and Moscow were currently on very bad terms. So the current Soviet government didn't want to help this hostile Hungarian government or its citizens in any way.

So Tivadar came up with a scheme to pass himself off

as an Austrian citizen. He spoke German well. He got a guide book for the Austrian city of Linz and memorized it. This way, he could claim Linz as his home town, if he were interrogated while trying to apply for passage to Linz. His plan worked and he was allowed to board a train for Vienna. From there he made his way to Budapest, Hungary. Tivadar arrived home just before Christmas, 1920. He had been gone six full years.

Tivadar resumed his studies and eventually passed the exam to become a lawyer. But he had lost most of his ambition. When he volunteered for the army in 1914, he had been a very bright, ambitious youth. Now he was 27 and his attitude toward life had changed. He had experienced so many hardships, seen so much suffering, and had so many near brushes with death, that he had the perspective of a very old man, though he was only 27. He just wanted to enjoy the rest of his life and work as little as possible.

In late 1914, when Tivadar was home on leave, prior to being captured, he had visited the home of his father's second cousin. There, the cousin's daughter, a girl of eleven named Erzebet, had met Tivadar, and had reportedly fallen in love with him. She and Tivadar met again after he returned. Erzebet, still smitten with Tivadar, was a very good catch. Her father had been very poor but had built a very successful business, so the family was wealthy. Tivadar, looking for an easy life, likely saw marrying a rich girl as just the thing. In Michael Kaufman's biography, <u>Soros, The Life and Times of a Messianic Billionaire</u>, the author suggests that marrying more for money and less for love may well have been Tivadar's motivation. In any case, they became lovers and married in 1924. Tivadar was 32 and Erzebet was 22.

When Tivadar came back from prison camp, he had not only lost his ambition; his experiences seemed to have wounded him in other ways. He had survived a life and death struggle from age of 20 to 27. This time frame corresponds with the developmental phase of Intimacy, a phase that he would not have been able to traverse normally. Tivadar had also had a tremendous amount of experience with how dangerous the world could be. These experiences would have damaged his Sense of Basic Trust. Both his damaged Intimacy phase and his damaged sense of Basic Trust would have left him with severe emotional injuries. These particular emotional injuries would have seriously interfered with the capacity for and quality of his emotional involvement in a marriage. Indeed, the evidence suggests, that while the marriage he made was financially convenient, he was not able to participate in it with sustained emotional depth.

He probably was not capable of deep intimacy with any marriage partner, after being so severely emotionally wounded by his experiences. Instead, womanizing became a feature of his married life. He was a good and faithful husband in other ways, but had romantic involvements with girlfriends from time to time. This probably provided him with some of the emotional excitement and satisfaction that he was unable to experience with a wife, because a deep marital connection would have reached too deeply into his wounds. Tivadar's pattern of marital emotional detachment was so apparent that George, as a young child, once described his father to neighbors as "a married bachelor."

Tivadar's incapacity for emotional depth in marriage matched a similar predicament for Erzebet. It turns out that she was deeply attached to her father; so much so that she may not have been very emotionally available to a husband. As with all couples, Tivadar and Erzebet were matched in their wounds, and specifically in their lack of capacity for marital emotional intimacy.

On their honeymoon in Italy, the couple received a telegram asking them to come home right away. Erzebet's father Mor had suffered a psychotic episode. Soon after Erzebet's departure for her honeymoon, Mor had gone into a violent rage, accusing his wife of having an affair with his lifelong bachelor partner Markus. Mor had attempted to strangle his wife. A diagnosis of paranoid schizophrenia was made. George remembers his grandmother, Mor's wife, as an uptight, boring, repressed woman. There was apparently no reality to the accusations. Mor's delusion about his wife's infidelity persisted but only surfaced when he was in the presence of his wife or partner Markus. So the family had to keep them separated for the remainder of Mor's life. Mor, not exposed to either his wife or his partner, resumed his calm soft-spoken character.

Without more evidence, including medical details to exclude the presence of an organic disease, it is impossible to be sure what afflicted Mor. Still, it is common in families where the marriage is extremely emotionally distant, for the marital relationship to be shored up by the deep love and attachment of a child which gets offered to one of the emotionally isolated parents. In these situations, one of two outcomes is common. Either the child is never able to marry, because to do so would be to abandon an isolated parent and thus risk triggering the collapse of the marriage. Or, the child does marry, and the fragile arrangement between the parents somehow falls apart.

If the child leaves the triangle they formed with their parents to pursue their own marriage, one parent may have a breakdown, either emotional (depression or psychosis, etc.) or physical (one spouses health breaks down and they die). The axiom "Where there is marriage without love, there is also love without marriage" is almost always true. Sometimes a lover replaces the child who has left the arrangement. Other times, the child is not replaced, and instead maintains an inappropriate lingering attachment to the parent, even after the child has outwardly left to pursue her own marriage. In this case the child, now married, continued to play the emotional role of "the boy with his finger in the dyke", keeping one parent's heart from dying of loneliness, so that the parental marriage, between distant emotionally inaccessible partners, can continue.

Since people usually marry into arrangements that resemble the patterns they grew up with, and since Erzebet's marriage to Tivadar was one of emotional distance, it is fair to say that her parents' marriage was probably similar, and she grew up caught in a triangle with her parents. This suggests a wound not only to the Intimacy Phase traveling through generations in Erzebet's family, but also a wound to the Oedipal Phase (part of the Initiative Phase). Thus, it appears that Oedipal triangular patterns persisted in her family long after the normative 3 -6 year old Oedipal phase, and to a much deeper degree than was developmentally appropriate.

So Tivadar and Erzebet started their married life with deep wounds to Intimacy and the Oedipal part of the Initiative Phase. Tivadar also had deep wounds to Basic Trust which were probably matched pretty well by wounds to the same phase in Erzebet's family. Remember couples marry into families with matching wounds. The fact that Mor's emotional breakdown took the form of a paranoid delusion (in this case, deep lack of Basic Trust in significant others) gives further evidence to this hypothesis of matching Basic Trust wounds.

Tivadar and Erzebet's first child Paul was born in 1926. George was born in 1930. From the start, Tivadar was very close emotionally to the children. His wife recalled years after his death that he had more capacity to be loving to the children than she did. It sounds like it was much easier for Tivadar to be loving toward his sons than toward his wife, given his wound to Intimacy. Since Tivadar was also the more loving parent of the two, he bonded to the first child more strongly than his wife did. That left the second child George to connect deeply to his mother emotionally. "He was the child she would turn to for solace and protection against the humiliations of a husband she worshipped and adored"[3]. Later, in a period of crisis when he was fifty, George would finally work to separate himself from his enmeshment with his mother. His childhood job as mother's ally would have marked long-term consequences for George's interpersonal functioning later in life.

With Mor incapacitated, Tivadar took over the administration of Erzebet's family's business interests. He also set up a small law practice. True to his desire to enjoy life as much a possible, he soon set up a semi-retired routine. Each day, he devoted only two hours to work. Though he had no career ambition, he was set financially through marriage. Tivadar put a lot of time and emotional investment into his children. In many ways, he was like a young grandfather. He put all of his energies into giving his children as much input as possible. All the energies that a father might have put into his own career, he put into his sons. And they both benefited enormously from his love and input. This emotional commitment and deep emotional investment of time and energy by both parents, but especially by Tivadar, set the stage for George and his brother to have deep emotional reserves to draw on later in life, no matter what wounds they would carry.

Tivadar spent a lot of time playing with his sons, teaching them, and talking to them. He told them all about his war and prison camp experiences. He did this not in a boastful way. Rather, he wanted to share with them what he had learned, so that they might benefit from his efforts to survive and the lessons he had learned. By telling them about his life, he was providing an integrative emotional experience for himself and his nuclear family. By sharing with them as much as he did, he protected them to some degree from carrying all of the wounds forward. In this sense, his approach to dealing with his traumatic history was intuitively correct, since speaking about the tragedy enabled it to be partially integrated.

Tivadar and his family lived a somewhat affluent lifestyle. When George was six, they bought some land and built a summer house on an island in the Danube, close to the city. They would reside there every spring and summer and come back in the fall. This vacation community was very nurturing and full of fun, especially for the two boys. But at the same time, the political situation in Europe was changing in dangerous ways. Germany had already passed many laws against the Jews.

At this point, Tivadar and Erzebet decided to change the family name. Up until this time, the family name had been Schwartz. Tivadar involved the whole family in the choosing of a new name. With everyone's input, he eventually decided on Soros, which in Magyar-Hungarian means "next in line." He seemed to be reflecting upon his sons. He knew at some level that his career aspirations were over even before they got started; finished off by the emotional wounds he received in the war and prison camp. Now it was his sons' turn and he was determined to put an emphasis on helping them to do well in the world, where he couldn't. The name also means "to soar" in Esperanto, the international synthetic language that he had learned in the prison camp. Again, he wanted his sons "to soar."

As Europe became engulfed in war, Tivadar was well prepared. After all, he had accumulated over one hundred average lifetimes worth of training in how to survive in chaotic and dangerous political environments. In 1939, as the clouds of war were gathering over Europe, Tivadar made a trip to the U.S. on behalf of a client. He was also trying to arrange the sale of a large building that his mother-in-law owned in Berlin. On his way back, he had his wife and sons meet him in Geneva. He had taken the trouble to obtain U.S. visas for his wife and sons, so that if a war began, they could leave Europe for the US. In the meantime, he arranged for them to stay in neutral Switzerland. His wife would have no part of it. At the time, Tivadar also happened to have an intense love affair going on in Budapest. Having his wife and sons out of the country would have greatly freed him up to pursue his love affair. His wife, apparently aware at some level of his love affair, refused to stay in Switzerland. She insisted the family remain together, so they all went back to Budapest.

The war began in September, 1939, but life stayed pretty much the same. However, the Hungarian government passed anti-Semitic laws in 1938. One law limited the participation of Jews in certain professions, including law, to 20 percent. In 1939, the percentage was decreased to 6 percent. In 1941, Jewish students began to be required to go to special schools. George and his brother had to conform to this law. Later, Jewish lawyers began to be required to have a non-Jewish partner in order to stay in practice. But these changes had come gradually. The family found they could adapt to them fairly easily.

Even before the war, Tivadar had begun to sell Erzebet's family's real estate holdings in Hungary, which provided the family with capital. It also meant that by the time Jewish property was confiscated, the family had avoided losses because their holdings had been sold previously. Hungary had been persuaded to join the Axis powers in 1941. Hungarian troops had participated in the attack on Russia beginning in June 1941. But even in 1942 and 1943, no fighting came to Hungary. Its location was out of reach of Allied bombing. And it was too far away for the allied armies on either the Eastern or the Western front to initially reach it.

But on March 19, 1944, the situation in Hungary totally changed. The German army entered Hungary and occupied the country. The next nine months and three weeks would be a most dangerous time for the Soros family. It would also be a most deadly time for the Jews of Hungry. "Though last to be attacked, Hungarian Jewry suffered the most concentrated and methodical deportation and extermination of any in Europe."[4] Once the Germans had occupied the country, Jewish children could no longer go to school and Jewish teachers could no longer teach. Instead, these pupils were directed along with their teachers to report to the Jewish Council.

The Jewish Council, an organization that the Nazis

always established once they had occupied a country, was formed of leading citizens in the Jewish community. "Council members were made personally responsible for the implementation of the various German measures relating to the Jewish population. As a reward they, their families and those who worked for them were exempted, at least initially, from these restrictions."[5] The Jewish Council was very effective in getting the Jewish population to follow German orders. Jewish Council members were under great personal pressure to succeed in getting the Jewish community to comply. They were led to believe that if they succeeded, they themselves would personally be safe. And if they failed to get the German orders carried out, they would be punished first.

The Jewish Council members fooled themselves into believing that they were actually protecting the Jewish community by getting them to go along with German orders. They thought that as long as they could get the Jewish community to comply with orders, the Germans would go easy on them. This ruse worked very efficiently as far as the Germans were concerned. They got the Jewish Council to carry out their orders for the Jewish population very effectively, without using any of their own manpower. When everything was accomplished, they would dispose of the Jewish Council members themselves. This scheme worked perfectly in country after country and in 1944 was employed in Hungary.

Since George was in a Jewish school that had been closed, he, his classmates, and his teachers were ordered to report to the Jewish Council. The Council employed the children as couriers for their work, under the direction of their teachers. George became a courier. After his second day on the job, his father asked him about his activities at the Council. George told his father that he had been directed to deliver summonses to different people. Tivadar asked him what they said. George said that he had brought one home. It read:

SUMMONS

You are requested to report tomorrow morning at 9'o'clock at the Rabbinical Seminary in Rokk Szilard Street. Please bring with you a blanket, and food for two days.

THE JEWISH COUNCIL[6]

Tivadar asked George if he knew what the summons meant. George answered that he guessed that those who responded to the summons would be interned. Tivadar wasn't sure George knew what would happen to these people who were interned. But George knew. He told his father that they would be transported to Germany and probably murdered. Tivadar forbade George to work there anymore, telling him that the Council had no right to send out such orders. He then asked George what kinds of people were receiving the summonses. George told him that they were all lawyers whose names began with either B or C. Tivadar found out, within a few days, that all the prominent lawyers in the city were getting these summonses. The Council had reached the letter G by the week's end. Tivadar felt he had a little time, since his name began with S. He also hoped that he was not on this list at all, since he did not consider himself to be a prominent lawyer. But he was taking no chances. He had no plan to answer such a summons. He asked around and found out that all of his lawyer friends were planning to respond to the summons. Not one was planning to disobey. Tivadar realized that they were all going to their slaughter willingly, without realizing it. When the war was over, a marble plaque was erected at the Bar Association listing the names of over six hundred lawyers who died answering the Jewish Council summonses.

Tivadar realized that he and his family members needed to disappear into hiding. All the lessons he had learned in World War I, in Soviet prison camp, and on the run in Russia would now pay off. One of the first things he did was to sit all the members of his family down. He explained to them that they were all now in a special situation. He said that all the normal rules of society no longer applied. He told them that if they continued to be law-abiding citizens and tried to continue with their present lives, they would all perish. He told them that the whole family would need to disappear by going into hiding and by assuming Gentile identities.

On March 29, ten days after the occupation began; an order went out that all Jews over 6 years of age had to wear a yellow star sewn on to their clothing. By April, all the immediate members of the Soros family had new Gentile identities backed by authentic or forged documents. Tivadar knew he needed to protect himself, his wife, his sons, and his mother-in-law. If he could help others, without taking large risks, he would. But he first needed to concentrate on his immediate family.

Tivadar, having secured the immediate family, tried to provide needed false documents to friends and acquaintances. For some, he provided the documents free. For others, he charged only his costs; and to a few wealthy individuals he sold the documents at a great profit. These profits would eventually come in handy. Since he was no longer working, he had only the money saved before the occupation began and this money eventually ran out. The profits he made selling false documents carried he and his family through the rest of the German occupation.

Tivadar also decided that the family needed to split up for safety. That way, if one of them was discovered, they would not risk the lives of all the others. All the members of the Soros family walked away from their current lives and went into hiding as other people. Tivadar hid with an architect friend in a makeshift room that Tivadar had remodeled specifically for hiding, in an apartment building where he knew and trusted the superintendent. His oldest son Paul, age 18 years, went out on his own. Paul kept moving from place to place to avoid compulsory military service, required of everyone 18 years or over. Tivadar told Paul to spend his time in libraries and movie houses were he would not be seen much. George, age 13 ½, took the new name and identity, Sander Kiss. Tivadar paid a man employed by the Ministry of Agriculture to take George into his home, and pretend George was his godson. The man was sympathetic to George's plight because he himself was paying someone to hide his Jewish wife in the countryside. Erzebet became Julia Besany. Tivadar paid a traveling salesman to let "Julia" live with him, but eventually she moved to an abandoned cabin that the salesman owned. Tivadar put his mother-in-law up in a hotel suite under an assumed name.

Tivadar instructed Paul and George to meet him each morning at a hotel swimming pool that was seldom used. This way, they would know from day to day whether each of them was safe. Tivadar gave money, as needed, to each family member to keep them afloat. The family arranged to keep tabs on the mother-in-law and kept in touch with Erzebet to make sure that she was alright. Still, it was a frightening time for all of them.

Tivadar's documents came from an acquaintance of his father, who lived in Tivadar's hometown in the countryside. Tivadar's brother and his family were still living there. When Tivadar's brother secured the documents, he tried to get Tivadar to return to the hometown to hide, saying that the countryside would be safer than Budapest. Tivadar decided against it. By late April 1944, the Germans had rounded up all the Jews living in this countryside area and had placed them in ghettos. By June 7, 1944, all these Jews living in ghettos had been put on trains bound for Auschwitz, where they would all perish, including Tivadar's brother and his family. Many other relatives of Tivadar and Erzebet perished during the war; including three of Tivadar's sisters, two of Erzebet's aunts, and Erzebet's grandmother.

For Tivadar and his family, there were a number of close calls. At one point, Erzebet was denounced by someone in the village where she was staying in the deserted cabin. Two policemen came to interrogate her. She was able to keep calm, and she managed to convince them that she really was Julia Besany. Any hint of anxiety on her part, or any failure to be convincing would have doomed her. But she played her part flawlessly and the police didn't bother her after that.

On another occasion, a classmate of George's from pre-occupation school days recognized him and called out to him by his real name. George told his father about the incident the next morning, when they met at the swimming pool. Tivadar knew that it was just a matter of time before George's cover would be blown. He told George not to return to the family he had been staying with. Instead, Tivadar sent him unannounced to the village were Erzebet was staying. Tivadar told George to pose as Erzebet's godson, but to find his own place to stay apart from his mother. Erzebet found George an unoccupied cabin to live in where she also sent Paul's girlfriend, who had been recently hiding with her.

George and Jutka, Paul's girlfriend, spent the summer together hiding in the unoccupied cabin. In late August 1944, Tivadar found another family in Budapest for George to stay with. George couldn't continue to stay in the cabin because it was unheated. Jutka also returned to Budapest, because she wanted to see her father and her brother, who had both recently escaped from a forced labor camp. Tivadar also found Jutka a place to stay in Budapest.

Jutka eventually had to leave the place that Tivadar had found for her. She moved to the city of Pest, where she stayed with a half-Jewish friend and the friend's parents. But when the radical Hungarian Nazi's came into power, things became desperate for everyone in hiding and Jutka was forced to move. The friend's parents no longer wanted her there. They didn't want to take any chances. So her friend's parents put a mattress into a nearby bombed-out building, and Jutka moved there.

The destroyed building was open to the elements and Jutka soon got sick, with tuberculosis. As the Russians started to lay siege to the city of Budapest, Jutka re-contacted Tivadar and his sons and moved in with them. But by then she was very sick. After Budapest was liberated by the Russians, Jutka moved in with her own father and brother. But by then, her tuberculosis had progressed and she soon died.

In November, Tivadar learned that his mother-in-law had been swept up into a ghetto that had been formed in Budapest. He arranged to pay a Gentile boy to try to get her out. The district chosen as a Jewish ghetto had not yet been cleared of all Christians who had been living there. So the boy was able to escort George's grandmother out by pretending that she was his mother. The boy and the grandmother simply walked out of the district and were not challenged. This was another close call but it had turned out well. Tivadar then placed her in a shared apartment but soon moved her to a suite in one of the nicer hotels.

In early October, the Russian Army had crossed into Southern Hungary. By November, the city of Budapest was coming under attack by Russian planes. Tivadar decided that it was now time to bring his sons back to hide with him. He thought it had become too dangerous for them to be walking around. Tivadar and his architect friend found a new place to live and Tivadar brought his two sons to hide with him. Jutka, who was ill with tuberculosis, also came to live with them. A doctor was summoned by Tivadar when Jutka came. But there was little the doctor could do. The tuberculosis was too advanced and there were no medicines that could effectively treat her.

At about this same time, George passed two dead bodies hanging from lampposts. Each had a sign attached to it. One sign said "This is what happens to a Jew who hides," and the other said "This is what happens to a Christian that hides Jews."[7] One day, George and his father were walking on the street, because though they were in hiding, they still needed to obtain supplies. George saw a low flying Russian plane coming toward them. He showed his father the red dots on the wings just in time for Tivadar to push the two of them into a doorway to take cover. The red dots were machine gun fire; the plane was strafing their location.

By Christmas, 1944, the Red Army began to lay siege to the city. The family heard, on the radio, the following announcement "Everyone sixteen or older must report for military service. Anyone who fails to obey this general mobilization is to be shot. Anyone who hides Jews is to be shot. Anyone who hoards merchandise, or sells at a high price, is to be shot."[8] The Hungarian Nazis were now under great pressure and were getting desperate. Fighting was occuring from street to street and from house to house. By Jan. 12, 1945, the Russians had gained control of the neighborhood where Tivadar and his sons were hiding. It took until Feb. 14, 1945, for the Russians to gain complete control of Budapest.

Now that they were liberated, Tivadar and his sons had to deal with the Russian soldiers. Once, two soldiers came to the apartment. They told Tivadar that they had come for Jutka and a girlfriend. The friend had just arrived to stay with them, after being raped by a Russian soldier. "My father talked them out of it,' George recalled. "Actually he took them to a nearby whorehouse."[9]

When the Russians arrived in the area where Erzebet was hiding, the residents of the area became panicked and started to flee into a forest area. The Russians reached this area the next day, and Erzebet was raped by two Russian soldiers. Once the Russians had established themselves as victors, things still remained dangerous. A few days after the city was liberated, Tivadar, George, and Paul went out to find grandmother. They reached the Hotel where Tivadar had put her up. They found her and she was fine. But when they went to leave, the Russians blocked their departure, telling them that there was a curfew. Tivadar tried to argue with the soldier in command, claiming that it was not yet dusk. The soldier said he would shoot them if they left. Then he accused Tivadar of being a spy and Paul and George of being enemy combatants in hiding. Tivadar, Paul, George and the grandmother had to spend the night in the cellar of the hotel, while trying to straighten things out. While in the cellar, a Russian soldier who had been deserted by a local woman he had fallen in love with threatened to blow everyone up with a hand grenade. The next day, they were allowed to leave.

Besides rape and random acts of violence, one of the main dangers of early liberation was deportation. In the immediate post-war period, the Russians began to round up men for work details. Sometimes, the men were released at the end of the day. On other occasions, the men were put on trains and shipped back to the Soviet Union as "prisoners-of-war" to be used as forced labor. On one occasion, before Tivadar learned what was happening, a detail of Russian soldiers came and demanded that Paul join one of these work details. Tivadar, not realizing the danger, didn't try to prevent him from going. Paul was transported to the outskirts of the city to work. After completing the days work they were detained. After sleeping outside overnight, the men were marched toward what Paul realized was a suburban rail yard. As the column of marching men made a sharp turn on its way up a road, passing through a forest toward the rail yard, Paul made a run for it and gained the cover of trees. He was then able to hide in an abandoned building. Later, he made his way back to the city. All tolled, the Russians deported 260,000 Hungarians to the Soviet Union. Only 60,000 ever returned.

With liberation, the family moved into their pre-war apartment. But they were out of touch with Erzebet, who didn't return until Easter, 1945. The city was in ruins and there was no power or running water for a long time. The family got involved in the black market business to survive. Tivadar's brother Zoltan, who had escaped deportation, started a wholesale business selling cigarette papers on the black market. Tivadar, with his knowledge of Russian, began working for a group of Swiss diplomats as a translator. This gave him access to foreign currency. So he began, with the help of his sons, to trade foreign currency and jewelry on the black market.

The period of Nazis occupation and early Russian liberation

was an extreme experience for the whole family. George, who was age 13-14 during this time, was in the developmental period of Identity. Specifically, he was reworking the issues of Self-Esteem, Autonomy and Control, and Separation-Individuation. All of these themes of adolescent development, a part of Early Identity phase, became severely wounded for him due to his experiences. In addition, there was so much terror and danger during this period, that the family's sense of Basic Trust, with regard to the community, was also severely damaged. This, as we will see, had a lasting effect on the family and specifically on George as a family member.

In spite of the post-war hardships, the family's fortunes started to improve. But by the middle of 1946, the post-war excitement was over. The Soviet system was firmly established. Things became more bleak and dull. George talked to his father about leaving the country. When his father asked him where he wanted to go, he said either Russia or London. He said he wanted to learn more about the world outside of Hungary. His father talked him out of going to Russia by explaining that he had already seen a lot of Russia and could tell George anything he wanted to know. Tivadar told him that the family also had a relative in London who perhaps could help George. So George, with his father's urging, began to write the cousin repeatedly.

The cousin eventually wrote that he had arranged to enroll George in a junior college in London. George needed to get a passport and a visa to allow him to travel. All summer, he tried to get the needed documents. If he could get a passport, he was promised a British visa. He and his father signed up as delegates for an Esperanto conference that was being held late that summer in Bern, Switzerland. Tivadar got a passport and left for the conference. George had to keep waiting.

Eventually, his passport came. He said goodbye to Paul and his mother, fearing that he would never see them again. He boarded the train for Austria, and then switched trains for Bern. When he arrived in Bern, the conference was almost over. His father gave him a small amount of money he had on deposit in Lichtenstein. This needed to last George until he reached London. George said goodbye to his father, again expecting he might never see him again. Tivadar took the train back to Budapest.

George stayed in Bern for two weeks, waiting for his British visa. When it came through, he took the train to Paris, hoping to connect with a relative there who might be able to help him buy a ticket to London. He was almost penniless at this point. The relative was away on a trip. But George, a survivor, had taken a precaution. While in Bern, he had spent the last of his money buying two Swiss wristwatches. When he found that he could get no help from his relative in Paris, he managed to trade one of the watches for enough money to buy his train ticket to London.

After he arrived, George initially stayed with his distant cousin and his family in London. But they were not pleased to have him. He was given a place to sleep on the couch. After a short stay, he left by bus for an Esperanto Youth Conference in Ipswich, England. When he returned, he did not go back to his cousin's house; he found a very cheap bed and breakfast to stay in.

George signed up for English courses for foreigners. His father had sent him a little money which would need to last him a long time. He had to ration every penny. Once the weather turned bleak, George became very depressed. He felt like an outsider. He had expected that when he arrived in London, people would find him quite interesting. After all, he came from a very educated family and he had survived the Nazis and then the Russian occupation. No one cared.

By the end of the semester, he had passed all of his courses except English. This meant that he would need to repeat it. George again turned to his relatives for help, but he found them very stingy. One was an ophthalmologist who Tivadar had helped a great deal in the past. On one occasion, the ophthalmologist took him out to dinner. At the end of dinner, knowing that George was penniless, the doctor offered to give him two dollars to buy a few cookies. This typified the meager help he received from his relatives.

George, at seventeen, was naturally interested in girls. He tried to socialize but his efforts went nowhere. He tried to socialize with some of the other foreign students but their predicaments seemed very different. Most of them had families to support them emotionally and financially, even though they were foreigners. For the next year and a half, George's depression remained severe.

He worked at a host of menial jobs and continued to study. At the end of the spring term, George managed to pass all of his exams. But his score was too low to realize his goal of being accepted to the prestigious London School of Economics. Instead, George matriculated at a commuter college in the fall of 1947. He was just 18 years old and felt his life was going nowhere. But after he made some money that summer, he started to feel a little better.

In the fall, George rented an apartment with a Dutch student and a fellow Hungarian who was somewhat older and had survived Auschwitz. George found classes at the community college very unchallenging. So he began to skip classes. He would instead sneak into classes at the London School of Economics. His pattern of cutting classes at the community college and class crashing at the London School of Economics was eventually discovered, and he was expelled from the commuter college. In the spring of 1949, he retook the entrance exams for the London School of Economics. This time, his score was high enough to be accepted.

George then moved in to a little attic room by himself. One of the other students in the building was also a London School of Economics student. This fellow student had a large collection of books and generously lent them to George. That summer, George got a job as a lifeguard. The pool was seldom used, so he had plenty of time to read. Things were now starting to look up. He began at the London School of Economics in the fall of 1949. He was 19 years old. George still had a long, slow climb ahead of him in England, but he had at least moved beyond the period of extreme isolation, poverty, and depression.

At the London School of Economics, he had a chance to revisit the Industry themes of his Identity Phase. He was revisiting these themes at a school with bright teachers and students. But six years of his adolescence had been fraught with extreme hardship. As is so often the case, this extreme trauma turned out to provide much of the emotional fuel for his enormous drive. That same trauma, however, would also eventually partially derail his career, when his developmental clock came back to revisit these same wounded themes.

George graduated from the London School of Economics in 1952. After graduating, George initially found a job working for L.S. Mayer, a family business that manufactured and sold leather handbags, and imported and sold jewelry and leather goods. The firm had no organized training program, so he was rotated through each of the firm's departments as a management trainee. When his rotations were complete, he was assigned to the sales department. George stayed there for several years. He eventually quit, having realized his position was leading him nowhere. He next took a job with a wholesale firm that sold knickknacks and souvenirs. He became a traveling salesman for the firm, selling trinkets in North Wales. He soon concluded that this new job was even less promising as a career path than his job with L.S. Mayer.

Realizing he was going further in the wrong direction, he began to think about what his parents would want for him in terms of a career direction. This helped him to redirect himself. He decided to make a radical change and look for a job in a merchant bank in London. While George found it very hard to obtain a job with one of the merchant banks, since most positions were obtained through family connections, he did eventually obtain a job at the firm of Singer & Friedlander. The firm's two principals were brothers who had originally come from Hungary, and who spoke Hungarian.

At first, he was again rotated through various departments in a kind of vague management training program. He was then assigned to do bookkeeping work and later to be an assistant to a gold trader. He performed both positions rather poorly. Eventually, he was assigned to the arbitrage trading department, which was adjacent to the research department. It was in the research department where he found a friend and mentor of sorts. This friend, John Ranyi, was a fellow Hungarian and one of the research analysts. John began to explain to George the work he was doing in the research department. George found himself very interested in what John was doing, and in a short time, George began to trade on his own, taking direction from the research department. He obtained the funds for trading from his doctor cousin. His doctor cousin agreed to put up a few hundred pounds and he and George would split the profits. George began to score some small successes with his own trading.

In spite of his small personal trading successes, the firm's management did not see George as an asset. They eventually told him that they didn't see much future for him at the firm, because he had not distinguished himself in any of the departments. Following this dressing down, George had lunch with Robert Mayer, a friend who was also a trainee at the firm. Robert's father owned a small brokerage firm on Wall Street and Robert asked George if he would be interested in a job as an arbitrage trader at his father's firm in New York. George told Robert that he was very interested. It took several months for George to secure the necessary U.S. visa under the quota system. But in September, 1956, George moved to New York to begin working at F.S. Mayer. He had $5,000 saved from his successes in his own personal trading.

George's new job in the arbitrage department involved buying foreign securities in one market and selling them in another, whenever there was a price differential between the two markets. Soon after George arrived in New York, a political crisis in the Suez Canal region began to affect the price of oil company shares in many world markets. George was successful in taking advantage of the resulting opportunities and began to excel professionally. By the time the oil crisis subsided, George had found other lucrative trading opportunities. Soon, he had established relationships between his small firm and 20 or more major Wall Street brokerage firms. Because George's salary was based on his performances, he began to do very well financially.

George married in 1960, when he was 30 years old. His son Robert was born in 1963, followed by a daughter Andrea in 1965 and a son Jonathan in 1970. George's career continued to do well and eventually began to soar. In 1968, while working at the brokerage firm of Arnold & S. Bleichroeder, where he had moved some years earlier, George hired Jim Rogers. This was the beginning of an extremely productive partnership that would make George and Jim both very wealthy. During these years, George started some investment funds at Arnhold & S. Bleichroeder that did extremely well.

In 1973, George realized that he could no longer continue to be both a broker for his firm and the manager of an ever-growing investment fund. So he and Jim Rogers left Arnold S. Bleichroeder and set up their own firm. Together, George and Jim Rogers established Soros Fund Management. George's departure from Arnhold & S. Bleichroeder was on friendly terms. And so, shareholders in the fund George had been managing at the firm could choose to stay with the firm's fund under a new manager, or leave the firm to follow George. The majority of investors chose to follow George, bringing 65% of the funds assets, or $13 million dollars.

From the beginning, George's partnership with Jim Rogers was very productive. By 1978, the fund's value had surpassed $100 million. But as the fund became larger and larger, the stresses of an ever increasing work load began to grow exponentially. By 1978, George was becoming more and more aware of how unhappy he was, in spite of his financial success. George's relationship with his wife was also in a crisis in 1978. In the late summer of 1978, George and his wife Annaliese separated. At this point, George left the family and got an apartment of his own. In spite of his wealth at the time, over $25 million, he moved into a tiny apartment that was very cheaply furnished. By 1979, it was clear that he and Jim Rogers were also no longer going to be able to work together. By 1980, George and Jim Rogers had split and George was now managing his fund on his own. Their partnership had lasted 12 years.

George was experiencing a personal crisis at this point. In 1979, he entered psychoanalysis. He wanted help with his emotional turmoil and with his dissatisfaction with the structure of his life and his relationship to his work. It was clear, at this point, that George was extremely successful financially. Yet he felt that his success depended on his retaining a crippling sense of insecurity at all times. He felt that if he let down his guard, his success would evaporate. Consequently, he was working non-stop like a dog. He felt he had to hold on to his profound sense of insecurity, or risk failure at any time. His relationship to his work made his success essentially useless, since he could not derive a real sense of safety and enjoyment from his colossal financial success.

After entering psychoanalysis, he started to work fewer hours and with less intensity. He wanted to change what he considered to be his very poor personal adjustment to his career. He went two or three times per week to therapy sessions over a period of several years. During his therapy, he began to discover the origins of his crippling insecurity. He also began to realize that he was somehow saddled with a profound sense of shame. At the same time, he realized that to compensate for this deep sense of shame, he had developed a grandiose sense of self. But underneath his illusions of grandeur, he had a deep sense of inferiority. He realized that, so far in his life, he was only a success at making money. As he continued his therapy work, he came to realize that his deep sense of shame was related to the attacks on his identity he suffered from age 13 to age 14. His Jewishness had been under attack by the Nazi invasion of his city, and he had to deny his real identity and live a false identity to save himself. As a result of having to deny his true identity as a matter of life and death, he had never really achieved a healthy, integrated sense of who he was.

As a result of his two or three years of psychoanalysis, he was gradually able to dispel his fears and his deep sense of shame. He emerged from his therapy effort feeling much more comfortable with himself. During this soul searching and re-creation of his sense of self; he had tried to find people he could hire to take over some of his duties, as he stepped back. But in spite of his effort to find the right person, he was not successful.

As a result of trying to carry the fund all by himself and at the same time putting his work commitment into better perspective, he found himself in a crisis in the summer of 1981. By September 1981, his fund was down 27%. This was the very first time his fund had been down in all the years of its existence. Many investors, sensing that George was experiencing some sort of crisis that was affecting his concentration, started to leave his fund. Eventually, so many investors abandoned his fund that the fund's assets shrank from $400 million to about $200.

However, in spite of this severe business setback, George saw the situation as a triumph overall. He had tackled his fear based dysfunctional relationship with his business; and he had emerged as the master of his career, rather that its slave. By the end of 1981, he was able to begin to reverse the downward spiral and he managed to finish the year with his fund down only 22%. But the business setback had been very costly for both he and his investors. For his investors, very wealthy individuals who had for years enjoyed his unbroken record of great success, the loss of 22% of their investment in one year was extremely painful financially.

George's revisiting of old emotional wounds, during the period beginning in 1978 and going through 1981, was a kind of perfect storm from the developmental perspective. George was the second son born to his parents. He was 13½ years old when the Nazi's invaded Budapest in March 1944. His brother was 18 years old, his father was 51 years old and his mother was 41 years old at the time. In 1978, he had been married 18 years, so his relationship with his wife was just the same age as his brother had been at the time of the invasion. His marriage's arrival at the same age as his brother during the invasion would have triggered some very upsetting revisitation of that traumatic time. An even more powerful trigger was that his second child, Andrea, was 13 years old in 1978, just as he had been when the Nazi's invaded. The simultaneous matching: of age of the marriage and age of his second child, to the age of his brother and him at the time of tragic past events, was a very powerful trigger to his unconscious to revisit his traumatic experiences. He had been the second child in his family, so his second child's arrival at 13 was all the more powerful a reminder of the trauma.

Since George had not previously revisited his traumatic war experiences with his family of origin, his daughter's arrival at the same age he had been when the trauma occurred re-awakened all of his old trauma. As we have seen in chapter 13, a spouse revisiting severe trauma can easily aim the associated feelings at his marital partner which can blow apart a marriage. This is what happened. Undoubtedly, his wife and her family's own traumatic experiences dovetailed with George's; her simultaneous revisitation of matching upstream wounds undoubtedly contributed equally to the stresses that broke up the marriage.

As George revisited his wounds from age 13 ½ to age 14, he was revisiting extreme trauma to his sense of Basic Trust, as it related to his relationship to the community. Just as the process of marriage forces the spouses to revisit their developmental phases in a chronology that corresponds to the length of the marriage, longstanding partnerships trigger the same kind of revisitation. In 1980, George's partnership with Jim Rogers was 12 years old. This resulted in George beginning to revisit his highly damaged Basic Trust themes of adolescence. These themes, which related to his sense of Basic Trust of community members, were severely damaged by his wartime experiences of living in terror for 9 months, while the most powerful segment of the community hunted him and his family. As George and Jim Roger's partnership reached the 12 year mark, they both began to revisit these Basic Trust themes as they relate to community members (non-family members), the Basic Trust themes of early adolescence.

At the same time, George was getting in touch with the horrific trauma he experienced to these very same themes at age 13. The emotions related to his severe trauma to Basic Trust themes could very easily break apart his partnership with Jim Rogers, and indeed, that is what happened. Again, the relationship and the revisiting of developmental themes are always bilateral. It has been my consistent experience that trauma revisited by one member of a marriage or partnership is always matched by equal and corresponding trauma revisited by the other member of the marriage or partnership. With this in mind, Jim Rogers was undoubtedly revisiting the exact same wounded themes with matching intensity. So Jim's simultaneous revisitation would have contributed equally to the partnership breakup.

Finally, George's father Tivadar was 51 when the Nazi's invaded. In light of the breakup of his marriage in 1978 and the breakup of his partnership in 1980, George's life was already going through a tremendous amount of upheaval. But, in 1981 George turned 51, the same age his father had been when the family began their crisis for survival. George's resonance with his own father's trauma would be activated, as George reached the same age.

George's father had died in 1968 at the age of 75. The death of a parent is the final very important developmental point. For, just as the developmental clock begins at birth and again at adolescence and again at marriage and again at the birth of a child etc., it also begins again with the death of a parent. This is the "death marker" I was referring to at the beginning of chapter 12 in the quote, "Three sex markers and a death marker". Birth, adolescence, marriage, and death are the four main points in the life cycle in all societies as identified by anthropologists. When a parent dies, the child starts a new life without that parent. This necessitates a readjustment of all of the child's developmental themes, because now the child is moving forward under the totally different family circumstances of being parentless. Thus the developmental clock begins again at the point of the parental death.

George's father Tivadar's death in 1968 meant that George began to revisit all of his developmental themes anew. At this restart of the developmental clock, he began to undergo the chronological readjustment of all his developmental themes to take into account the absences of Tivadar, to whom he had been very close. In 1981, Tivadar had been deceased 13 years, so George's developmental clock that started with his father's death had been ticking for 13 years. Consequently, George would be 13 years into the chronology of this developmental clock and would begin to relieve his war experiences as a 13 year old. However this time, he would be revisiting these themes in his father's absence. Thus, George was triggered simultaneously for two powerful reasons related to his father in 1981. First, George was now 51, as his father had been when the Nazi's invaded. Second, in 1981, George was 13 years into the reworking of his developmental themes in his father's absence; and age 13 was when his own personal trauma began. So, George was predictably revisiting the horror of he and his family's trauma very intensely in 1981.

What is more, George was now without the support of his long term business partner. In 1981, his ability to master the situation faltered and his fund lost 27% by the end of the summer. As I mentioned previously, this was the first time in the existence of the fund that the fund's value had fallen. Considering that the fund's value at the beginning of the summer of 1981 was about $400 million dollars, the drop in value represented a loss of over $100 million dollars. At this point, many investors in the fund defected. As a result of the defections, his fund shrank further to a value of $200 million dollars.

From a strictly career point of view, this amounted to a huge setback. The emotional cost of his divorce, and the huge loss of his long-term partnership with Jim Rogers, undoubtedly played a role in making George vulnerable to this setback in his fund's success. But the underlying cause of the upheaval was the developmentally scheduled and predictable revisitation of his upstream emotional wounds. Like Winston Churchill, George Soros would come back from this setback stronger than ever. However, he and his investors paid a very high price for his developmentally scheduled and predictable career derailment.

At the end of 1981, to take some strain off of himself, George began to farm out some of the money under his management to other outside fund managers. And in 1982, George began to place more responsibility in the hands of Jim Marquez, a fund manager working on this team. By the end of 1982, George's Quantum Fund was again in fine form. He ended 1982 with the fund up 57%. This recovery began another fabulous period of gain which would end up making him incredibly wealthy.

In 1983, George married his second wife, Susan Weber. As his perfect storm crisis began to resolve, George also began to further rework his identity. As a result of the painful transformation he had just gone through, he began to become more and more interested in philanthropy and in world affairs. He then began to give away his money, slowly at first and gradually faster, in an effort to make an impact on the world.

He was now reworking the Identity themes of adolescence, at the same time as his children, but with his focus being an attempt to rework the world that he had to connect with. As an early adolescent, he had had to face a community that wanted him and millions of other people like him dead because of who they were or what they stood for. In adolescence the developmental focus is on revisiting each of the developmental themes of childhood, with the emphasis on the relationships between the individual and his or her community, with regard to these themes.

In adolescence, George had been introduced to a particularly evil segment of the world community and its peculiar totalitarian political arrangement, the Nazi regime. The Nazis hunted and killed millions of people precisely because of their identities. George and his family happened to have identity profiles that put them squarely on the Nazi death list. He and his family had managed to escape by falsifying their identities, but they were helpless to save hundreds of thousands of fellow Hungarian Jewish community members who were killed in the Nazi hunt.

Now that his children had reached adolescence he was required to revisit his own adolescent Identity formation. He began to focus on how he could be instrumental in transforming totalitarian communities that still existed in the world. These remaining totalitarian communities were continuing to cause the kind of destruction that had made a satisfactory adjustment to his community and a satisfactory identity formation impossible for him during his own adolescence. He was now setting out to try to influence the remaking of these various parts of the world; communities that he knew from his own personal experience with the Nazis were impossible to form a workable personal identity in conjunction with.

Meanwhile, as he slowly moved further into philanthropy and endeavors to promote open, tolerant societies, his investment fund continued to soar. In late 1984, he resumed more complete command of his fund from Jim Marquez, and hired Gary Gladstein to manage his staff, in order to concentrate on broader economical and political issues that affected world markets and his investment decisions. He also took back much of the money that he had farmed out to outside managers at the end of 1981. By the end of 1985, his Quantum Fund's value had reached over a billion dollars, the first fund ever to reach that level.

In 1985, George's first son from his new marriage, Alexander was born, and in 1989, his second son from the new marriage, Gregory was born. George continued to look for the right kind of person to help him with his Quantum Fund. In 1988, George hired Stanley Druckenmiller as his new partner. The Quantum Fund continued to soar and in 1992, earned more than $2 billion dollars on currency trades related to European currencies. George's Quantum Fund was going up and up.

If an individual's emotional turmoil belonged to them alone, we would reasonably expect that George would have gotten past his, with the help of his several years of psychoanalysis. He had weathered his emotional crisis of 1978 – 1980. He had weathered his business crisis of 1981. And he had emerged in 1982 with a new sense of his own identity, ready to remake his personal and professional life in accordance with his new identity. However, as we know from the material presented in this volume, emotional wounds belong to one's entire family system, not just to the individual themselves. So no matter how much excellent individual therapy a person receives to help them integrate their emotional difficulties, the old emotional wounds will persist in their family system until the entire extended family system finishes the integration of those upstream wounds.

With this in mind, we might predict that George and his family would in time be in for another difficult period of revisitation of upstream wounds. Based on the material presented in this book, the next major revisitation would occur when one of his son's from his new marriage turned 13 years old, the age that corresponded to George's horrific emotional wounds. What is more, we might predict that George might well eventually have difficulty with his second really significant business partner, Stanley Druckenmiller. George's partnership with Stanley represented another deep relationship with an outsider (non-family member), and George's emotional wounds from age 13 ½ to 14 ¼, when the Nazi's invaded, basically shattered his sense of Basic Trust as it applied to his relationship to the community or "outsiders". Thus we might expect that George would start to run into difficulties around 1998, when Alexander turned 13 years old. And we might predict that his partnership with Stanley Druckenmiller would become strained in 2000, 12 years after its inception, when the partner relationship began revisiting themes of Basic Trust between community members.

And sure enough, this is what happened. As Yogi Berra said, it was "déjà vu all over again". In August of 1998, the Quantum fund had reached its high water mark, with an aggregate value of $22 billion. Following that peak, it began to slide. This happens to coincide with George's son Alexander arriving at age 13 ½ . During the first half of 1999, the Quantum Fund dropped by about 20%. Following this drop, Stanley Druckenmiller, with George's acquiesces, tried to reverse his strategy, and succeeded in getting the fund back up by 35% for 1999. But the strategy that Stanley employed was fundamentally flawed. George had disagreed with Stanley's new strategy, but he had allowed Stanley to go forward anyway. By the spring of 2000, the Quantum Fund was now down by 35 % or $7.6 billion dollars from its high of $22 billion in 1998. $7.6 billion dollars is quite a loss.

This major business reversal coincided with George's revisitation of major upstream emotional wounds, just as it had in 1981. In the spring of 2000, George and Stanley Druckenmiller also dissolved their partnership. The breakup of this partnership was again right on schedule. The partnership had lasted 12 years, as George's partnership with Jim Rogers had. Clearly, George's emotional wounds to his sense of Basic Trust vis à vis the community (which gets revisited starting at 12 years into a deep relationship with a non-family member, or "outsider") had remained so pronounced, despite his individual efforts to integrate them, that his partnership with Stanley Druckenmiller was doomed at the same developmental, chronological point as his partnership with Jim Rogers had been. Furthermore, the disruption to George's life this second time around, when he came again to the major revisitation of his severe emotional upstream wounds, matched the areas of functioning that had been disrupted in 1978-1981.

George's father Tivadar was found to have abdominal cancer in 1966, at the age of 73 and had died at age 75 on Feb., 22 1968. George had experienced great difficulty with his father's illness and death, and had left matters largely to the healthcare professionals. This final parting between George and his truly beloved father had been extremely difficult for George. In 2003, George arrived at the age of 73, the age his father had been when his father had been diagnosed with cancer. This triggered, in George, a difficult revisitation of the death of his father. This revisitation of deep loss also put enormous strain on his relationship with the current deepest relationship in this life, his marriage to Susan. By 2004, George and his wife Susan had separated and by 2005, they divorced. Their divorce coincided with George's arrival at the same age that his father Tivadar had been at his death.

For George, the business disruptions and deep personal disruptions that affected his career performance had been a matched set. The emotional wound revisitations of 1978-1981 had brought divorce, the breakup of a longstanding and productive business partnership, and a great financial loss. The emotional wound revisitations of 1998 – 2005 had again brought the breakup of a longstanding and deeply productive business partnership, great financial loss, and the breakup of a second marriage. In spite of George's two to three year effort in psychoanalysis, the revisitation of his old powerful emotional wounds occurred again right on schedule, and the career impact was equally devastating the second time around, in terms of important relationships ruptured and money lost.

There is no question that George's first major revisitation of his old upstream emotional wounds in 1978-1981 produced some very valuable integration for him. George emerged from this first revisitation with a more comfortable and more powerful sense of self. He was able to open up a whole new aspect of himself which he expressed in his philanthropic and political work. Yet George's second major revisitation was just as personally devastating as the first. And since his fund was holding more money at the time of the second revisitation, the devastating impact of this second revisitation produced a much larger financial loss of $7 billion dollars.

Which of George's developmental themes were heavily damaged by his early adolescent experiences? When George was 13 ½ and the Nazis invaded his city, he was 1 ½ years into his Identity Phase. He and his family's survival depended on evading the Nazis by masquerading in false identities for 9 months. It is clear that this seeking of refuge in a false identity to survive had a profound impact on George's early building of his Sense of identity. Also, his family's experience produced a profound wound to his early adolescent Basic Trust themes. At age 13, he would have just finished revisiting his adolescent Basic Trust themes, which are related to Basic Trust in terms of his relationship to his community. What sense of Basic Trust George had managed to work out in relationship to his community from age 12 to age 13 was profoundly disrupted within 6 months by the total failure of his community to prove trustworthy and protect him and his family. Instead, the community, under Nazi leadership, began to hunt him and his family and tried to kill them; and succeeded in killing a large number of his extended family. This surely would result in a profound difficulty trusting one's community.

From age 13 to age 15, George was revisiting the adolescent themes of Autonomy and Control, which make up a part of the early development of Identity. 6 months into George's revisitation of these adolescent themes of Autonomy and Control, he was faced with 9 months of life and death struggle, most of which he had to endure and survive alone. It is true that his father provided him with invaluable guidance, emotional support, and material resources. But during most of each day, he had to risk exposure and death alone. This extreme survival experience would have greatly skewed his developing sense of adolescent Autonomy and Control. While most adolescents from age 13 to age 15 struggle with how to manage their affairs with appropriate autonomy, while at the same time learning how to share power with others in the community, George had to learn how to use his Autonomy and Control to save his life, hour by hour. This extremely critical exercise in Autonomy and Control, to literally save his life from hour to hour, gave George an immense training in quick, momentous, decision-making, where the consequences were enormous. George eventually found a career niche as the manager of an enormous hedge fund, where such extremely developed skills were essential. But it was this need to exercise Autonomy and Control under extreme survival circumstances that characterized his dysfunctional relationship to his business prior to his first major wound revisitation period of 1978-1981.

From age 12 to age 15, George was also revisiting the adolescent themes of Separation-Individuation. This revisitation would come to govern George's closeness and distance from his involvement with his community. During the heart of this adolescent revisitation period, George Soros and his family had to completely disappear from the community into a false life, in order to avoid certain death at the hands of the Nazis. This created a very dysfunctional adjustment for George as an adult, in terms of his involvement with the community prior to his first major revisitation crisis of 1978-1981. During George's adulthood prior to 1978-1981, he essentially kept himself removed from most involvement with the community, just as he had remained removed from the community during his critical 9 months in hiding.

Finally, from age 12 to age 19, George was working on the early part of his adolescent revisitation of the developmental themes of Sense of Self-Esteem. Remember that adolescents rework their Sense of Self-Esteem from age 12 to age 19, and then their adolescent Sense of Self gets further solidified between age 19 and age 24. An adolescent's revisiting of Sense of Self-Esteem is at its most impressionable and most vulnerable at the beginning of the reworking of these Self-Esteem themes at age 12. George was still in this very impressionable and vulnerable adolescent Self-Esteem period from age 13 ½ to age 14 ¼, during the Nazi invasion and occupation of his city. The constant struggle for survival as a fugitive created enormous wounds to his Sense of Self-Esteem during this critical and very sensitive developmental period.

All of the above themes that had been wounded for George from age 13 to age 15: Basic Trust, Autonomy and Control, Separation-Individuation, Sense of Self-Esteem, and his overall Sense of Identity had gone through major upheaval. And their revisitation, triggered by inevitable family chronology, resulted for George in a three year crisis. This three year crisis of inevitable emotional upheaval was at the root of each of his career crises. Many leaders under such circumstances never recover their previously successful career trajectory. But like Winston Churchill, George used this period of upheaval to achieve some healing of each of his profoundly affected developmental themes.

The healing George achieved during the crisis of 1978-1981 allowed him to get over his cripplingly insecure relationship to his investment business (Basic Trust) and to take a more balanced approach to control issues in his business activities (Autonomy and Control). This period of career derailment and associated healing also allowed George to move past his career adjustment as an isolated, workaholic hedge fund manager and become a very involved global citizen. In fact, he became deeply invested in the world community in terms of both philanthropy, and of using his vast wealth to affect political outcomes to promote open and just societies. From an almost total career isolate, he became a very connected world citizen involved in a wide array of interesting and enriching relationships (Separation-Individuation). His 1978-1981 emotional wound revisitations also allowed him to rework his Self-Esteem themes. After this, he was able to consider himself successful, and to allow others in the world community to get to know him and appreciate his success (Sense of Self-Esteem). With these changes to the components of George's Sense of Identity, his overall Identity had undergone an extremely positive metamorphosis from 1978-1981.

Yet, in spite of the healing that George accomplished in 1978-1981; another matching career derailment and emotional upheaval emerged with the next set of chronologically determined triggering family revisitations. The career derailment repeated itself, the personal losses were again huge, and the financial losses were colossal, due to the vast scale on which George's investment fund operated at the time. The emotional wounds to the family system had only been very partially integrated during the first 1978-1981 revisitation upheaval. And, because emotional wound revisitations by themselves rarely complete the needed integration, the extended family revisited the wounds again as chronologically scheduled. That second major revisitation is also unlikely to have fully integrated the remaining upstream wounds; so in the future, an additional generation of family member's careers (George's children's careers), will be scheduled for upheaval when George's grandchildren arrive at the critically wounded developmental period of age 13 to age 15. Since the upstream wounds belong to the whole extended family, the next powerful revisitation of the remaining unintegrated wounds will inevitably be triggered when George's grandchildren reach the critically wounded developmental period from age 13 to 15.

George made very prudent use of the most sophisticated emotional integration technology available at the time of his first upheaval, psychoanalysis. But imagine if the Extended Family Integration Process had been available to him in 1978 to 1981, when it was clear to him that he was in crisis. With the use of the Extended Family Integration Technology, a much more complete integration could have been achieved. This could have effectively prevented the next round of career and emotional upheaval in 1998-2005. It could have saved George and his family tremendous emotional distress, and it could have saved his investors $7 billion dollars, no small sum. It also could save the family from subsequent upheavals.

In the future, the Extended Family Integration Process will play a critical role in both preventing and recovering from serious career derailments. Because career derailments are both predictable and potentially devastating, leaders will make use of this new people technology both to safeguard their career trajectory and as an extremely valuable tool in strategic career development. Two hundred years from now, the Herculean efforts that Winston Churchill and George Soros had to make to keep their careers on track will be seen as both extremely heroic and very antiquated.

Chapter 18

Health

"It is easier to maintain good health ... than to regain it once it is lost."

Kenneth Cooper MD

We go to great lengths to try to preserve our health, or to regain it, if it has been compromised. Yet nothing can compromise our health faster than too much stress. According to Michael F. Roizen, MD, in his book, Real Age, a year of overwhelming stress can make us function as if we were up to 32 years older during that stressful year and in the year or two that follow. As early as 1929, Dr. W. B. Cannon's "experimental work provided a necessary link in the argument that stressful life events can prove harmful. That is, he showed that stimuli associated with emotional arousal can cause changes in basic physiological processes."[1] Other researchers found that if these changes in basic physiological processes were allowed to persist, eventually these chronic imbalances could lead to the development of serious disease.

Following the work of Dr. Cannon, researchers began to try to answer the questions: how much stress is caused by different life events, such as marriage, the birth of a child, or a job change, and how much stress is too much? In the 1960's and 1970's, researchers began to find the answers to these questions. In the 1967, Dr. Thomas Holmes and Dr. R. H. Rahe published an article called "The Social Readjustment Rating Scale".[2] In the article, they described a Social Readjustment Rating Scale, based on a large body of research. They presented a list of 43 life events, which were ranked from most stressful to least stressful, and given a point value. The most stressful life event, the death of a spouse, was given a point value of 100. All other items on the list were given a point value in relationship to the value (100) assigned to the death of a spouse. So, for example, marriage, considered by all the research groups questioned to be half as stressful as the death of a spouse, was given a point value of 50. The list was developed by questioning large groups of people. The people in these groups were asked which life events where stressful and to what degree. Groups of people from adolescents to the elderly and from all walks of life were questioned, including people from other cultures.

Dr. Holmes and Dr. Rahe developed the Social Readjustment Rating Scale from the answers given by these groups. It was found that there was a high degree of agreement from one group to the next on the items in the Rating Scale and their point value. The idea was that any item on the list was stressful because it required the person experiencing it to make an adjustment in their lives. The list these researchers came up with was as follows:[3]

Rank	Life Event	Mean Point Value
1	Death of spouse	100
2	Divorce	73
3	Marital Separation	65
4	Jail Term	63
5	Death of a close family member	63
6	Personal Injury or illness	53
7	Marriage	50
8	Fired from work	47
9	Marital reconciliation	45
10	Retirement	45
11	Change in health of family member	44
12	Pregnancy	40
13	Sexual difficulties	39
14	Gain of new family member	39
15	Business readjustment	39
16	Change in financial state	38
17	Death of close friend	37
18	Change to different line of work	36
19	Change in number of arguments with spouse	35
20	Mortgage over a $100,000[4]	31

21	Foreclosure of mortgage or loan	30
22	Change in responsibilities at work	29
23	Son or daughter leaving home	29
24	Trouble with in-laws	29
25	Outstanding personal achievement	28
26	Wife begins or stops working	26
27	Begin or end school	26
28	Change in living conditions	25
29	Revision of personal habits	24
30	Trouble with boss	23
31	Change in work hours or conditions	20
32	Change in residence	20
33	Change in schools	20
34	Change in recreation	19
35	Change in church activities	19
36	Change in social activities	18
37	Mortgage or loan less that $100,000	17
38	Change in sleeping habits	16
39	Change in number of family get-togethers	15
40	Change in eating habits	15
41	Vacation	13
42	Christmas holidays	12
43	Minor violation of the law	11

Notice that all the items on the list are life events that a person has to make an adjustment to. A life event may be a positive or negative experience, but it still requires an adjustment.

Dr. Holmes and Dr. Rahe, with this tool, began to look at the relationship between a person's total Life Event Points for a given year and their susceptibility to the onset of a disease in that year. What they found was that if a person experienced life events in a year that totaled more than 150 points, they were more at risk to develop a disease. They labeled any point value over 150 for a given year as "life crisis". They went further to classify yearly total Life Event Point Scores above 150. They listed the following total yearly point groupings and associated each grouping with the chance of a health change developing during that year:

	Life Crisis associated with Health change (%)
Mild Life Crisis (150-199)	37%
Moderate Life Crisis (200-299)	51%
Major Life Crisis (300+)	79%

They found "that the greater the life change or adaptive requirement, the greater the vulnerability or lowering of resistance to disease, and the more serious the disease that does develop."[5] They also found that, while too much stress could predict the onset of a serious disease, it could not predict which disease a person would develop. It is as if a person is like a steel hoist chain. If you stress the chain too much by putting too much weight on it, you increase the likelihood that the chain will break (onset of disease). But even when you stress the chain past the breaking point, you cannot predict which link is the weakest, and thus the one that will break. Each person's weakest link will be their particular organ system that is the most vulnerable and the one that will develop a disease.

While this scale is very useful for predicting who will develop a disease as a result of too much stress, it relies on external stressful events, events you can see. What my work has found is that when a person and their family's developmental clock gets around to revisiting a powerful emotionally wounded phase, the revisitation can put the person under tremendous stress. Unlike external stressful events, these revisitation stresses are for the most part not visible to people. But they can be just as dangerous, or even more so, than the more obvious external stressful events.

While my work is more preliminary in correlating a family and its members' arrival at the revisitation of a developmental wound and the related onset of an illness, what I have observed tells me that there is a high correlation between the two. Whenever a family and its members' developmental clock revisit a wounded phase, the family will experience some sort of disruption. Often, the disruption is in the emotional or behavioral functioning of one or more of its members. But sometimes, the most pronounced disruption is the onset of a serious illness in a family member. When I evaluate a person with the onset of a serious illness, sometimes, I find an associated occurrence of a high level, stressful, external current life event; but often, I find that the person and their family's developmental clock had arrived at a very powerful wound revisitation. And frequently, I find the occurrence of both a recent stressful life event, and the revisitation of an old powerful wound. Over time, I have come to believe that the recent stressful life event and the concurrent revisitation of an old wound are interconnected. I have come to believe that the arrival at a powerful developmental wound revisitation appears to have triggered the external stressful life event to occur.

I will now share with you some examples I have encountered of families where the revisiting of upstream developmental wounds is related to the onset of serious illness in a family member. While much future research will need to be done in this area, I think that the relationship these examples reveal is very important.

Arnold was an exceedingly bright, energetic man of 47. He owned and managed real estate and was a self-made multimillionaire. He was the youngest of three siblings, with an older sister 12 years his senior, and a middle brother 6 years his senior. When he was 8, his mother died of kidney failure after a 6 month illness. At 12, his father died suddenly of a heart attack. The family had been poor and his father left a tiny estate, not enough to provide for Arnold. His eldest sister Sally was newly married, and since Arnold had nowhere to go, Sally and her husband took him in. His brother joined the service when their father died.

Though he appreciated all they did for him, Arnold said that life with Sally and her husband was very stressful. So when he was 16, he got a job in a supermarket working every afternoon from 4 pm until closing at 10 pm and all day Saturday and Sunday. He worked 50 hours a week and he made enough money to move out on his own. He continued to go to school while supporting himself. At 18, he joined the Air Force and served for 4 years. When he was 22, he left the Air Force and began working and putting himself through college. By 26, Arnold had graduated with a business degree and by his early 30's, he was a millionaire.

At 35, Arnold married. He was happily married but he and his wife were never able to have children. For Arnold, the developmental clock began again with his marriage at 35. Eight years into his marriage, when he was 43, he had completed his first new multi-story office building. In the past, he usually bought large existing buildings with several partners. This was the first large building he had contracted to have built on his own. When he was 47, two things occurred. First, he was now in the final stages of completing his second new large office building, which he had again contracted to have built by himself. Second, he moved from a small town house in the city where he had lived all his adult life, to a large beautiful house in the suburbs.

In spite of these two successes, at age 47, he became very depressed. His family physician urged him to seek psychiatric treatment but he refused, stating that it would probably do no good. Instead, he pushed on as he always had. The emotional wounds he had suffered at age 8, when his mother died, were rooted in his Industry phase. As a result, this phase was misconfigured and in his case, the misconfiguration took the form of a marked overemphasis on Industry Themes. This pattern continued into adulthood by which time he was clearly a workaholic. The completion of his first building was 8 years into his marriage and the completion of his second building was 12 years into his marriage. According to his developmental clock, which, as we noted above, began again when he married, each building's completion coincided with the revisiting of the death of one of his parents. In fact, the two buildings were only a few blocks from each other; and on one occasion, he had even remarked that the two buildings were a kind of monument to his parents, one building for each.

In spite of the depression he suffered as he was completing the second new building, he pushed on as usual (Industry Phase misconfiguration – workaholism). By fall, he began to feel very poorly physically, and went to see his family physician. His physician did an EKG and discovered that Arnold had suffered several recent silent heart attacks. A few days later, he caught the flu and within a week he was diagnosed with "walking pneumonia". But Arnold didn't quit or even let himself slow down. There was a schedule to meet to complete his second building. So he took the medicines prescribed for his pneumonia, and after two days rest, went back to work overseeing the new building's completion.

After seeing the results of his EKG, Arnold's family physician had referred him to a cardiologist. Arnold postponed the appointment because of his flu. Ten days after his family physician had diagnosed the "walking pneumonia", Arnold was seen by the cardiologist. The cardiologist wanted to do a stress test to determine the degree of damage to Arnold's heart from the silent heart attacks. Arnold reported he was feeling better from the "walking pneumonia" so the cardiologist arranged for Arnold to have a stress done in the office on this first visit. Arnold pushed ahead enthusiastically with the stress test. He collapsed on the treadmill machine, with a sudden cardiac arrest. He could not be revived. His last words were "How am I doing?"

Arnold had been in very good physical condition before his silent heart attacks. He regularly swam a mile or more each day. He watched his diet intelligently and his cholesterol was low. In terms of external stressors, he had the stress of overseeing the completion of the second new building, and he was working hard to keep construction on schedule. He wanted to have the building occupied as soon as possible by the business tenants he had already lined up. But his external stressors were not alarmingly high. After all, he had completed a building on his own before. And he was an old hand at commercial real estate.

Arnold also had no obvious reason for the sudden onset of severe depression that preceded his silent heart attacks. But if you look at the emotional stress that was being engendered by his developmental clock arriving at the point of revisiting his father's death, the stress he was under was enormous. After his mother died, his father represented all the security he had left. His father's death had orphaned him. His sister Sally helped all she could, but by 16, life on his own looked preferable. Arnold had never dealt with any of this emotional trauma. What is more, his wife also lost a parent at eight, and had a very traumatic year when she was 12. So the couple was revisiting their respective massive emotional wounds at the same time. For Arnold, the stress was beyond what his system could bear. I am convinced that his depression, silent heart attacks and sudden death could have been averted; if only Arnold had, together with his sister, brother and their families, revisited the loss of his parents in an Extended Family Consulting Process before or at the point that his developmental clock reached the traumatic 12 year point. It would also have helped enormously if his wife and her extended family could have done similar Extended Family Integration Work in parallel. The two spouses and their extended family systems reached matching wound segments at the same time, leaving neither in a position to lend much support to the other. They were simultaneously overwhelmed, a recipe for something to break. In this case, what broke was Arnold's cardiovascular health.

The next case involves a 45 year old woman and her family. Joan was a vice-president of a bank. She was married to Fred, a very successful corporate attorney who worked for a large firm. The couple had a 15 year old son Harry and a 10 old daughter Carmen. Things were going along well for this very successful couple and their children. Both careers were sailing. The children were doing exceptionally well in private school and both had several good friends. The family enjoyed travel and went on two or three nice trips a year. However, in the fall of Harry's sophomore year, he became severely depressed for no apparent reason. The parents made an appointment with a child psychiatrist who began seeing Harry twice a week and prescribed medication. But Harry got worse week by week. Within 9 weeks of the onset of his depression, Harry had to be hospitalized. He was hearing voices and had the delusion that the world would soon be destroyed. He had also threatened to kill himself, which resulted in his hospitalization at a well-respected teaching hospital. He was diagnosed with a Major Depression with psychotic features. He remained in the psychiatric hospital for two weeks while he was stabilized on several medications.

When he was discharged, Harry seemed stable. But 3 weeks later, his mother found him in the bathroom with blood all over himself. He had tried to cut his wrists. The wounds were deep and he was bleeding profusely, but he was still conscious. He was rushed to the ER and admitted to the inpatient psychiatric ward. He stayed a month. When he was discharged, he was on heavy doses of a mood stabilizer, an antipsychotic medication, and an antidepressant. He continued individual therapy, now going three times per week. A few weeks after his discharge, he seemed to be doing better. He had caught up on some of his school work, and he was seeing some friends again. But one afternoon, 11 weeks after his most recent discharge, his father arrived home from work and found Harry in the bathroom. He had swallowed a whole bottle of pills which he had taken from the medicine cabinet at a friend's house.

Fred called the ambulance and Harry was taken to the ER. His stomach was pumped. Fortunately, Fred found him in time to rescue him. He was placed in the intensive care unit, and in three days, he was stabilized. He was readmitted to the inpatient psychiatric unit. Again he was stabilized with medications. This time, he stayed in the psychiatric hospital for 5 weeks.

After he had been home a month, Harry's mother Joan noticed a lump in her left breast. She scheduled an exam with her doctor. Upon seeing Joan, her doctor referred her to a breast surgeon and her lump was biopsied. The pathology report came back malignant. Joan underwent a series of tests and no evidence of metastasis to other organs was found. Joan was scheduled for surgery. During surgery, the surgeon found that the cancer had spread extensively to surrounding lymph nodes. The surgeon did a radical mastectomy and Joan was treated with radiation and chemotherapy. Post treatment, Joan seemed to have aged twenty years. Her cancer was under control for the time being but the entire ordeal had devastated her. Harry was also stable for the time being but the family never knew when he would have a setback. He was heavily medicated and he had fallen so far behind in school that he would have to repeat his sophomore year.

Eighteen months later, Joan was finally looking better. Her cancer was in remission and her doctors said that her outlook was now finally looking good. Harry was doing reasonably well in his junior year, after repeating his sophomore year. He was still heavily medicated and was seeing a psychiatrist twice a week for therapy. Because of his condition, the family did not feel that he would be able to go away to college.

At this point, Joan confided to a colleague that she felt that the ordeal with her son's psychiatric illness had caused the onset of her cancer. She said that the months between when her son got sick and when she was diagnosed with cancer were horrific. She felt there was no relief anywhere and she realized now that she herself had often felt so desperate that she wanted to die.

Bernie Siegel, MD, the surgeon who wrote <u>Love, Medicine & Miracles,</u> said in his book that out of every 100 cancer patients, only about 15 to 20% had a strong desire to get well. He found that about "15 to 20 percent of all patients unconsciously, or even consciously, wish to die. On some level they welcome cancer or another serious illness as a way to escape their problems through death or disease."[6] Dr. Siegel found that the middle 60 to 70% where willing to go along with the treatment their doctors recommended, but they didn't really want to expend great effort to fight for their life. Evidently, life for them had become so difficult that they could take it or leave it. Joan admitted that she felt like that. Her son's problem was such a nightmare and there seemed to be no satisfactory resolution in sight.

Dr. Lawrence LeShan is a psychotherapist with a lifetime of professional experience working with cancer patients. As he explained in his book <u>Cancer as a Turning Point,</u> he asks his cancer patients questions such as: "What kind of a life and lifestyle would make you glad to get up in the morning and glad to go to bed at night? Dr. LeShan has found in 35 years of experience working with cancer patients that invariably, cancer patients have somehow gotten themselves painted into a corner in their lives, and their position in that corner makes them feel that their life isn't worth living. They are usually very caring people who are afraid to change for fear that their changes will seriously upset their relationships with the other important people in their lives. They would prefer to try to keep going with a life that doesn't feel worth living, rather than cause their loved ones extreme discomfort or pain. Dr. LeShan has found that, if he can help his patients find an acceptable way to change their lives, it seems to allow these patients' immune systems to mobilize to fight off their cancer. Dr. LeShan reported that using this approach, "over the past thirty years, approximately half of his (cancer) patients with poor prognoses have experienced long-term remission and are still alive."[7]

When we analyze Joan's situation, we can see that the persistence of Harry's devastating emotional problems had significantly changed Joan's feeling about her life. It had gotten so horrific for her during the months that Harry was in and out of the hospital that, at times, Joan no longer wanted to live herself. And the lowering of Joan's immune system function, in response to her not wanting to go on with her life as it was, had given her cancer cells a chance to grow. It is reported that a normal healthy person makes about 250,000 cancer cells a day. A healthy person's immune system chases these newly created cancer cells like criminals and eliminates them before they can get a foothold. But Joan's lower immune system function in response to her ongoing emotional turmoil and distress had allowed some of the cancer cells her body normally produced to escape destruction. So the onset of Joan's breast cancer was intimately connected to her son Harry's emotional problems.

When we analyze Harry's emotional problems, we invariably find, as we do with all such emotional distress, a process, in the extended families on both sides, of a revisitation of very severe emotional wounds. Harry was simply the most recent member in his two extended families to crumble emotionally. He happened, at the time, to be at the focal point of a huge amount of unresolved and unintegrated emotional woundedness.

What if Harry's emotional breakdown had been recognized as an indicator that both Joan's and Fred's families were suffering from massive unintegrated emotional wounds? And what if Joan's and Fred's extended families had each mobilized to come together and do the work to integrate their old wounds that had been crippling them for 3 to 5 generations? For one, Harry would have rapidly gotten out from under the massive stress. The two extended families would have taken back the stress, which they are powerful enough to integrate and resolve. Harry would then no longer be the patient. His symptoms would recede and he would soon be functioning well again, no longer in need of medication. With the two extended families' persistence, their old emotional wounds would become integrated and all their family members would start to enjoy a new, much more successful level of functioning. And Joan's life predicament would never have approached hopelessness. Consequently, her immune system would not have lowered its surveillance, and her breast cancer would never have had a chance to develop. This alternative sequence of events would have resulted in the maintenance of good health, rather than in an attempt to regain it once it was lost. Which would you rather have?

The last case I will present is one in which the onset of a serious illness was actually recognized as the body's pathological response to the patient and her family's revisiting of a massive old emotional wound. Mary was a graduate student in a health care field. She had been well until she was 25, when she began to develop serious food allergies. At first, her only allergy was to string beans. She had not been allergic to them previously. But now, Mary found that when she ate them, her mouth and throat became swollen and she began to have trouble breathing. The first time this occurred, Mary was rushed to the ER where she was given an injection of epinephrine, standard treatment for a life threatening allergic reaction. Her symptoms subsided after the injection of the epinephrine and she was instructed by the ER doctor to scrupulously avoid string beans. The doctor told her that she had become highly allergic to string beans and that if she ate them again, she would most likely have another severe reaction, her airway could close off and she could die. She was given an epinephrine injection pen (Epi Pen) that she was told to keep with her at all times. The doctor told her that if she ever ate string beans inadvertently and had these symptoms again, she should inject herself with the Epi Pen and get to the nearest ER immediately. He said the injection could save her life.

Mary was careful about string beans, but within two months, she had developed a similar allergy to strawberries. She went to the ER again and was told by the doctor that she had developed a second serious food allergy. In the next 4 months, 2 serious food allergies became 5 serious food allergies and then 8 serious food allergies. Within another 5 months, she was getting a new serious food allergy almost every week. It got to a point were she had developed over 20 serious food allergies, all potentially life threatening. Her family doctor referred her for a complete medical evaluation at the University Hospital. Based on her evaluation and the results of all of her medical tests, the doctors at the University Hospital told her that she either had early lupus erythematosus, a severe disorder where the immune system attack's the body's own skin, blood vessels, and other organs; or some kind of very early leukemia. Both possible diagnoses were devastating.

Mary was a colleague of mine at the time and she shared with me what was happening to her in terms of her health. She also shared with me some of her family's history of several generations of extreme emotional distress and dysfunction. Mary's health problem occurred at a time well before I had worked out the theory of the extended family transmission of emotional wounds presented in this volume. But I was aware that massive stress could unbalance the physiological system, causing disease. And I was aware that unresolved family issues that an individual participated in, because they were a family member, could create tremendous stress. I concluded, even then, that Mary's disease process could very well be occurring due to unresolved family stress. I therefore convinced Mary to bring her family in for a consultation with Dr. Carl Whitaker, who was going to be visiting the University in the near future. I was hoping that Dr. Whitaker could perhaps reveal a link between Mary's serious condition and the current level of emotional stress in Mary's family. Mary got her family to attend the evaluation with Dr. Whitaker. She told me after the evaluation that Dr. Whitaker had agreed that her medical condition had its origins in tremendous unresolved stresses in the family. He recommended that she and her family become involved in therapy to see if a strong effort at family stress reduction could help her medical condition.

Mary was 25 at the time and was in the Intimacy Phase of development. The Intimacy Phase is both a distinct phase in its own right, and, at the same time, a revisitation of the Basic Trust Phase, when we encounter the deepest intimacy of our lives: the intimacy between infant and mother. Mary had one sister, who had a history of a psychotic episode. As noted in a previous chapter, a psychotic episode can be a symptom of a major family wound to the Basic Trust phase. Mary's parents both had problems with alcohol, which is another symptom that indicates a major wound to the Basic Trust Phase.

After Dr. Whitaker's evaluation, Mary and her family found a family therapist and started to actively explore their family's emotional wounds. By the time the family had completed six months of weekly family treatment, all of Mary's food allergies had completely gone away. What is more, all of Mary's abnormal laboratory test values which had led the doctors to conclude that she had an early serious disease had returned to normal. 12 years later, Mary was still free of food allergies and she never showed any evidence of a serious disease.

Mary's case is an example of a situation where the family stress patterns were recognized early as being the cause of a serious disease process. With that knowledge, Mary's family got together as a group and worked hard to lower the level of stress in the family. As a result, Mary and her family's stress level went down. Since the physiologic changes triggered by the enormous stress had not been going on for too long, the substantial lowering of Mary's stress resulted in her physiologic processes going back to normal. Had Mary waited for many years before lowering her and her family's stress, the chronic physiologic imbalances in her body being produced by her stress would most likely have caused a clear cut disease with some irreversible damage.

I am still in the early stages of investigating the relationship between massive, unresolved extended family stress (from upstream wounds) and the cause and timing of serious disease. However, I can now rapidly determine during a two hour evaluation, whether or not an extended family has serious upstream wounds. If the extended family has serious unresolved emotional wounds, I can predict with significant accuracy when the family system will revisit these wounds, based on the theory being presented in this volume.

Consequently, with the application of this new knowledge, extended families are now in a position to find out ahead of time when their group will encounter a period of massive re-experiencing of stress. And since these periods of massive re-experiencing of stress are frequently associated with the onset of serious disease, extended families are now in a position to know ahead of time precisely when they are at risk. What is more, if an extended family or pair of families connected through shared grandchildren wishes to undertake the work, they can finish the integration of their serious upstream emotional wounds using the Extended Family Consulting Process. This will remove for them the danger periods ahead, as there will now be no major stresses to revisit.

Finally, people who are now struggling with a serious

illness could use an extended family evaluation to determine if family stress patterns might be playing an important role in their disease. If a seriously ill person finds, after such an evaluation, that upstream emotional wounds are indeed involved in a major way, they could get the extended family together to do the work of integrating the wounds and thus relieving their stress. While it may not always result in the sick individual reverting completely to a state of normal health, as it did with Mary, it might well help significantly in moving their disease toward remission. The degree of benefit would undoubtedly depend on how long their disease process has gone on and how much irreversible physiologic damage has occurred. But the body is known to have remarkable curative power under the right circumstances. When combined with modern medical techniques for disease treatment, the results might well be very significant.

Chapter 19

Disaster Prevention

"All the King's horses and all the King's men, couldn't put Humpty together again."

or

"An once of prevention is worth a pound of cure"

Benjamin Franklin

When my father was raising us, he always supported our adventurousness and independence. He encouraged us to try any activity we were interested in, as long as our behavior was moral. But he always said "Come home in one piece." He was always aware that if we made foolish choices that endangered our wellbeing, the results could destroy our future. His solution wasn't to curtail our activities. Rather, he wanted us to use our heads, be prudent, and take sensible precautions to avoid calamity. We could try white water canoeing or take scuba lessons. But he always expected us to take precautions so that we would remain safe.

He would be scornful if he thought we had acted in such a way as to foolishly risk our safety. After we had done something that could bring unnecessary harm to us, he would say "Use your head for something other than a hat rack." And if others were acting unsafely, he would say "If everyone goes and jumps off the Brooklyn Bridge, are you going to jump too?" Because I grew up steeped in this orientation; the notion of preventing a problem always seemed far superior to me than trying to solve it after it occurred, especially if the negative results were devastating. Fixing the disaster after it occurred always seemed a stupid failure compared to preventing it in the first place.

But to prevent disasters, we have to be able to predict

them. The admonition "Don't go swimming for at least an hour after you have eaten a meal" is based on the bad experience of others who didn't follow this advice. People have come to recognize over the years that swimming on a full stomach might lead to an abdominal cramp. Undoubtedly, some people had experienced this and the unlucky ones drowned because of it. In Boy Scouts, they taught us never to dive into water unless we knew for a fact that it was deep enough and was free of underwater obstructions. Experience had taught that some of those who broke this rule struck an underwater obstacle or hit the bottom on their dive and broke their neck. One mistake like that and the victim is a quadriplegic for life. There is no opportunity to take the turn over again like you can in a game of Monopoly.

Our ability to predict disasters and avoid them is always dependant on our ability to anticipate the future; to predict ahead of time what will harm us and what to avoid. But many serious dangers are unseen. The underwater reef that can wreck a ship cannot be seen. Hundreds of years ago, sailors entering unknown coastal waters had to proceed slowly and with great care. The captain always placed a man with a weighted line that was marked every six feet at the bow of the ship. This sailor would repeatedly toss the line in and call out how many marks the depth measured. We now use sonar to do the same thing, but with more speed and accuracy. Likewise, one of the most valuable applications of the body of knowledge presented in this volume is its predictive use. This knowledge can be used to predict upcoming, previously unseen, "stress" reefs that will surely wreck part of the "family flotilla" if they are not dealt with effectively. I will give some example of disasters that could have been prevented had this knowledge been used and effective action taken.

Evelyn was a vivacious, attractive, high spirited teenager. She had a sister Jeana who was six years younger. Her father Don owned a small lumber yard which he inherited from his father. His business was very successful. Kathleen, the mother, was a high school teacher. Don, born in 1932, was the oldest of three brothers. When he was 15, his father, Albert, who had started the lumber business, was diagnosed with stomach cancer. It was 1947 and there were no effective treatments at the time. Albert slowly became incapacitated. He had no appetite and lost a lot of weight.

He died by inches in front of his sons. The end came in 1950, when Don was 18. Albert was 52 at the time of his death. Don had always wanted to follow his father in the lumber business so he and his mother took over the business once Albert died. Don's middle brother became a lawyer and his youngest brother, Sam, who was 13 when dad died, became an oncologist. Apparently, watching helplessly as his father died had fired up Sam to do battle with "the hopeless diseases", as cancer was known in 1962, when he finished medical school.

Although the illness and death of his father had been devastating to Don, he grieved some and then put it behind him and looked to the future. All was well over the years until Don's daughter Evelyn turned 15 years old. In the fall of her sophomore year, Evelyn became very surly at home. She began to fail several subjects and got in trouble at school. The family sought family therapy, but they didn't want to delve too deeply into painful subjects. So after 5 sessions, they decided to quit and struggle with Evelyn's issues on their own.

We know from the material in this volume, that Don suffered a big loss starting at age 15. His agony continued for three years until his father died when Don was 18 years old. The family's developmental clock began again with Don and Kathleen's marriage and then a second clock started with the birth of Evelyn in 1966. The time line for the family would look something like this:

1963	1966	1981	1984
marriage	Evelyn's birth	Evelyn's problems begin 15	Don 52 Evelyn 18, has stroke

Knowing what we do about familys revisiting unresolved emotional wounds, we could predict that Don and his family will begin to revisit the upstream wound of the onset of Albert's illness, to some degree, 15 years into the marriage; and to a much stronger degree, when Evelyn turned 15 years old and the couple is 18 years into the marriage. So, stormy revisitations of upstream wounds were on the horizon.

Not everybody is temperamentally cut out to go back and revisit painful memories. And family therapy doesn't usually afford the great anesthesia that soothes everyone which can be achieved when three or more generations come together to revisit the past. So it is totally understandable that Don and his family decided to forgo nuclear family therapy, a laborious and sometimes very painful process. The family felt that they could muddle through and that this was easier than dredging around in the family's emotional wound closet. But we can see from our diagram that things will get worse. In 1984, Don will turn 52, which was the age of his father, Albert, when he died; and at the same time, Evelyn will turn 18 years old, which was the age Don was when his father died. Arriving at this point in the developmental clock will strongly trigger the unconscious revisiting of the family's upstream wounds. Also, without delineating them here, Kathleen's family had matching wounds that were further back on her side, but as it turns out, Don and she will arrive at the revisiting of matching wounds when Evelyn turns 18 years old.

Back in 1984, this knowledge had not been worked out. I wasn't even aware of any of these timing dynamics back then. But with our present knowledge, we could predict that the family would revisit major emotional wounds with the accompanying overwhelming stress in 1984, when Evelyn turned 18 years old. Evelyn turned 18 years old in March of 1984. At Don's birthday party in June of that year, Evelyn collapsed. She had suffered a stroke. She was only 18 years old and she had previously been entirely healthy. How was this possible?

Evelyn had been taking birth control pills and occasionally smoked, against her doctor's advice. It had been reported in the medical literature that a few young women who smoked and took birth control pills had suffered strokes. But the incidence was rare. However, the massive stress of the family's revisiting of the old emotional wounds, coupled with the increased risk from the combination of birth control pills and smoking, had caught up with Evelyn and her family. The stroke was major and it took Evelyn over a year before she could walk unassisted. And even after one year of recovery, her paralyzed arm remained weak and only partially functional. While this theory does not allow us to predict which link in the family chain of emotional and physical health will break, it does allow us to predict that the family chain of health will become massively overloaded and during what time period. Under massive unrelieved emotional stress, the family can "break" in a variety of ways. The break can be to any of the corners of the triangle below:

Emotional or relationship functioning

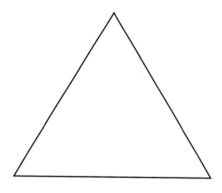

Health   Judgment and Behavior

The next example, the death of John F. Kennedy Jr., is a tragedy that is familiar to all of us. John Jr. was born Nov. 25, 1960. On Nov. 22, 1963, his father was assassinated in Dallas. He was 3 days short of 3 years old. After his father's death, John became very impulsive and this behavior became a serious problem. In addition, for at least the next year, his mother was acutely depressed, often thinking of suicide, which is understandable, given the magnitude of her loss[1]. When John began school, his behavior was frequently disruptive and his work was poor. This is clear evidence that from the age of 3, John had been having great difficulty dealing with both the death of his father and his mother's subsequent deep depression.

John's mother eventually took him to see a child psychiatrist in New York City. Given the murder of his father at 3 years old, and a severely depressed mother for a long period following, we would expect that John would have trouble with the developmental themes, starting from 3 years old and for at least the next several years. John would then revisit these same wounded developmental themes starting when he was 15 years old. And with the revisiting of these wounded developmental themes, we would expect that he would have significant trouble from 15 years old onward, for at least the next few years. In fact, John did have such trouble. He failed the eleventh grade at Phillip Andover Academy, the boarding school he was attending, and he had to repeat the grade.

John married Carolyn Bessette in a hushed wedding on Sept. 21, 1996. With John's marriage, the developmental clock would start again. The year before he married, John also started the magazine *George*. As John was approaching his developmental clock's revisiting of his father's death three years into his marriage, his magazine *George* was failing financially. It was anticipated in the summer of 1999 that the magazine would loose over $9 million dollars for that year. His financial backer had gotten cold feet, and was ready to terminate the magazine. In the weeks before John's death, he was shopping around for new sources of financing. His marriage was also failing as it approached its 3 year anniversary. He and Carolyn had entered marriage counseling in March, 1999. But by July, John was talking to close friends about the possibility of divorce. His life, both business and personal, was falling apart. This is no surprise, given the huge amount of emotional trauma that he was getting ready to revisit.

The day before his fatal flight, John had gone to see his orthopedic surgeon. John had broken this ankle in a hang gliding accident at the beginning of June, 1999. His surgeon removed the cast but told him he should not fly or bear full weight on it for at least 10 more days. However, the next day, John decided to fly anyway, against his doctor's advice. This was a clear lapse in judgment on the part of a man of 38 years old, who was "old enough to know better" as my father would say.

John had a new personal airplane, a Piper Saratoga II

HP, a high performance aircraft. At the time of his fatal flight, John had only accumulated 37 hours of experience in this new plane. Because high-performance airplanes are so complex and unforgiving if you make a mistake, insurance companies require that the pilot of such a plane log a minimum number of hours of practice with a knowledgeable flight instructor before they are considered safe to fly the plane on their own. John did not yet have the required number of hours by the day of his fatal flight.

John also did not have an instrument rating. In flying, the pilot relies on sight to know where they are going. If the weather becomes too bad to see clearly, the pilot can switch to using a set of complicated instruments and radio signals to guide the flight. But flying by instruments takes a long time to master. John did not yet have that level of proficiency to fly using instruments alone. In fact, he was not licensed to fly if the weather was not clear.

John decided to take off for Hyannis, MA on the evening of July 16, 1999, despite his limitations, and despite his knowledge that weather in the Cape Cod area is very changeable and can quickly become overcast or foggy. This decision on his part showed very poor judgment. And poor judgment is precisely what one sees when people are under enormous stress. John's magazine and his marriage were failing. And he was about to revisit the worst emotionally traumatic period of his life, whether he wanted to or not. Whatever difficulty John had with his airplane, his decision to fly that night, given all of the circumstances, was what killed him and his passengers.

And for what? He was certainly wealthy enough to hire an instrument trained pilot for the evening, who would have had no trouble whatsoever with the flight. In the 36 years since his father's death, his family had not yet managed to defuse the impact of the emotional trauma. They had not yet integrated their emotional wounds, incorporating them into an updated and better prepared family culture that would be more successful in avoiding tragedy in the future. Instead, John, his wife, and her sister perished on the upcoming unseen "reef" of stress that was scheduled to be revisited, according to the rules of the developmental clock. Had John's family been able to recognize the upcoming danger, they could at least have taken precautions. Had his family come together to integrate their upstream emotional wounds, such as the death of John's father and any other wounds that have been playing havoc with the family over the years, they could have cleared away the "Kennedy curse" that was operating that fateful evening. Such work, done ahead of time, would be real prevention.

The final case I will present is a disaster that has not yet occurred. The case is based on core elements of a real family situation. The details have been changed as with all case studies in this volume, to create a fictional case, thus protecting the privacy of the model family. Richard is a very successful, high profile professional. At 43, he is at the top of his field, and he is young enough to go even higher. Richard was the oldest of three children. His father Fred, was a successful professional and his mother Louise, was a stay-at-home mom. Fred did well in his career, and the family enjoyed a prosperous lifestyle. Even though Fred had a busy career, he always took time out to spend a lot of time with his children. He loved them deeply.

All of this love and prosperity was cut short when Fred died of a sudden heart attack at age 47. Richard was 14 years old at the time. His father's death was a huge loss for Richard. What is more, once Fred died, his income stream was gone. The family had to struggle to make ends meet and mom had to go to work.

Richard postponed marriage until he had become thoroughly successful professionally. At the age of 39, he married Judith, a younger professional woman. A year later, when Richard was 40, they had their first child. Two years later, when Richard was 42, they had their second child. Because Richard was 14 years old when tragedy struck, he and his family will revisit the unresolved emotional stress of the loss of his father when the family is immersed in the 14 year old themes. These 14 years old themes include Autonomy and Control, Self-Esteem, Separation-Individuation (Closeness and Distance), and Affect Regulation (Mood Stability). These are also the themes of 2 years of age. So the family's revisitations will occur when the developmental clock reaches 2 years and when it reaches 14 years.

The points where the family will revisit high emotional stress will start when the marital developmental clock reaches 2 years into the marriage. The second revisitation will be stronger, when the first child is 2 years old. But a major revisiting will occur at the point when the marital developmental clock reaches 14 years. And the biggest emotional stress "reef" will be reached by the family when the first child reaches 14 years of age. Our new knowledge tells us that these stress "reefs" are out there in time, waiting for this family. It further predicts when these emotional stress "reefs" will be reached and even how big they will be.

Richard will reach the smallest of the "reefs", the 2 year marital reef, when he is 41 years old. He and his family will reach a larger 2 year reef when he is 42 and his first child is two. Either one of these stress "reefs" could stress the marriage or the eldest child's behavioral adjustment. But, while these first two reefs may cause some distress, they probably won't be cause for great alarm. However, the next two emotional stress "reefs" will be much larger and may cause massive damage to the family, or to some of its members.

Remember George Soros's emotional wounds at age 14. When he and his family revisited them when his second child was 14 years old (he had been a second child), the massive stress broke up his business partnership, his marriage, and cost he and his investors a lot of money. George and his family's revisitation could just as easily have cost someone in his family their health, as it did with Evelyn in the previous chapter.

We cannot predict what kinds of damage the massive stress of the revisitation at 14 years will produce for Richard and his family. What we can predict is that unless those 14 year old emotional wounds have previously been integrated by the family as a whole, they will cause massive stress when the developmental clocks strike 14 years. And that stress may cause serious illness, major emotional dysfunction, marital rupture, or major lapses in personal or professional judgment and behavior. When a 60 foot yacht hits a reef at full speed, one cannot predict exactly what the damage will be. The yacht may break in half, there may be an explosion, and there may be serious injury among the crew. What we can predict is that the damage, whatever it is, will be great. IT IS BEST TO AVOID STRIKING THE REEF! In yachting one does this by anticipating the position of the reef and changing course. In families, one avoids the stress "reefs" by removing them. If the upstream emotional wounds are integrated by the extended family as a team, there will be no stress "reefs" left to strike.

Part Three   Neuroscience

Chapter 20

The Brain

"Every cubic inch of space is a miracle."

Walt Whitman

This book sets forth a theory of how extended family members influence the development of each other from before birth to death. It suggests that their ongoing communicative interactions result in the development of a "living" extended family culture and that this is somehow written into the brains of each extended family member. What's more, the theory suggests that the continuing communication, mostly non-verbal, between extended family members, serves to maintain in each member's brain, the structures responsible for maintaining this extended family culture. Finally, it puts forth the idea that communicative interactions within the extended family, under the right circumstances (Extended Family Consulting Process), can result in a rapid, mutually coordinated shift in the brain structures of each member. These mutually coordinated shifts result in the "living" extended family culture undergoing a profound updating process (integration of an emotional wound experience) which can be of great benefit to the extended family group.

At the most fundamental level of brain structure, this theory suggests that extended family members' ongoing interactions with each other actually end up influencing the synaptic structure (tiny connections between individual brain cells that allow them to communicate with each other) of each other's brains. What's more, the theory suggests that the continuing relationships or relative lack of relationships between extended family members on an ongoing basis serves to maintain the brain structures that have been built in this interactional way.

How is it possible that the interactions between extended family members influence the precise development of each others important brain structures? While this is not primarily a book about brain science, I want to address the above question in this chapter. If the reader can gain some measure of understanding of what the brain is capable of, then all of the information in the preceding chapters will make more sense; since the reader will have a better appreciation of how truly wonderful and capable the human brain really is.

There is much talk these days about biochemical changes in people's brains resulting in the onset of certain emotional difficulties. And there is much targeting of the genetic makeup of individuals as causing these negative biochemical changes. This is very simplistic thinking, even though it is currently fashionable. While there is no doubt that the brain communicates using a special set of chemicals, the real power of the brain is due to its fantastically precise and complex three dimensional structures; that it is able to build and modify based on experience.

This reality is not very popular to focus on at the moment, because we are only beginning to understand the nature of these complex brain cell relationships. And we are far from being able to directly influence brain structural configuration. Imagine how many billions of brain cells have to be able to talk to each other in precise ways in order for a musician to play the violin skillfully. Do we have any scientific capacity at this point in time to directly intervene inside a person's brain, who has no skill with the violin; so that after our intervention they will become a virtuoso? The answer is a resounding No! We currently have less scientific capacity to accomplish this feat than a 2 year old boy with a hammer has of rearranging circuits on a tiny computer chip.

The human brain is a huge colony of cells that has developed the capacity, over a long evolution, to develop precise relationships among its cells based on the individual person's experiences. But the astounding capacity of the human brain goes way beyond this initial capacity. The human brain can coordinate its capacity for relationship building between its brain cells with the parallel relationship building between brain cells going on in the brains of the other members of the individual's extended family. And this creates the capacity for humans to build highly coordinated teams;

where their teamwork has its underpinnings in the coordinately built brain structures of the team's members.

As you can see, this concept goes way beyond focusing on the individual's brain alone. In fact, the theory in this book recognizes the extended family as functioning like a "team" brain, which indeed it is. It is not a team brain in lock step, like the coordinated brains of the members of an ant colony. Rather, it is the "team" brain of a set of related independent individuals who have the biological capacity and destiny to influence each other's brain development profoundly throughout the life cycle. Is there any neurobiological evidence to support these team brain ideas? And if there is such evidence, how do the brains of extended family members actually accomplish this coordinated extended family team functioning?

To answer these questions, I want to set forth some information about what the brain is and what it is capable of. It is easiest to think of the brain as a huge collection of cells. If you are not sure what a cell is, think of it as the basic microscopic building block of life. Each cell is made up of complex chemicals to form a living unit. Cells have the unique property of being able to grow (enlarge in size) and divide (and thus multiply). All living matter is made up of collections of cells. Humans are made up of about 200 cell types, from skin cells to muscle cells to lung cells. In the brain there are basically two different kinds of cells. First, there are the neurons, the cells that are able to "talk to each other". Second, there are the supporting cells, whose job it is to take care of the neurons. The supporting cells are very important. If they don't function properly, we would get sick and die. But it is the neurons that allow the brain to perform its miracles.

The brain is an organ with a job to do, just like the heart. The heart's job is to pump blood. The brain's job is related to pattern formation and communication. Think about a marching band that provides entertainment during half time at a football game. The band's job is to create patterns (coordinated patterns of notes we call music and visual patterns to dazzle our eyes as they march across the field) and to communicate those patterns. The job of neurons is the same. Their job is to create and perceive patterns that have meaning or significance and to communicate them.

Neurons are made up of three parts, a cell body (think of a more or less round shape) and two types of fibers that extend out from the cell body. The fibers are sort of like telephone wires. The first type of fibers send signals out from the cell body and are called axons. The second types of fibers bring signals in toward the cell body and are called dendrites. While neurons vary in structure, a typical neuron will have about 10,000 dendrites and only one axon. In the human brain, there are somewhere between 10 and 20 billion neurons.

Imagine the earth with between 10 to 20 billion people living on it (each person is a neuron). Imagine that each person has their own apartment (cell body) and that on average, each apartment has 10,000 telephones lines coming into the apartment (10,000 dendrites). Imagine that each person (neuron) has to act like a kind of voting machine whose job it is to tally the votes that come in to them on a second by second basis. Each second, they add up all the signals coming in on the 10,000 incoming lines (they have a special adding box that tally's the signals for them). If the tally is high enough, they cast a vote by sending a signal out on their outgoing line. If the tally is too low, they abstain from sending out a signal. Similarly, the neuron is a kind of moment by moment voting machine. The output of the neurons is used to communicate patterns that tell other cells in the body what to do.

Take a pianist for example. In order to play the piano well, the pianist's brain needs to send millions and millions of the right kinds of signals, from moment to moment, to the muscle cells of all parts of the pianist's body, but especially to their arms, hands and fingers. If the signals sent to the millions upon millions of muscle fibers are just right, the pianists muscle's will relax and contract in just the right patterns so that they can hit the right keys with just the right amount of force for each key to play beautiful music. The cells sending the right pattern of million upon millions of signals to all of these muscle cells are the neurons in the pianist's brain.

A great pianist is also listening to the musical tones she is producing from moment to moment, to make sure that that her music sounds right. Vibrations are created when the hammers connected to the piano keys strike the piano strings. This sets the air to vibrating in precise patterns, creating the sound that the pianist and the audience hears. The sound enters the pianist's ear canal and sets the eardrum vibrating in precise patterns, reflecting the sound coming in. The ear drum then vibrates three linked bones in the middle ear, which in turn vibrate a structure in the inner ear. The precise pattern of vibrations is then picked up by nerve cells in the inner ear. These nerve cells then send signals to the brain neurons in precise patterns that reflect the vibrations they are receiving. Vast networks of neurons receive these patterns and make auditory sense out of them. These receiving networks of neurons, in turn, send patterns of signals to other appraising networks of neurons in the brain. These subsequent vast appraising networks of neurons allow the pianist to evaluate the quality of sound she is producing. Other vast networks of memory neurons then receive these evaluation signals. Based on their extremely precise but complex relationship configuration, which these memory neurons use to create the musical memory they hold built up over hours and hours of practice, these memory networks send out precise signals telling other vast networks of motor neurons what signals to send out to millions of muscle cells. These vast networks of motor neurons send the right kinds of signal patterns to the muscle cells all over the pianist's body to produce the next notes correctly. The concert pianist is able to do all of this automatically, which is the essence of her mastery.

Notice that neurons talk to two different classes of cells. They either talk to other neurons, or to some other types of cells in the body, in this case muscle cells. Neurons are also receiving input from two types of signaling cells. Either they receive input from sense organ cells (hearing nerve cells, sight nerve cells, touch nerve cells, smell nerve cells, and taste nerve cells) or they receive input from other neurons. Notice that some vast groups of neurons have the job of receiving patterns. Other vast groups of neurons have the job of interpreting patterns and still other vast groups of neurons have the job of holding a memory of specific patterns. Finally other vast groups of neurons have the job of producing patterns.

All nerve fibers that send a signal out from the neuron's cell body are called axons. Each axon has a special knob at the end of its long fiber. This knob is precisely positioned to connect to the structure that will receive the signal from the axon. Receiving structures are either another neuron's cell body, the receiving fiber (dendrite) of another neuron, or the receiving structure of another type of cell, such as a muscle cell.

This connection point, between the end of an axon (signal sending fiber of a neuron) and the receiving structure is a special kind of connection called a synapse. While there are 10 to 20 billion neurons in the brain, there are over 1,000,000,000,000,000 synapses. While the number of neurons remains mostly the same once we become a young adult, the connection between neurons, or synapses, are slowly but constantly changing, based on our experiences.

Every time we have any experience, it sends signal traffic through the brain's neuron fibers and across its synaptic connections. The more traffic we send over certain fibers and across certain synaptic connections, the more new parallel fibers and synaptic connections get built. Signal activity across synaptic connections promotes the building of new synaptic connections and the fibers needed to carry the extra signal traffic. If synaptic connections (called synapses) go unused, those synapses eventually get pruned. So neuron synapses are subject to the "use it or lose it rule".

Throughout our life, the patterns of synaptic connections in our brain are constantly being added to or pruned, based on each of our neurons' unique experiences. Neurons can have experiences that are initiated from the outside (external experiences) and they can have experiences that are initiated from signals they receive from other neurons inside the brain (internally initiated experiences).

When a pianist practices, she slowly builds new useful synaptic connections between neurons. Some patterns of connections she builds through practice will allow her to execute the playing of notes more and more correctly. Other patterns of connections will be used by her brain to store memories of how music pieces should sound. Pianists have to practice their musical pieces over and over. This is because only extensive repetition slowly triggers the building of enough of the right kinds of synaptic connections to enable them to play well.

Pianists can however practice "in their head" instead of

being seated at a piano. They can send traffic over the necessary circuits by initiating the practice of their music internally, by thinking about playing. The brain can thus have formative experiences either through the person having an actual experience, or by the person thinking about or "feeling" an experience, that originates in their imagination. This is why Olympic athletes practice thinking about winning, in addition to actually practicing their sport. In the "imaginative" practice, they can think through each step of a winning performance, controlling exactly how it unfolds in their mind, so as to make the "imaginative" experience a stellar quality performance. This perfect "imaginative" practice initiates the building of the right kinds of synaptic connections that will support such winning behavior when the time comes to actually compete.

You can see that the brain has a lot of work to do, constantly building and pruning synaptic connections. But the brain is basically very frugal. It will not waste resources building intricate patterns of connections that are not needed. If you practice the violin for only one day, your brain will build very few useful violin playing circuits. If, however, you practice a skill day after day, year in and year out, with great diligence, striving for perfection during each practice session, your brain will make more and more useful circuits. Eventually, if you keep up your practice, you will become a master of that skill.

Let me give you a very famous example of skill building that all of our great grandparents would have been familiar with. At the beginning of the 20th century, there was a famous markswoman named Annie Oakley. She was very well known because she performed widely in a traveling Wild West Show. When Annie Oakley was a girl of about eight, her father died. The family was poor and had depended on the father to shoot game for the family to eat before he died. Annie was the oldest child, so after her father's death, she assumed the responsibility of trying to use her father's shotgun to hunt game. If she hit something that day, the family ate meat. If she didn't hit anything that day, the family went without. Also, since the family was poor, Annie couldn't waste ammunition. She had to try very hard to make every shot count. After years and years of dedicated practice trying to make every shot count, she had built enough of the right kinds of synaptic connections in her brain to make fantastically accurate shots over and over again. She became perhaps the best shot in the whole U.S. at the time. This is how fantastically precise and skillful brain circuits get developed, over years of precise practice.

Now that I have introduced you to how the brain is wired, through billions upon billions of synaptic connections; and how this wiring changes over time based on repetitive experience, I now want to explain something about how these networks are positioned in the brain. While some vast groups of neurons that work together to perform a function (functional groups) are all more or less located in one place (ie. visual neurons, grouped in the visual cortex at the back of the head), other functional groups of neurons are spread out in interconnecting networks throughout the brain. The neuronal networks that are responsible for an individual's capacity for music are an example of an interconnecting network of neurons that are very spread out in many areas of the brain.

By analogy, the structural elements that make up the fireplace and chimney of a house are all connected together in one place. But the structural elements that provide the electricity, while interconnected, are spread out throughout the house structure. One result of these two differing location patterns of neurons that work together is that, over the years, scientists mapping the brain have found it easier to locate and identify those functional groups of neurons that happen to be grouped together.

At the present time, many functional neuron groups of the localized variety have been identified. For example, we know where the auditory and the visual neurons are located. We also know where the language neurons and the motor neurons responsible for movement of facial muscles are located. However, we are only just beginning to map out where the functional neuron groups are located that are distributed throughout the brain, rather than grouped locally. Neuroscience's experience of trying to map the brain has been like a young child's learning to draw a house. At the beginning, the child becomes aware of how to draw localized structures like a chimney, for they are much more evident. It takes much longer for a young person to be able to draw the map of all the electrical wires and fixtures in a house, because the wiring interrelationships are much less obvious. At the present time, neuroscience can only map out a few distributed functional neuronal groups. In fact, brain science doesn't even know of the existence of most of these distributed circuits, for their functions are just too subtle and interconnected to be teased out as of yet.

But localized or distributed, whether we know how to map them yet or not, everything that each of us is capable of depends on our having built up an appropriate network of synaptic connections. That network is the brain infrastructure that supports the memory, evaluation, and execution of each particular function. Some functional synaptic networks are built relatively quickly. If we are an adult and have built up a synaptic network that embodies all of our life experiences about the category, fruit; we can add the new connections needed to include a new fruit that we encounter, such as pomegranates, fairly quickly. We can build the needed synaptic networks to include pomegranates in our repertoire of known fruits if we handle one, peel it, and eat it. On the other hand, to build a synaptic network sufficient to play the piano professionally takes years and years of daily, diligent practice.

Some synaptic networks that we build are individually oriented. That is, we build them ourselves and we don't need to coordinate these synaptic networks with the behavior or reactions of other people. Learning to juggle involves building such an individually oriented synaptic network. A study reported in the May 2004 issue of the journal Nature found that volunteers had an increase in certain gray matter in areas of the brain that handle visual information after learning to juggle, as revealed on brain scan.[1] Pair skating, on the other hand, requires that the skater build appropriate synaptic networks that are coordinated with the matching and complementary synaptic networks that their partner is building at the same time, during their joint practice sessions.

Basketball players need to build synaptic networks that depend on at least four other teammates, not just one other person, as in pair skating. A basketball team, that has practiced and played together for years, can run circles around a team made up of players of equal ability that have never played together before. The team that has practiced and played together has slowly built up unique synaptic networks in each member that correspond to the playing style of each other member. Once built, these synaptic networks allow team members to automatically anticipate each other's game behavior under a wide variety of circumstances. This allows their behavior as a team to be coordinated, seamless, and vastly superior to the team behavior of a team of strangers.

Now, we are getting to the heart of what is important about brain structure, in terms of the new knowledge presented in this volume. The synaptic networks that handle all the tasks that come under the heading of a developmental phase or theme are shared and coordinated networks; and the group sharing them is a particular extended family. Like basketball players' synaptic networks, the developmental phase synaptic networks of a particular extended family serve to coordinate each family member's behavior with regards to each developmental theme. This allows the extended family to function together in an automatic and seamless way. It really makes them a team down to the matching synaptic networks in their brains. And the coordinated team behavior, that these matching synaptic networks make possible, has great survival value.

The ability to build coordinated synaptic networks within an extended family does for Homo sapiens what the hard wired brain connections do for ants. It makes smooth team behavior possible. For humans, the kind of team behavior that is ultimately built is based on the extended family's experiences with the environment, including the environment of other competing extended family teams. And the "game plans" an extended family employs in dealing with their environment successfully is encoded in their coordinated synaptic networks and is very updateable.

By contrast, ants of any particular species have to wait for a lucky genetic mutation modification of just the right sort in order to update their particular species specific game plan. It takes an enormous number of random mutations, spread out over a very long time, to hit upon a significant update to a particular species of ant's hard-wired environmental game plan.

To make an analogy to football, there was a time when no one had thought of the forward pass. Then one team initiated the forward pass behavior. Competing teams, experiencing the devastating effect of the forward pass being used against them, quickly made it part of their own team's repertoire. If the football teams had been ants with hard-wired game plans in their brains, the team who came up with the forward pass would have had to wait for a very unique genetic mutation that would result in the forward pass being included in their game plan. If they were lucky enough to experience this helpful genetic mutation, they would now outclass all the other competing ant teams. For the other teams could not imitate their newly more formidable competitor's behavior. These other less competitive ant teams would now be stuck waiting for their own lucky forward pass genetic mutation to occur. What would happen, most probably, is that they would never be so lucky as to get the same mutation, so their foe would outclass them right out of existence. You can see, from this example, that the kind of synaptic network system humans have, with its infinite capacity for modification, is vastly superior to the hard-wired ant system.

Brain science has progressed far enough, at the present time, to show that the brain builds vast synaptic networks to handle the execution of complex human functions. And this synaptic network building is not just a capability of children, but goes on throughout the life cycle. This underlying structural brain process in humans, the building of highly coordinated, modifiable, synaptic networks within individual member's brains, is the mechanism that allows extended families to function as very coordinated teams. I will now discuss some other important aspects of this most marvelous capability of the human brain.

The relationship experiences among extended family members that are formative for building the synaptic networks related to each developmental phase happen to be coded or encrypted, which is a very important feature. By this, I mean that extended family members can influence each other, and the synaptic networks that they then build in response to each other, in a way that strangers cannot. Like a fingerprint or an iris scanning system, that allows only authorized individuals access to sensitive areas in a government or industry building, family members' unique non-verbal communication styles (their unique voice prints, transactional behavior patterns, thinking, judging, perceiving, and emotional styles) serve as an authorizing screening system. This screening system only allows true extended family members, or those outsiders we have developed a deep bond with (spouses, adoptive parents, very deep friends), to have deep access and impact on each other; in such a way as to allow them to be a part of the joint synaptic network building process. Strangers and ordinary friends do not have deep enough access to affect the joint synaptic network building process.

Remember when you were a child of 5. If your mother said something was ok, then it was ok, no matter what anyone else in the neighborhood said. You might have had to deal with the reactions of outsiders, but you accepted your mother's responses to you as formative. Over their long evolution, extended families developed great exclusivity over who could influence them deeply (affect the types of coordinated synaptic networks members built) for the same reason that corporations exercise great exclusivity over who gets to attend strategic planning meetings as a voting member. In both cases, their very survival depends on this exclusivity. Extended family members have lived or died together for millennia, depending on the success of their collective approach to the environment. Thus, early man developed, over an extended period of time (millions of years), an exclusivity as to who was allowed to influence deeply their joint synaptic networks, and thus their game plan for survival in their environment.

Grandparents, parents, children and siblings qualify, as do aunts, uncles and cousins. These people are qualified members whose influence can shape the very synaptic networks we build because these people are all part of the same genetic team. The qualified members' unique extended family style or culture is a product that they develop and use together to coordinate their survival behavior. At the same time, their unique family culture or style also serves to identify them to each other.

This style, or extended family culture, and the underlying coordinated synaptic networks in its members, that make their family culture neurologically possible, is so unique that it is recognizable to family members who share the same extended family cultural roots, but didn't actually grow up together. Take two brothers who grew up together and were thus synaptically programmed to participate in the same extended family culture. Now separate these two brothers just before their marriages. Let us suppose that one brother stays on the East coast and the other brother moves to California. Twenty years later, their children, cousins who did not grow up together, will nevertheless have a great deal in common, from an extended family cultural point of view.

I know of just such a situation. Ellen, an only child, and her parents left the Midwest and their extended families and moved to California when she was 14 years old. When Ellen became an adult, she married Stefan, a man who was also an only child. The couple had only one child, Celeste. When Ellen and her husband Stefan died in their eighties, their only child, Celeste, was left without siblings, without aunts or uncles, and without cousins. Feeling lonely, Celeste found her mother's cousins and their descendants in the Midwest and planned a visit. When Celeste met these distant relatives, she said that they felt entirely familiar, even though she was 50 years old at the time, and was meeting them for the first time in her life. And these relatives were familiar to Celeste, even down to the synaptic level. For Celeste shared almost as much coordinated synaptic structure with them as these relatives shared with each other. Indeed, Celeste's mother, Ellen, had been formed in that synaptic network - extended family culture, and Celeste had been half formed by her relationship with her mother Ellen. Celeste's father and his extended family had been the other formative system.

So our extended family members provide the human interactive experiences that form our coordinated synaptic networks. And the coordinated synaptic networks, which are formed in extended family members, get used over and over again in interacting with each other. This perpetually repeated use serves to maintain the coordinated circuits that get built. An extended family culture is thus self-sustaining, even down to the substrate synaptic network level. This is because the extended family members' continual communicative interaction with each other serves to reinforce the shared synaptic circuits they have built together.

What do we know so far?

1.   Extended family members, through their mutual interaction, trigger the building of coordinated synaptic networks in each other's brains.

2.   These coordinated synaptic networks enable group

members to exquisitely coordinate their collective behavior toward the environment.

3. The coordinated synaptic networks thus built are actually the neurological infrastructure of the extended family's culture, or "game plan of dealing with the environment".

4. Only family members who share the same extended family culture written synaptically into their brains can influence each other in a formative way, in terms of building such circuits. The uniqueness of an extended family's culture serves both survival and identification purposes. Only "authorized" people have ready access to our deep synaptic networks. A criticism from our mother has an immediate and deep impact, whereas a similar comment from a stranger can be shrugged off comparatively easily.

How is the brain able to store so much coordinated uniqueness? Remember the 1,000,000,000,000,000 synaptic connections in the brain? Think about how many unique ways all of those connections could be arranged. The number is so huge, that it is "hyper astronomical" – on the order of ten followed by millions of zeros. There are about ten followed by eighty zero's worth of positively charged particles in the whole known universe."[2] So if we counted up every positive particle in our universe (with each atom containing from one to 250 positive particles in its nucleus) and then took about 10 with 3 ½ pages of zeros after it (10 with a total of 10,000 trailing zeros) worth of universes like ours and added all of the positive particle from these universes together, that is about how many unique ways there are to arrange the synapses in one human brain.

By contrast, a computer screen has about 480,000 dots on the screen, and these dot's, lit up uniquely each time, can display an almost infinite number of different images. The computer screen's capacity is tiny compared to the brains capacity for configuring uniqueness through varying its synaptic connections.

For another comparison, take the game of chess. There

are 32 pieces and 64 squares in the game of chess. Yet there are about 10 to the 120th possible moves in one game of chess. When computer scientists first attempted to have computers beat human chess masters, their initial idea was to have the computer calculate all possible moves and then select the best one each time. But they soon realized that this was impossible. It would take all the supercomputers in the world, working together, 10 to the 80th years to compute all the possible moves in just one game of chess.[3] By then, even God would be old, never mind the poor human opponent. So, there is no question that the brain has virtually unlimited capacity to store unique synaptic sequences and relationships, and thus to store unique representational patterns that encode meaning.

In this sea of brain uniqueness, it is a great advantage for human extended family members to be able to coordinate their developing brain structures, so as to support exquisitely intricate coordinated extended family team behavior.

We have looked at the capacities and workings of the brain and have seen how the synaptic structure of the brain is actually able to accomplish this feat of coordinated extended family team functioning. We now get to the last brain problem that is presented by the acceptance of my theory. How can extended family members trigger in each other a relatively rapid revision in their synaptically determined "game plan", when the environmental circumstances favor such a rapid adjustment?

First of all, is the change really rapid? If we compare the rate of change produced by the Extended Family Integration Process to the rate of change, using current methods of helping family members to change, the rate is rapid indeed. But when you compare the rate of change using the Extended Family Integration Process to the rate of change in normal development, that is, the laying down of the original synaptic networks corresponding to the extended family's current working of developmental themes; the time it takes is quite similar. It takes a child about a year to lay down the basic synaptic networks of Basic Trust. And it takes an extended family about a year to rework very damaged collective Basic Trust circuits. If the emotional wounds to a particular set of developmental synaptic circuits are less extensive, the repair process can often be completed in a matter of months.

What makes the Extended Family Integration Process fast compared to current therapy methods is that the changes occur to all family members at the same time. Any process where all the extended family members change simultaneously is much faster than a process that changes them one by one. What also makes it seem fast, compared to current therapy methods, is that it manages to work at all with severe cases of emotional dysfunction. Current therapy methods with these severe cases seem to take forever, because for the most part, they don't actually ever resolve the problems. Never resolving the problem is the same as taking forever, and it is the very essence of slowness.

I recently finished working with an extended family where the adolescent who was at the focal point of the stress was manifesting bipolar symptoms. This adolescent had been treated previously with individual therapy and medication for a period of seven years with little improvement. Compared to that, 12 months to completely resolve the problem and revise the functioning of the extended family at the same time seemed very fast. In fact, the Extended Family Consulting Process freed up the potential of the extended family to trigger the revision of the relevant group synaptic circuits in a very natural way. And the time frame needed was similar to the time frame that was required to build the relevant synaptic circuits in the first place.

The Extended Family Integration Process seems fast because by comparison, other therapy methods are so slow. The human brain has developed, over the millennia, a kind of synaptic lock on profound group developmental change. As a result, most change is slow. If change is going to be triggered rapidly, the synaptic lock must be opened. To open the synaptic lock in each individual family member, the members have to be in the presence of most or all of the other extended family members that will be affected by the change. If this lock is not triggered to open, then change in the synaptic circuits of the developmental phases proceeds slowly, indeed, if at all. If the lock is opened by simultaneous intra-group triggering between a sufficient number of critical family members, then change can proceed freely and rapidly.

This synaptic lock mechanism is a kind of biological insurance policy. The survival of the group depends on how their extended family culture is configured. Any changes to this group configuration could affect profoundly the welfare or even the survival of members. The synaptic lock ensures that a critical number of family members are taking part in the change process, and thus implicitly consenting to the updating of the group's family culture. This mechanism evolved to ensure that updating can only take place easily and rapidly if the basic core of the extended family group is giving their implicit consent to the developmental revisions.

In essence it is a kind of internal voting process. Each individual family member needs to receive the right kinds of signaling from a sufficient number of other extended family members to allow their developmental synaptic circuit configurations to be revised. And it needs to be a simultaneous process. Family members need to trigger each other at the same time as they all move toward the loosening of their synaptic locks. The synaptic locks of members cannot be released one by one. They have to arrive at release simultaneously, in a unified process.

It is interesting to note that individual neurons have to reach their threshold to fire (to send out a signal) by being stimulated simultaneously by many inputs which are carried up their dendrites or reach their cell bodies directly. These multiple stimuli need to add together at the same time to reach a threshold sufficient to trigger the neuron to fire and send out a signal. Extended families, during their updating process, need to cross-trigger each other simultaneously, so as to get past their individual thresholds, so that group developmental change can be triggered.

Synaptic networks in each human brain provide the locking circuits that need to be released in order for group updating to be allowed to proceed. This is an inherent biological characteristic of the human brain that developed over millions of years of primate evolution. In humans, the extended family group collectively exerts the most powerful influence governing group cultural change. Change initiated by a single individual is significantly inhibited by the synaptic lock mechanism. It can occur but it takes forever. This is the hero's journey we talked about earlier in the book. It will be a long time before we are able to exactly map these critical synaptic locking circuits. But we know they are there, because synaptic networks account for all sophisticated functionality in the brain. And we can observe that the group updating process only proceeds easily under simultaneous group communicative triggering, when the synaptic locking circuits are released.

Just in case you are not very familiar with how powerful group communicative triggering of synaptic circuits can be, let me remind you of a few startling biological examples that were mentioned previously. In Grouper fish, the lead female of a school of these reef fish turns into a male after the lead male dies. Simultaneous group communication determined which was the lead female, prior to the lead male's death. And simultaneous group triggering communication initiates a profound change in the physiology of this lead female, which leads to her undergoing the automatic sex change. In Clown fish, the opposite occurs. After the lead female dies, a male gets communicatively triggered to turn into a female. Pretty interesting!

I will give you one more example. An article was published in the April 29, 1993 issue of Nature, a leading scientific journal. The article was called Kinship affects morphogenesis in cannibalistic salamanders. In this article, the authors described the results of a very interesting experiment. The experiment was done with Arizona tiger salamanders. The larvas of these salamanders were found to develop different forms of their jaw structure, depending on whether they were reared in a sibling group or in a group of stranger salamanders. If sibling salamander larva were reared together, they were found to most likely develop a smaller form of jaw that is associated with non-cannibalism. When they were reared in a mixed group of unrelated individuals (strangers), they were found to most likely develop a large jaw that is associated with cannibalistic behavior.

The authors concluded that smell signal recognition between larvae acted as a trigger to determine which jaw the larva developed. Siblings tended to signal each other to develop the non-cannibal jaw, which resulted in them not eating each other. Non-sibling smell signals tended to trigger the development of the cannibal jaw structure, so that non-related individuals responded to each other by trying to eliminate or eat each other. So, salamander family members triggered a kind of biological change in each other that resulted in cooperation. In the absence of these kin signals, individuals developed in such a way as to be able to maximally compete (trying to eliminate each other through cannibalism).

The human brain is indeed a miracle. Gerald Edelman MD., a Nobel Prize winner for Physiology and Medicine, says that it is the most complex structure we know of in the universe. Its capacity for uniqueness is essentially infinite. And it is able to perform its miraculous functions based on its carefully crafted synaptic architecture. This synaptic architecture is built, in a human way, to be responsive to the environment. And among the most important synaptic systems in the brain are the synaptic systems that are responsible for the configuration of the developmental phases. These synaptic systems ultimately control the form of the extended family's culture, and the precise ways in which kin members cooperate as a team to ensure their survival.

These synaptic systems are endowed with special features: the ability to be updated by family group interaction and resistance to modification by individual effort. "Teamness" really is built into the brain and these "teamness" brain structures are at the heart of a wide variety of very profound people problems. An understanding of how these systems works allows extended families to take advantage of their extended family group updating capacity. And this extended family group updating capacity allows extended families to solve very important people problems, with the accompanying creation of great value for themselves in the process. This is an entirely natural process, not unlike the body's ability to heal a bone if it is set properly and then immobilized for a sufficient time. And now, with the knowledge that is being presented in this volume, this healing capacity can begin to be available to all.

Notes

Part One - Theory

Chapter 1

1. Hughes, James, Jr., *Family Wealth, Keeping it in the Family*, Princeton: Bloomberg Press, 2004.
2. Roizen, Michael F., *Real Age, Are You as Young as You Can Be?*, New York: HarperCollins, 1999.
3. Williams, Roy O. and Preisser, Vic, *Preparing Heirs: Five Steps to a Successful Transition of Family Wealth and Values*, San Francisco: Robert D. Reed Publishers, 2003.
4. Ibid., p 2.
5. Ward, John L., *Keeping the Family Business Healthy*, San Francisco: Jossey-Bass, 1987.

Chapter 8

1. Bruchac, Joseph, "1491, America Before Columbus", *National Geographic*, Oct., 1991.

Chapter 9

1. Campbell, Joseph, *The Hero with a Thousand Faces*, Princeton: Princeton University Press, 1949, 29.
2. Ibid., 327.
3. Quote of Benjamin Franklin

Chapter 10

1. Ekman, Paul, *Emotions Revealed: Recognizing Faces and Feelings to Improve Communication and Emotional Life*, New York: Henry Holt and Company, 2003.
2. Bateson, Gregory, *Mind and Nature, a Necessary Unity*, New York: E. P. Dutton, 1979.
3. Ibid., 8.

Part Two- Practical Applications

Chapter 13

1. LeDoux, Joseph, *Synaptic Self: How Our Brains Become Who We are,* New York: Penguin, 2002.
2. *Diagnostic and Statistical Manual of Mental Disorders, DSM-IV-TR,* Washington, DC: American Psychiatric Association, 4th Ed. 2000.

Chapter 14

1. Hughes, *Family Wealth*, p xv- xvi.
2. Iyengar, B.K.S. , *Yoga, The Path to Holistic Health,* London: Dorling Kindersley, 2001.
3. Pfennig, David W. and Collins, James P., "Kinship affects morphogenesis in cannibalistic salamanders", *Nature,* Vol. 362, April 29, 1993, 836-838.
4. Canfield, Jack, *The Success Principles: How to Get From Where You Are to Where You Want to Be*, New York: HarperCollins, 2005.
5. Watson, Tom Jr. and Petre, Peter, *Father, Son and Company: My Life at IBM and Beyond,* New York: Bantam, 1990.
6. Condon, Gerald M. and Condon, Jeffrey L., *Beyond the Grave*: *The Right Way and the Wrong Way of Leaving Money to Your Children (and Others),* New York: Harper Collins, 2001, p 131.
7. Ibid., 128.
8. Ibid., 131.
9. Ibid., 129.
10. Ibid., 130.

Chapter 15

1. Useem, Jerry, " Jim Collins on Tough Calls", *Fortune*. June 27, 2005, 89-94.
2. Ibid, 89-94.

3. Peter, Paul, and Mary, *A Song Will Rise,* "Monday Morning", Warner Brother Records, 1965.
4. Kuhn, Thomas S., *The Structure of Scientific Revolution*, Chicago: The University of Chicago Press, 2nd Ed., 1970.
5. Berra, Yogi, Quote.

Chapter 16

1. Stanley, Thomas J. and Danko, William D., *The Millionaire Next Door*: *The Surprising Secrets of America's Wealthy*, London: Longstreet Press, 1996.
2. Astrachen, Joseph H., Ward, John L., and Aronoff, Craig E., *Family Business Sourcebook II,* Marietta, GA: Business Owner Resources, 2nd Rev. Ed., 1996.
3. Gersick, Kelin E., Davis, John A., McColllom Hampton, Marion, and Lansberg, Ivan, *Generation to Generation: Life Cycles of the Family Business,* Boston: Harvard Business School Press, 1997.

Chapter 17

1. Stanley, Thomas J., *Marketing to the Affluent*, New York: McGraw-Hill, 1988, 140.
2. Erikson, Erik H., *Childhood and Society*, New York: W.W. Norton , 2nd Ed., 1963, 267.
3. Tichy, Noel M., *The Leadership Engine,* New York: HarperCollins, 2002, 10.
4. Tichy, Noel M. , *The Cycle of Leadership: How Great Leaders Teach Their Companies to Win,* New York: HarperCollins, 2002, xxii.
5. Ibid., p 28.
6. Tichy, *The Leadership Engine,* 8.
7. Conger, Jay A. and Benjamin, Beth, *Building Leaders: How Successful Companies Develop the Next Generation*, San Francisco: Jossey-Bass, 1999, 239
8. Dotlich, David L. and Cairo, Peter C., *Why CEOs Fail: The 11 Behaviors That Can Derail Your Climb to the Top - And How to Manage Them,* San Francisco: Jossey-Bass, 2003, xv.

9. Ibid., xi.
10. Ibid., xiv.
11. Ibid., xxiii.
12. Ibid., xxiii.
13. Ibid., xxiv.
14. Ibid., xxii.

Chapter 17 - Part II

1. Manchester, William, *The Last Lion, Winston Spencer Churchill, Visions of Glory, 1874-1932,* New York: Dell, 1983.
2. Kohut, Heinz MD., *The Analysis of Self, A Systematic Approach to the Psychoanalytic Treatment of Narcissistic Personality Disorders,* Madison, CT: International Universities Press, 1971, 108-1009.
3. Ibid., 108.
4. Ibid., 109.
5. Ibid., 109.
6. Ibid., 109.
7. Manchester, *The Last Lion,* 114.
8. Manchester, *The Last Lion,* 177.
9. Manchester, *The Last Lion,* 179.
10. Manchester, *The Last Lion,* 179.
11. Manchester, *The Last Lion,* 182-3.
13. Manchester, *The Last Lion,* 203-4.
14. Manchester, *The Last Lion,* 183.
15. Keegan, John, *Winston Churchill,* New York: Viking, 2002, 63-4.
16. Hayward, Steven F., *Churchill on Leadership: Executive Success in the Face of Adversity*, Rocklin, CA: Prima, Publishing, 2004, 24.
17. Churchill, Randolph S., *Winston S., Volume II, Young Statesman, 1901-1914,* Boston: Houghton Mifflin, 1967, 237.
[18] Ibid, 349.
[19] Ibid, 352.
20. Manchester, *The Last Lion,* 414.
21. Manchester, *The Last Lion,* 428-9.
22. Manchester, *The Last Lion,* 430.

23. Gilbert, Martin, *Winston S. Churchill, Volume III, The Challenge of War, 1914-1916,* Boston: Houghton Mifflin, 1971, 110-122.
24. Manchester, *The Last Lion,* 503.
25. Gilbert, *Volume III,* 159.
26. Gilbert, *Volume III,* 40.
27. Gilbert, *Volume III,* 86.
28. Gilbert, *Volume III,* 144.
29. Manchester, *The Last Lion,* 437.
30. Gilbert, *Volume III,* 147.
31. Gilbert, *Volume III,* 191-193.
32. Manchester, *The Last Lion,* 511.
33. Gilbert, *Volume III,* 237.
34. Gilbert, *Volume III,* 350.
35. Gilbert, *Volume III,* 419.
36. Gilbert, *Volume III,* 420.
37. Gilbert, *Volume III,* 420.
38. Gilbert, *Volume III,* 426.
39. Gilbert, *Volume III,* 431.
40. Gilbert, *Volume III,* 431.
41. Gilbert, *Volume III,* 432.
42. Gilbert, *Volume III,* 441.
43. Gilbert, *Volume III,* 441.
44. Gilbert, *Volume III,* 441.
45. Gilbert, *Volume III,* 440.
46. Gilbert, *Volume III,* 452.
47. Gilbert, *Volume III,* 453.
48. Gilbert, *Volume III,* 453.
49. Gilbert, *Volume III,* 473.
50. Gilbert, *Volume III,* 825.

Chapter 17 - Part III

1. Kaufman, Michael T., *Soros, The Life and Times of Messianic Billionaire,* New York: Random House, 2002, xiv.
2. Ibid., 272.
3. Ibid., 156.

4. Levin, Nora, *The Holocaust, The destruction of European Jewry 1933-1945*, New York: Schocken, 1973, 597.
5. Soros, Tivadar, *Masquerade, Dancing around Death in Nazi-Occupied Hungary*, New York: Arcade, 2001, 16.
6. Ibid., 17.
7. Kaufman, *Soros*, 42.
8. Soros, *Masquerade*, 187.
9. Kaufman, *Soros*, 45.

Chapter 18

1. Dohrenwend, Barbara S. and Dohrenwend, Bruce P., Editors, *Stressful Life Events: Their Nature and Effects*, New York: John Wiley, 1974, 3.
2. Ibid., 45.
3. "Reprinted from *Journal of Psychosomatic Research, Vol 11 (2)*, Holmes T.H. and Rahe, R. H, " The Social Readjustment Rating Scale", Table 3, 213-218, Copyright 1967 with Permission from Elsevier"
4. Amount increased by this author to reflect today's dollar.
5. Dohrenwend, *Stressful Life Events*, 67.
6. Siegel, Bernie S., *Love, Medicine & Miracles: Lessons Learned About Self-Healing From a Surgeon's Experience with Exceptional Patients*, New York: Harper Row, 1986, 22-24.
7. LeShan, Lawrence, *Cancer as a Turning Point: A Handbook for People with Cancer, Their Families, and Health Professionals*, New York: Plume, 1994, 1.

Chapter 19

1. Klein, Edward, *The Kennedy Curse: Why Tragedy Has Haunted America's First Family*, New York: St. Martin's Press, 2003

Part III - Neuroscience

Chapter 20

1. Draganski, B., Gaser, C., Busch, V., Schuierer, G., Bogdahn, U., and May, A., "Neuroplasticity: Changes in grey matter induced by training", *Nature,* Vol. 427, Jan. 22, 2004, 311-312.
2. Edelman, Gerald M., *Bright Air, Brilliant Fire,* New York: Basic Books, 17.
3. Peters, Thomas J. and Waterman, Robert H. Jr., *In Search of Excellence: Lessons from Americas Best Run Companies,* New York: Warner Books, 1993.

Appendix I

Developmental Stages

1. Basic Trust - Birth to 1 year
    The infant is learning to have trust in the family members that are providing basic care, in the family environment, and in the wider environment in which the infant and family are embedded.

2. Sense of Self - Birth to 7 years, then the stage gets solidified
                    between 7 and 12 years
    The infant or child is gradually gaining the experience that he or she is valued, first by the parental figures and then by others in the community. There are three components to self esteem. The first is "being" self esteem, the sense that the parental figures are made deeply joyful by the child's mere presence. The second is "appearance" self esteem; the sense the child has that their appearance is acceptable and pleasing to others. The third is "performance" self esteem; the sense the child gets that they can do things that are considered worthwhile accomplishments by others.

3. Gender Identity - Birth to 4 years
    The growing sense the infant or child has that they are a girl or a boy and all that means within their family and community context.

4. Separation – Individuation   - Birth to 3 years
    The child moves from a period of bonding at birth to a period of great attachment to the parenting figures from 6 months to 12 months. Then the child begins to gradually separate from the parental figures, coinciding with the emerging ability to walk. At about 2 ½ years, the child becomes more clingy and dependant, as if she or he is becoming aware of how large and potentially overwhelming the world is. Finally, at about age three, the child becomes more independent again and is now his or her own little

person.

5. Affect Regulation - 6 months to 3 ½ years

The gradual attainment by the child of the ability to regulate his or her own affect (emotional responses). By about 3 ½, the child has achieved the ability to calm themselves down under normal circumstances.

6. Autonomy - 1 year to 3 years

The child gradually gets the sense, in relationship to the parents, of what he or she has control over, what the parents control, and what is mutually controlled.

7. Initiative - 3 ½ years to 6 ½ years

The child gains the capacity to initiate all sorts of purposeful behaviors. The child also learns that he or she has the capacity to charm the opposite sex parent. The child gradually learns that some initiated behaviors are upsetting or hurtful to others. The child, through his or her experiences with the family and with others, gradually develops a rudimentary conscience. By the time the child is about 6 ½, he or she has a firm sense that they have the capacity to charm the opposite sex, and at the same time, they have come to learn that charm has its limits. They now start to become deeply attached to the same sex parent, who they start to strongly identify with, and from whom they will start to learn how to be competent during the next stage.

8. Industry - 7 years to 12 years

The child is highly identified with the same sex parent and is working on gaining the capacity to be good at things and to complete tasks well.

9. Identity - 12 years to early adulthood (18 years to 24 years)

The adolescent is gaining a sense of who he or she is vis à vis the community. They will have achieved a sense of identity when they have a sense of who they are that matches the sense of who others see them to be, as manifest in a career. During this developmental phase, the adolescent revisits each of the previous developmental themes of childhood in the same chronological order and for the same length of time. During these revisitations, the adolescent reworks each of the developmental themes of childhood, but this time, the emphasis is on the adolescent's relationship to the community, with regard to each of the developmental themes.

10. Intimacy - Early adulthood (18 years to late twenties)

The young adult has achieved the capacity to commit themselves to affiliations and partnerships and has developed the ethical strength to remain loyal to such commitments, even though doing so may require significant sacrifices and compromises. This is the stage during which people pair off to marry and begin their own families.

11. Generativity - Adulthood

During this stage, the adult is concerned with establishing and developing the next generation.

12. Ego Integrity - Senior Adulthood

It is the coming together of one's sense of one's life and the gradual achievement of wisdom. It includes accepting the roles of "elder" in one's extended family and in one's community.

Selected Bibliography

References for the Developmental Stages Framework:

1. Erickson, Erik H., *Childhood and Society,* New York: Norton, 1963.

2. Call, Justin D., Galenson, Eleanor and Tyson, Robert L., *Frontiers of Infant Psychiatry, 2 Vols.*, New York: Basic Books, 1983.

3. Mahler, Margaret, *The Psychological Birth of the Human Infant, Symbiosis and Individuation,* New York: Basic Books, 1975.

4. Kohut, Heinz, *The Analysis of the Self: A Systematic Approach to the Psychoanalytic Treatment of Narcissistic Personality Disorders,* Madison, CT: International University Press, 1971.

5. Schore, Allan N., *Affect Regulation and the Origin of the Self: The Neurobiology of Emotional Development,* Hillsdale, N.J., Lawrence Erlbaum Associates, 1994.

6. Money, John and Ehrhardt, A., *Man and Woman, Boy and Girl: The Differentiation and Dimorphism of Gender Identity from Conception to Maturity,* Baltimore: Johns Hopkins Press, 1972.

References: Family Therapy Background for Theoretical Framework

1. Napier, Augustus. and Whitaker, Carl, *The Family Crucible,* New York: Harper and Row, 1978.

2. Neill, John R., and Kniskern, David P., *From Psyche to System: The Evolving Therapy of Carl Whitaker,* New York: Guildford Press, 1982.

3. Whitaker, Carl. and Bumberry, William, *Dancing with the Family,* New York: Brunner/Mazel, 1988.

4. Whitaker, Carl and ed. Ryan, Margaret O., *Midnight Musings of a Family Therapist,* New York: Norton, 1989.

5. Haley, Jay, ed., *Changing Families*: *A Family Reader,* New York: Grune and Stratton, 1971.

6. Minuchin, Salvador and Fishman, Charles H., *Family Therapy Techniques,* Cambridge, MA: Harvard University Press, 1981.

INDEX